Latent Structure Analysis

PAUL F. LAZARSFELD

Quételet Professor of Social Science, Columbia University

NEIL W. HENRY   *Cornell University*

Latent

Structure Analysis

HOUGHTON MIFFLIN COMPANY · BOSTON

New York   Atlanta   Geneva, Illinois   Dallas   Palo Alto

Frontispiece from *Complete Poems of Robert Frost*. Copyright 1942 by Robert Frost. Reprinted by permission of Holt, Rinehart and Winston, Inc.

Appendix B: Large Sample Distribution Theory for Estimates of the Parameters of a Latent Class Model, Copyright © 1968 by T. W. Anderson.

THE SECRET SITS

We dance round in a ring and suppose,
But the Secret sits in the middle and knows.

Robert Frost, A Witness Tree

Preface

The present volume has developed from numerous memoranda which were written for class use or for different research projects in the years since the publication of *Measurement and Prediction*. During this period we have had the help of many colleagues. In particular, we cite the work of T. W. Anderson, W. A. Gibson, Robert Somers, and Lee Wiggins.

A paper by Anderson on sampling theory in the latent class model is included as an appendix; and Robert O. Carleton's and his analysis of randomly generated samples has been summarized in Chapter 4. Gibson's contribution is documented by his many articles on the latent class model, and includes the extension to continuous variables; a selection from his work appears in Chapter 4. We drew on the work of Somers and Wiggins in preparing Chapters 6 and 9, respectively. A short selection from Somers' dissertation is included in Chapter 6.

The senior author greatly appreciates the encouragement which Fred Mosteller and the late Sam Stouffer provided in the early stages of the development of latent structure analysis. Jack Dudman, Peter Rossi, and Dean Harper made important contributions as well. L. J. Savage and Leo Goodman were, on more than one occasion, valuable consultants on technical matters.

Major financial support came from the RAND Corporation, thanks to Hans Speier, and later from The National Science Foundation. Able assistants on these projects included Lotte Bailyn, Arnold Simmel, and David Elesh. Harry Milholland wrote the computer program described in Chapter 4 as part of the NSF project.

The Bureau of Applied Social Research at Columbia University was the administrative center for the complex system of collaboration and technical assistance. We would like to give special thanks to Miss Clara Shapiro, and to Allen Barton, the present director, who in the early stages was also a staff member, and offer our sincere appreciation to the many colleagues at the Bureau who have talked and listened to us over the years.

Paul Kelly has been a patient and helpful representative of the publisher. The editorial staff at Houghton Mifflin has done a fine job with our often awkward manuscript.

Paul F. Lazarsfeld
Neil W. Henry

Contents

4

The Latent Class Model: Estimation of Parameters 71

5

The Problem of Ordered Classes 122

6

Latent Structure Models with Continuous Latent Space: I 157

7

Latent Structure Models with Continuous Latent Space: II 197

8

More General Models 226

1

History and Synopsis

1. Introduction

All the social sciences deal with concepts which seem to have a certain vagueness. Who has not read many discussions of the real meaning of the term "public opinion," or of "folk society," or of "extrovert personality"? There are various reasons why the social scientist's language has so many of these terms, which at first sight seem to be ill-defined or at best "fuzzy at the fringe." In some cases we can, by the nature of the concept, only observe symptoms, behind which we assume a more permanent reality: this would be true, for example, in the case of personality notions. In other matters, the object of investigation is so vast that we can only analyze certain aspects of it: notions like patterns of culture or *Zeitgeist* belong here. For still other purposes, the problem itself seems to require a looser kind of formulation: wherever we study adjustments, e.g., in marriage, in job performance, or in standard of living, we find that large numbers of actual solutions may serve the same functional purpose.

This peculiarity of the social scientist's intellectual tools has been deplored by some, considered as unavoidable by others. Most of all, however, it has been covered with nomenclature. Syndromes, genotypes, underlying concepts, hypothetical constructs, and many other terms have been used. It is hard to say to what extent we have today a clear formulation of the problem behind all these terms, let alone clear directions on how to deal with them in the pursuit of empirical research. And yet, it is in the course of these actual investigations that some clarification is most needed. For, if we have to decide whether there is increased bureaucratization in government, or whether city life makes people progressively neurotic, we have to get some measurable representations of these ideas. No matter what measure we choose to use, some assumptions, whether explicit or implicit, must be made concerning the *meaning* of the term in question.

1

The general character of the problem has not escaped the attention of logicians. They talk of *disposition terms*, which refer not to directly observable characteristics, but rather to dispositions on the part of some physical objects to display specific reactions under specifiable circumstances. The definition of such terms seems to create considerable difficulties. A famous paper by Carnap has convinced most of his fellow philosophers that for the introduction of such a term a somewhat different kind of logical operation is needed, which operation he calls partial definition or reduction.[1] Following Hempel's simpler presentation, one way to "define" the disposition term "magnetic" would be as follows:[2]

If a small iron object is close to X at time T, then X is magnetic at time T, if and only if that object moves toward X at time T.

This definition is partial for one obvious reason. If there is no way to approach X with small iron objects, if, say, X is at the bottom of a lake, we could not determine whether it is magnetic or not.

Thus, e.g., if the concept of electric current has been introduced previously, the first partial definition might be supplemented by the additional reduction sentence: If X moves through a closed wire loop at time T, then: X is magnetic at T if and only if an electric current flows in the wire at T.

But when several reduction sentences are used for the same concept they have to be reconciled. What happens in the example of magnetism, where attracting metal and inducing currents are used as two test conditions? Hempel points out that when

two test conditions are not mutually exclusive, i.e., may be jointly satisfied by a physical body, the two reduction sentences together entail the assertion that whenever this is the case, the two corresponding reactions will occur jointly, too; more specifically (the two definitions) together imply a statement to the effect that any physical body which is near some small iron object and moves through a closed wire loop will generate a current in the loop if and only if it attracts the iron object. But this statement surely is not just a stipulation concerning the use of a new term — in fact, it does not contain the new term, 'magnetic,' at all. *Hence, while a single reduction sentence may be viewed simply as a notational convention for the use of the term it introduces, this is no longer generally true of a set of two or more reduction sentences for the same term, for such a set implies, as a rule, certain consequences which have the character of empirical laws.*[3]

In the social sciences one more complexity enters. A "magnetic personality" is one which is *likely* to attract other people, which is *likely* to induce in them currents of enthusiasm. The items of observations are linked to the concepts

---

[1]Rudolf Carnap, "Testability and Meaning," *Philosophy of Science* III (1936), pp. 419–471, and IV (1937), pp. 2–40. It might not be a coincidence that Carnap explained the history of his idea by a reference to a problem of introspection:

> The members of the [Vienna] Circle did not wish in former times to include into our scientific language a sentence corresponding to the English sentence S: 'This stone is not thinking about Vienna.' But at present I should prefer to construct the scientific language in such a way that it contains a sentence corresponding to S.

[2]C. G. Hempel, "Fundamentals of Concept Formation in Empirical Science." *International Encyclopedia of Unified Science*, Vol. II (Chicago, University of Chicago Press, 1952), p. 19.
[3]Italics occurring in quoted passages throughout the text are ours.

to be defined by *probability relations*. If we have two test situations it is not necessary that their outcome be related by a rigid law. To turn once more to the example of magnetism, it would be sufficient to say that attracting iron objects and inducing electric current are correlated, that they frequently occur together, but not necessarily always. Such covariation can be of different degree, and we are free to decide what amount of it entitles indicators to be included in the list which serves as the basis for the specification of meaning. And what is more important, the list of specifying items need not be final, but can change as a result of improved inquiries. To put it still differently: Hempel notes that empirical laws arise when reduction sentences are combined. We say, similarly, that if several indicators are strongly related to a single concept, then they will have a certain well defined pattern of correlation with each other. Now, conversely, *we realize that in the real world we are surrounded by indicators, and we observe their covariation, and we ask whether the patterns of covariation we observe may not tell us something about the defining nature of a concept.*

Our starting point is, then, the problem of how concepts may be *inferred* from indicators. More specifically, we have in mind classificatory concepts which are intended to divide people, or collectives, or other objects, into different groups. Thus the notion of "relative deprivation" can be used to interpret a set of empirical findings. The more specific problem concerns us: given a particular group of people, we want to know how deprived each is, and relative to whom. In this sense, we speak of an *inferential classification* which can have a number of different forms. Sometimes we are satisfied with a dichotomy: deprived — not deprived. At other times, we require a ranking of the members of the group, and, occasionally, we try to approach the measurement on a real number scale that is common in the physical sciences. What we are concerned with in latent structure analysis is the probability relation between the set of observed indicators and the inferred position of the units involved in an empirical study.

2. Some Historical Comments

Only slowly did social scientists and philosophers come to realize the necessity of specifying this probability relation between underlying concept and behavioral indicators. William James has written in *The Meaning of Truth:* "Suppose that we say a man is prudent. Concretely, that means that he takes out insurance, hedges in betting, looks before he leaps. . . . As a constant habit in him, it is convenient to call him prudent in abstraction from any one of his acts." Actually, one would not expect a "prudent" man to hedge in betting always, or to take out insurance on all possible risks; instead, one would talk about the probability that he will perform any specific act as compared with a less prudent individual. And one would know that the appropriate indicators might vary considerably, depending on the social setting of the individual.

John Dewey saw a looser connection between concepts and indicators. He warned that one should *not* "assume that there is or ever can be an exact equation of disposition and outcome." It was characteristic for habits (Dewey's equivalent to dispositions) "that their outworking in any particular case is subject to contingencies, to circumstances which are unforeseeable and which carry an act one side of its usual effect."[4]

The notion of probability is now explicitly or implicitly built into any systematic discussion of traits. For example, consider Allport's article concerning the problem of defining a trait. Two of his points are especially pertinent here:[5]

4. The evidence of a trait may be established empirically and statistically . . . in order to know that an individual has a trait it is necessary to have evidence of repeated reactions, which, though not necessarily constant in type, seem nonetheless to be consistently a *function of the same underlying determinant.*

7. Acts and even habits that are inconsistent with a trait are not proof of the non-existence of the trait . . . there are in every personality instances of acts that are *unrelated to existent traits, the product of the stimulus and of the attitude of the moment.* Even the characteristically neat person may become careless in his haste to catch a train.

If one studies collectives, large or small, one is, of course, as much concerned with inferential classifications as if one studies personalities. In 1895 Durkheim tried to write for the new science of sociology a Magna Carta. In *The Rules of Sociological Method* the central and reiterated proposition was that "social facts are to be treated as things." The first of his six chapters is entitled: "What is a Social Fact?" And when in the introduction to the second edition he wanted to clarify his ideas against his critics, he tried to sharpen his definition.[6] We read there statements like these:

Things include all objects of knowledge that cannot be conceived by purely mental activity, those that require for their conception data from outside the mind, from observations and experiments, those which are *built up from the more external and immediately accessible characteristics to the less visible and more profound.* (p. xliii.)

Here Durkheim clearly approaches the idea of indicators (external and immediately accessible) and disposition concepts (less visible and more profound). But as far as we know, he never expressed himself clearly on the relation between the two.[7]

A few years later, Max Weber has already quite explicitly introduced the notion of probability in his definitions. We frequently find in his writings passages like the following one:[8]

. . . it is only the existence of the probability that a certain type of action will take place which constitutes the 'existence' of friendship. Thus that a *friendship exists* or has existed *means this and only this:* that we, the observers, judge that there is or has been a

[4]John Dewey, *Human Nature and Conduct* (New York, Henry Holt and Co., 1909), pp. 48–49.
[5]Gordon Allport, "What Is A Trait Of Personality?" *Journal of Abnormal and Social Psychology,* 1931, pp. 368–372.
[6]E. Durkheim, *The Rules of Sociological Method,* George E. G. Catlin, ed. (Chicago, University of Chicago Press, 1938).
[7]Some of his pertinent statements are reported and analyzed in another paper: P. F. Lazarsfeld, "Notes on the History of Quantification in Sociology: Trends, Sources, and Problems," *ISIS,* 52, Part 2 (June 1961), pp. 277–333.
[8]Max Weber, *The Theory of Social and Economic Organization,* T. Parsons, ed. (New York, Oxford University Press, 1947), p. 119.

probability that on the basis of known subjective attitudes of certain individuals there will result in the average sense a certain specific type of action.

Weber specifically stresses that only in such probabilistic terms can the meaning of social relationships be caught. They cease to exist, he says, "Whenever there is no longer a probability that certain kinds of meaningful oriented social action will take place."

Implied in all our examples was the idea that a large number of indicators will be necessary. This is almost obvious from the probabilistic point of view: if you want to estimate the proportion of white balls in an urn you will make a better guess with several independent drawings than with one. Of course, the sociologist cannot ask the same question five times. We thus resort to using several different questions in order to come to a more accurate judgment. This procedure raises a new problem: how to combine the responses to these several questions.

Thus Max Weber defined a bureaucratic organization by a set of criteria[9]; among them were the requirements of hierarchy, of separation of professional and personal obligations, separation of the members from ownership of the tools of work, etc. He defined "ideal-typically" those organizations which satisfied all the criteria, failing to consider the question of the existence of organizations which satisfied only a proportion of them. Carl J. Friedrich, in a critique, correctly pointed out that omitting an answer to this question precluded any empirical study of organizations.[10] He wanted to compare bureaucracies in various countries and wanted to use the Weber criteria, or similar ones, as "measuring rods for determining the degree of bureaucratization"; he needed "the judgment of more or less." Because Friedrich compares only five countries, his ranking could still be made in somewhat impressionistic terms, but if he had wanted to study scores of organizations, he would have been in the same position as a psychologist who wants to order people according to their degree of extroversion, and his problem would have been to combine the *degree of absence or presence* of indicators into one or more indices of bureaucratization.

Among psychologists, the discussion of *intervening variables* provides much material for our present theme.[11] In a variety of ways, this notion served the purpose of reconciling the strong behavioristic trend of the 1930's with the need to continue using concepts based on verbalized introspection. How to define and measure such intervening variables was a major problem. Tolman, for instance, who was the leader in this effort, accepted any concept which was connected to *one* indicator by an empirically or theoretically derived numerical

---

[9]Max Weber, "The Essentials of Bureaucratic Organization," reprinted in *Reader in Bureaucracy*, R. K. Merton, A. Gray, B. Hockey, H. C. Selvin, eds. (Glencoe, Ill., The Free Press, 1952), pp. 18ff.
[10]Carl J. Friedrich, "Some Observations on Weber's Analysis of Bureaucracy", *Ibid.*, p. 27.
[11]For a more detailed presentation of pertinent material see Paul Lazarsfeld, "Concept Formation and Measurement in the Behavioral Sciences; Some Historical Observations." *Concepts, Theory and Explanation in the Behavioral Sciences*, Gordon J. Di Kempo, ed., (New York, Random House, 1966), pp. 144–204. This is a much extended version of the historical remarks made here.

function: e.g., hunger could be measured by the amount of electric shock a rat was willing to take after varying periods of food deprivation.[12]

Twenty years after he did his main experimental work, Tolman joined a group of sociologists in work on a theory of action. He developed a series of elaborate paradigms, illustrated with down-to-earth examples.[13] One such was "a hungry actor going to a particular restaurant and ordering and eating a particular food." In the course of this process, the "Actor's Belief-Value Matrix" would come into play. It would be studied by means of questionnaires.

Thus, for example, one could ask the actor: (1) "What are you ready to do when you haven't eaten for a considerable length of time?" (2) "What kinds of food do you like? Name six varieties of food in order of preference. What do you like about each of these six?" (3) "For each of these six foods what types of restaurants would you go to and in what order? List all the considerations you would take into account in choosing the one kind of restaurant or the other."

The repeated references to questionnaires make it easy to predict what problems Tolman would face if he were really to attempt to develop measurements along this line of argument: the student experienced in social research knows that answers to questionnaires vary considerably if wordings are slightly changed, if the interview is done under slightly varying conditions, etc. There is just no way to develop a "standard experimental set-up" or "standard-defining experiment." We shall have to face the fact that to an intervening variable there will correspond a variety of indicators and that they will have to be reconciled in some way.

There has existed for quite a while an important technique for studying the interrelation of indicators and their connection with underlying concepts: factor analysis. The procedure is too well known to need an introduction. One of its important proponents used the apt aphorism that a factor analyst is "like a plumber who is given no map of the underlying conditions, but is asked to deduce from the rates of flow from many faucets — and their mutual interferences — what conduit system exists."[14] It is less well known that Cattell was one of the first to apply factor analysis to sociological data, to characteristics of collectives. He created the term *syntality* "to refer to that in a group which corresponds to personality in an individual."[15]

Latent structure analysis is in some ways similar and in many very basic ways different from factor analysis. But one should never forget that either procedure is as applicable to sets of groups as to sets of individuals. That more examples in this volume come from observations on individuals is due to the fact that these are much more easily obtained. Now that cross-cultural data have become more widely available the balance, we hope, will be reached in the near future.

[12]Lazarsfeld, *Ibid.*, p. 155 and the original references given there.
[13]Talcott Parsons and Edward A. Shils, eds., *Toward a General Theory of Action* (Cambridge, Harvard University Press, 1951), p. 295, pp. 363ff.
[14]R. B. Cattell, *Description and Measurement of Personality* (World Book Co., 1946), p. 110.
[15]R. B. Cattell, "Concepts and Methods in the Measurement of Group Syntality," *Psychological Review*, 55 (1948), pp. 48–63.

3. The Development of Latent Structure Analysis

One can unify the probability aspect and the need for using a variety of indicators into one slogan taken from medicine: the *diagnostic procedure*. The medical doctor needs to use a variety of tests to find out what degree of damage is done to an organ to which he has no direct access. The present publication presents such a diagnostic procedure. The observable material is (usually) a series of dichotomous observations. The intended classification is defined by a set of latent parameters, and relations linking the latent variates to the manifest data contain the main "theory." It will be useful to recall the state of affairs at the time latent structure analysis had its start.

For a long time there had been discussions of how the items of a test should be weighted: by the opinion of competent judges, through bi-serial correlation with a total score, and so on. The full weight of the problem came to the fore only with the appearance of the SSRC monograph on prediction in 1941.[16] It made three major contributions. The main text made clear the distinction between two kinds of "scales": those for which outside criteria were available and those for which this was not the case. The typical example is concerned with efforts to predict the success of marriage. Studies of this kind require two kinds of classificatory instruments. On the one hand, marriages have to be ordered somehow according to how successful they are. To do this, the investigator has to decide on some criteria of marital success, and has to combine them into one scale which we might call, typically, *intrinsic*. But he also collects information on the state of affairs which existed at the time the marriage was planned: length of engagement, length of time the couple have known each other, similarity of social background, age difference, and so on. These items have to be combined into a predictive instrument to be used to gauge the chances of a successful marriage in the future: this is an *extrinsic* scale because it is derived from its relation to the established scale of success. The main purpose of the study is to get appropriate weights for the items in the predictive scale, based on their correlations with the happiness classification.

In an important appendix to the SSRC study, Louis Guttman brought to light one basic aspect of intrinsic scales. Because there is no external criterion against which to validate the various items, it is necessary to weight them according to their relations with each other, and this required some mathematical model. Guttman's idea was to weight the items so that the dispersion between the objects to be classified be maximized. The mathematical procedures which Guttman introduced in this appendix have had considerable consequences, but they don't concern us in the present context. What matters here is the clear insight that *mathematical models were needed for intrinsic scales;* this was the second contribution of the SSRC volume.

A third contribution was less explicit, but nevertheless definitely implied: the necessity of dealing differently with attributes as compared to quantitative variables. Guttman implicitly challenged the justification of applying correlation

---

[16]Paul Horst and others, eds., *Prediction of Personal Adjustment* (New York, Social Science Research Council, 1941).

analysis to attributes, that is, manifest classifications for which only a few categories are available (yes, no; agree, disagree, undecided; present, absent).

This third contribution proved to be, in the long run, the most important one for latent structure analysis. The problem to be dealt with can be demonstrated in its basic form by thinking of two dichotomous attributes. Suppose we want to gauge the socioeconomic level of people by whether or not they own two objects. Obviously, those who own both are on top and those who own neither are at the bottom. But how should we compare those who own the one but not the other? Guttman proposed to circumvent the issue by his notion of a perfect scale. A pair of items would belong to such a scale only if one of the two unranked types never existed. Some people might own a color television set and others an electric typewriter without being able to afford both. But it is a social fact that almost everyone who owns a color television also owns a refrigerator. There would be no ambiguity, therefore, in deciding how to rank the people, based on the ownership of the television and the refrigerator, due to the "natural" ordering of the objects (items). The most famous precedent for this idea is the Bogardus Social Distance Scale: people are asked whether they would marry and work with members of another ethnic group; the assumption is that no one would approve of marriage who disapproved of collaboration at work.

Guttman's perfect scale has had a great vogue of popularity. The hope was that by a proper choice of cumulative indicators one could obtain pure instruments with which to classify people into a uni-dimensional order. This whole trend of thought overlooked the one element which we have stressed so strongly in our preceding pages: the probabilistic character of indicators. In nearly every social science application, we are quite sure, *a priori*, that no manifest observation will be completely determined by the assumed position of a respondent on an underlying latent scale. A typical problem is the following.

Suppose we want to know to what extent a person favors economic intervention by the federal government. We ask two questions: should the government run railroads, should it own the banks? A convinced interventionist will say yes to both questions; a convinced free-enterprise man will say no to both. But someone in a more intermediate mood might pick either of the two other possibilities. He might want the government to own the banks because of their far-reaching power, but might fear an inefficient management of the railroads. Or he might favor government ownership of railroads because that might be the cue for unravelling the national transportation problem, but be willing to leave banking operations to the free play of the marketplace. Which of the two intermediate answers indicates a stronger desire for government controls in a "pure" form can only be found out by adding additional questions regarding, say, more control over television programs, building houses, etc.

By ruling out, *a priori*, certain combinations of possible response patterns, one eliminated the possibility of gaining a great deal of additional knowledge. By admitting a much greater variety of manifest information to analysis, one was faced with the problem of how to deal mathematically with them. Factor analysis had provided one model for relating such observations to an intended classification, but it had become clear that this model was inappropriate for dealing with non-quantitative data; and the growth of social research had greatly increased the amount of such data. Answers to questionnaires, observations on actual behavior, membership in significant social groups, do not provide the kind of variables to which the factor analysis models should be applied. Louis Guttman opened up a new world when he emphasized the need to apply new mathematical methods to qualitative data. It is the purpose of latent structure analysis to broaden these possibilities. A brief preview of the content of the present volume will show in what directions these efforts have been made.[17]

4. The Plan of the Present Volume

Chapter 2 can be considered a bridge between this conceptual introduction and the mathematical treatment which dominates the rest of the book. The chapter deals with the simplest possible case. A sample of people have answered a number of dichotomous questions which are arbitrarily classified as positive or negative. The manifest data thus come from each person's response pattern, which is made up of a series of plus and minus signs. Given the relative frequencies of these ultimate response patterns, it is easy to compute a variety of other data: the proportion of positive responses to each single item and the fourfold tables for pairs of items, or the joint frequencies for triplets, quadruplets, etc.

The intended classification requires that the respondents be assigned to one of two "latent classes." These latent classes are characterized by a set of latent parameters telling the probability of a positive response for each item in each class. A series of accounting equations links the latent parameters and the empirically observed response frequencies. These equations derive from the central substantive idea of the whole system, called the *principle of local independence*, following a suggestion of Mosteller. The chapter discusses the substantive implications of this axiom and its mathematical formulation. The algebra involved in solving the accounting equations is traced in considerable detail because it forms the foundation of all subsequent, more difficult, mathematical analyses. Even someone who has difficulties with the later chapters can gather from Chapter 2 the main ideas of latent structure analysis and the type of mathematical developments to which it leads.

The case of two latent classes was described in detail in the fourth volume of *The American Soldier*.[18] There, one will also find a chapter written by Sam

---

[17]The work of Guttman has only been traced up to the point where it led, almost by opposition, to the development of latent structure analysis. Guttman has since made many new important contributions which, however, go in other directions. For an introduction to Guttman's later work, see his articles in Lazarsfeld's *Mathematical Thinking in the Social Sciences*. It should be added that very early Guttman created the notion of an "universe of items" of which a particular scale represents a subset. This volume does not deal with the selection of items at all, but only with their mathematical treatment; and, therefore, this point is not further pursued.

[18]S. A. Stouffer, *et al.*, *Measurement and Prediction* (Princeton, Princeton University Press, 1950), Chapters 10 and 11.

Stouffer comparing with great insight Guttman's ideas on the perfect scale and latent structure analysis.[19] It is very much to the credit of the late Professor Stouffer that he sponsored both developments in spite of the fact that, at that time, they seemed somewhat at odds with each other.

The content of Chapter 2 can be summarized in a symbolic form which some readers might find helpful. The manifest data consist of all possible combinations which can be formed from a series of n items, such as presence or absence of observable group characteristics, answers to a true-false question, or anything else which can be put into dichotomous form. For two items, we get the well-known fourfold table, the cells of which report the frequencies of the four possible joint occurrences. For three items, we get what has been called a dichotomous cube, with eight entries. For n items, we get 2^n frequencies which can be thought of as making up an n-dimensional cube or multinomial system S. Such a system will be called homogeneous if all the higher-order relative frequencies are products of the marginal proportions. The problem then is to decompose S into the "sum" of two H's. It is our obvious intention to raise the question of what conditions are necessary to solve the more general decomposition problem when

$$S = H_1 + H_2 + \cdots + H_k.$$

While each H_i is itself homogeneous, corresponding entries in a sequence of $H_i(i = 1, 2, \ldots, k)$ may be linked by specified conditions. The remaining chapters of this book are devoted to solving and discussing a number of such specific models.

In the original publication, now 20 years old, it was pointed out that it was easy to set up accounting equations where the latent classification consisted of any number of classes. The algebraic solution of these equations, even for the three-class case, was not available, however. During the next few years, various efforts were made to solve these equations. By trial and error the senior author finally selected a combination of manifest data which provided the answer. The procedure required the introduction of sums of "semi-stratified determinants" which had previously not found the attention of algebraists. (This concept is explained in Chapter 3.) These compounds turned out to equal relatively simple functions of the latent parameters, namely, the symmetric functions of the within-class probabilities of an item. The senior author remembers with gratitude the help he received at that time from Professor Jack Dudman (now at Reed College), who assisted him on a project generously financed by the RAND Corporation.

The mathematicians of, say, 1910, were much interested in the theory of determinants, but had not been confronted with the type of equation which arose in the study of the latent class model. The mathematicians of 1950, on the other hand, considered our type of problem uninteresting. Once a solution had been found by "brute force," however, competent colleagues gave it an elegant and efficient form. The "basic solution" presented in Chapter 3 equates the latent probabilities to the roots of determinantal equations, and is due to

[19] *Ibid*, Chapter 2.

Professor Theodore Anderson. At the same time, coincidentally, Bert Green, then a Psychometric Fellow at Princeton University, also solved the multiple class equations by a different method that resembled traditional factor analysis in its consideration of symmetric matrices. Because Green's procedure required the estimation of quantities which were not really required by the structure of the model,[20] it remained a "first" without further developmental consequences.

It is helpful to distinguish several steps in the development of a latent structure model. The accounting equations establish relations between manifest data and latent parameters. Once the equations are set up there is the algebraic problem as to how they can be solved. The general procedure is to form complex combinations of manifest data which correspond to simple forms of the latent parameters, but each model requires special mathematical inventiveness for this phase. Finally, there is the task of deciding whether a given set of empirical data fits the model under investigation.

The fit is, of course, never perfect, partly because a model will almost always be an over-simplification of the real situation and partly because any set of empirical observations is subject to sampling errors. Chapter 4 is devoted to a review of the sampling problem in the latent class models; it is the exclusive contribution of the junior author. Interestingly enough, much of the literature on latent structure analysis written by other authors has concentrated on questions of estimation. There exist now several computer programs for dealing with particular aspects of latent structure analysis, but, as we note later on, there is no single system which will automatically analyze a set of data. While, obviously, any practical applications of latent structure analysis require estimation procedures, it is possible to follow the general theory of latent structure analysis without going into the details of Chapter 4.

Readers who have examined the discrete class case in Chapters 2 and 3 and who are acquainted with factor analysis, will notice the way in which the two procedures are similar, or different. The main similarity lies in what we call the *conditions of reducibility*. Both models impose conditions on the rank of a covariance or correlation matrix. In an m-class model, for instance, the covariance matrix of a set of items has rank $m - 1$; the correlation matrix of a set of tests reducible to k-factors has to have the rank of k. The main difference lies in the fact that latent structure analysis has no rotation problem. This is because the discrete class case can make use of information about the joint frequencies of three or more items in order to determine the proper rotations. The equations of factor analysis which link manifest scores with latent factors involve assumption of normal distribution and therefore do not permit the use of data more complex than pairwise correlations, since all such higher-order data is uniquely determined by the second-order correlations. Finally, latent structure analysis is specifically designed for dichotomous items, attributes, and does not require the use of correlation coefficients.

There exists, also, a difference in intuitive interpretation. A system of latent classes is best thought of as a typology where each type reacts differently to the

---

[20]These quantities play the role of the unknown communalities of ordinary factor analysis.

stimuli represented by the questions. No special order is assumed to exist between these types. Other models permit latent classes to be placed in relation to one another; two of these are described in Chapter 5. The first is a generalization of Guttman's "perfect scale." In the language of latent structure, the perfect scale makes the following two assumptions: that people are ranked on a latent continuum; and every item is of such a character that below a certain point of this continuum no one gives a positive reply, while beyond this point everyone does. The second assumption is the one that we relax: below the cutting point, any item has a very small probability of drawing a positive reply, and then, above that point, it has a very large probability for a positive reply. The parameters of this *latent distance model*, i.e., these two probabilities for each item, can be fairly easily computed. The model can be applied much more generally to empirical data than the perfect scale model.

The second model of Chapter 5 is a modification of the model introduced in Chapter 3. The assumption there is that people are concentrated at discrete points whose location along a continuum can be computed with the help of accounting equations. But this additional knowledge is gotten for a price; in the *located class model* the probabilities of each item must be made subject to certain restrictions.

As in other models discussed so far, the distribution of people in the latent space can also be identified. The question then remains, however, to what class (or at what point) a specific respondent belongs. For each of the models, *recruitment probabilities* can be computed which state how likely it is that a particular respondent is located at a given place in the latent space. This implies that a latent structure model does not necessarily assign to every respondent a specific score. It may assign a whole distribution of recruitment probabilities and some average of them might correspond to the traditional idea of a score, if it were possible, in fact, to *order* everyone in the population.

This is also true for those models where people can be thought to be distributed continuously over a latent dimension. Chapter 6 discusses a characteristic case where just this assumption is being made. It introduces the notion of *traceline:* a continuous function which links the probability of a positive response to an item to a position on the latent continuum. In such a model, then, the accounting equations will involve integrals rather than sums, as in the discrete class models. Only in very simple cases do these models permit a closed analytical integration. The model of Chapter 6 is not very realistic, but it was chosen because it permits one to show the algebraic properties and analysis of such continuous models in all detail. Two points in this chapter deserve special attention. There are again conditions of reducibility specified by the model, but they are radically different from the ones that arise in factor analysis; and also, the model permits a geometrical interpretation involving an "hyperbolic rotation," which is quite different from the orthogonal rotation in factor analysis.

Chapter 7 develops further the models of continuous tracelines. The located discrete class case assumes that the latent probabilities are subject to polynomial restrictions and that the population is concentrated on specific points. If we drop the latter assumption, then we have a model with polynomial tracelines and a density distribution of the population over the whole admissible range of the latent continuum. It can be shown, in principle, that the moments of this distribution can be computed if we have enough manifest items. But the solution of the accounting equations is not yet available.

In the same chapter, we discuss comparisons with other measurement models, especially those developed by a group of Princeton psychometricians, under the leadership of Frederic Lord. The traceline they introduce is the normal ogive, but there is another more important difference. Lord makes no assumption on the latent distribution of the population. Rather, by his estimation procedures, he ends up with a specific latent position for each individual. This part of Chapter 7 is closely related to Chapter 4. Another model of a population-free latent structure has been proposed by the Danish statistician Georg Rasch. These models permit us to develop further the parallels with, and the difference from, the classical notion of test scores.

Chapter 8 raises the question of how far latent structure analysis can be applied when the manifest data are non-dichotomous. Gibson's *latent profile* model deals with manifest variables which can assume any real value. He shows that under these conditions one can also assume the existence of latent classes which now are characterized by mean values rather than by latent probabilities. The junior author extended the idea and demonstrated that one can also compute the higher-order moments of each variable within the latent classes. The correlations between variables within a class are assumed to vanish, of course, following the axiom of local independence. Latent profile analysis lends itself especially well to the analysis of ecological data. Here the basic units of the analysis are not people, but collectives. An example applied to all counties of the State of Ohio helps to clarify the idea.

Another extension is offered for the case where the manifest data fall into a *finite number of categories larger than two*. The accounting equations are straightforward and easily solved. But the model puts so many restrictions on the manifest data that its practical application seems doubtful.

Chapter 9 introduces variations on the theme of latent classes. Suppose that the position of an individual within the latent class is not fixed, but changes with time. More specifically, we assume that individuals move back and forth between latent classes along a Markov chain. Such a model would apply especially to so-called panel analysis where repeated observations are made on the same people, for instance, what magazines they read; for which party they vote; whether they are employed or unemployed, etc.

Throughout this book we have been guided by a number of editorial policies. Wherever suitable, we used data from actual studies to illustrate the mathematics. We did not hesitate to present artificial examples at several points, however, when this helped to clarify a more difficult point. Some mathematical ideas, interesting, but not essential for the main flow of the argument, are either treated in "Asides" or relegated to exercises. Computer programs mentioned in the text can be obtained by writing to the Bureau of Applied Social Research at Columbia University.

While we have tried to present a full picture of the present state of latent structure analysis, we were much concerned with its future development. We emphasized the existence of unsolved problems, indicating what efforts have been made toward their solution, and in what direction we think answers lie. The basic ideas of latent structure analysis are of a very general nature, and the specific models this book presents are those for which the mathematics is relatively easy. Readers concerned with substantive problems will quickly think of further applications; as a result they should investigate *other* models which undoubtedly will require different mathematical procedures.

2

Basic Concepts of Latent Structure Analysis

1. Introduction

A public opinion poll investigates attitudes about the UN by asking a series of yes-no questions which deal with specific issues involving the UN. The agency wants to devise some kind of index which will enable it to separate the population into three groups: Pro-UN, Anti-UN, and neutral.

A doctor observes the presence or absence of symptoms of a certain disease. He knows that when the patient is sick he may not necessarily show all the symptoms of the disease, while on the other hand, patients who are not sick will sometimes exhibit some symptoms. How should the doctor make his decision as to the condition of the patient?

These examples are typical of a problem that often arises in the social sciences. The concern is with measurement of characteristics which are not directly observable, such as the attitude of the public, and the health of the patient. Measurement models attempt to answer these questions by making certain assumptions that appear plausible about the *nature* of the attitude, health, etc., and then seeing what conclusions can be derived from the assumptions. As was discussed in Chapter 1, it is necessary to make some assumptions about the nature of what we called the "latent variable." In the situations that concern us, there is no objective criterion for directly measuring this variable, no yardstick against which it can be evaluated. A test, a poll, a set of symptoms are imperfect indicators, but there do not exist any perfect indicators. Thus we choose to define the latent variable by specifying its effect on a certain class of indicators.[1]

[1] We would agree that in some cases an objective criterion may theoretically exist: e.g., eventually the patient will die, and a post-mortem examination may ascertain whether the disease was really present. Most of our examples, however, will come from the field of attitude research, where such examinations are not meaningful alternatives.

Latent structure analysis in its primary form is concerned with responses to dichotomous items.[2] An *item* may be a question asked directly of an individual, as in an opinion poll, or it may be a certain characteristic of the respondent, such as the ownership of certain objects or the presence or absence of a particular symptom. In any case, we shall speak of the *response* to the item, even when referring to collectives rather than individuals. One of the two alternatives will be called the positive response, and the other, the negative response. A set of items is called a *test* or *item list*.

In order to be able to treat precisely statements such as "student *A* is more likely to pass than student *B*," and to take into account our inability to predict behavior with 100% accuracy, we introduce the notion of probability into our models. In the above example, we would characterize *A* and *B* by two numbers, p_A and p_B, between zero and one, which are the probabilities of the two subjects passing. The statement then implies that p_A is greater than p_B. We can also think of p_A as being the proportion of people "similar" to *A* who pass, and usually this is how we estimate probabilities: by counting how many in a certain population have the desired property.

In practice, we work with an item list made up of items related to a single ability, attitude, attribute, etc. These items can be thought of as elements of a larger universe which consists of all possible items which are related to that latent variable. We postulate the existence of a *latent space* in which the members of a population are located, with the probability of positive response to any item in the list determined completely by one's position in this latent space. A particular latent structure *model* is a specification of the nature of the latent space, and of how the *item probabilities* vary within the space. The latent space is thus a space of the variable which we are interested in measuring.

For example, in the case of the poll concerning the UN, the latent space is supposed to consist of three distinct points, these points representing the people who are Pro-UN, Anti-UN, and Uninterested. We might believe that the probability of a positive response to any relevant item would be high for the first group of people, low for the second group, and intermediate for the third group.

Similarly, in the case of diagnosing illness, we might postulate that the latent space consists of *two* points, representing presence and absence, respectively, of the disease. Those who were really sick would have a higher probability of exhibiting any one symptom than those who were not.

In the case of an intelligence test made up of dichotomous items, we might suppose that underlying the responses to the questions is the *ability* of the students, and that ability is distributed in a continuous fashion. Then the latent space might be the entire real line, the linear continuum, the students being, perhaps, normally distributed. For each point on the line (each ability), there exists a probability of a correct answer to any question. This is formally stated by defining a function for every question, called the *item traceline*, which generates the appropriate probabilities.

The examples dealing with attitudes toward the UN and the diagnosis of

[2]This requirement may be relaxed. See Chapter 8.

illness fall into the class of *discrete class models*, the latent space consisting of a finite number of points. The example of the intelligence test belongs to the class of *continuous distribution*, or *traceline*, models. Of course, we must remember that a model is only an attempt to describe a situation or population, and may not succeed in this description. Only by looking at the relevant empirical data can we decide whether a particular model serves its purpose. We are concerned throughout this book with showing how to relate the theoretical models to the actual data.

Latent structure analysis includes many different models, all of which are derived from a few basic assumptions. In this chapter, we shall present a simple model, the latent dichotomy, in order to illustrate the nature of these assumptions. In later chapters, we shall generalize and apply the assumptions, obtaining other, more complex models.

2. The Latent Dichotomy: Definition

As the first step in the definition of the latent dichotomy, we postulate the existence of two latent classes. While there will be many situations in which the objects of our analysis are not individual people, we shall consider now, for the sake of clarity, that a population of individuals is being studied. The division into two classes may be thought of as corresponding to the presence or the absence of a *latent attribute* or *quality* in these individuals.

The relation between the latent classes and the observable items is defined by the *axiom of local independence*, which states that within a class the items are all independent of one another. This definition is our way of stating mathematically that the latent variable explains why the observed items are related to one another. In the next section, we shall try to justify this definition by considering the problem of explaining the association between two items in terms of a third observable variable.

2.1 *An Observable or Manifest Dichotomy*

Consider the following hypothetical example.

Example. A group of 1,000 people are asked whether they have read the last issue of magazine *A* and magazine *B*. Their responses can be easily presented by means of a fourfold table, i.e.,

TABLE 1

Readership of Two Magazines

	Read *A*	Do not read *A*	
Read *B*	260	240	500
Do not read *B*	140	360	500
	400	600	1000

From Table 1 we see that there is some association between reading magazine A and reading magazine B. A simple indicator of this association is the percentage difference, which tells us that readers of A tend to read B more often than do non-readers of A: $65\% - 40\% = 25\%$. Other coefficients of association might be used: the ϕ coefficient; Yule's Q; or the x^2 statistic.[3] All of these measures have a common factor and that is the *cross product* of the 2×2 table, defined by:

$$\frac{ad - bc}{n^2},$$

where the table is

a	b	$a + b$
c	d	$c + d$
$a + c$	$b + d$	$a + b + c + d = n$

In the terminology of matrix algebra, $ad - bc$ is the *determinant* of the matrix:

$$\begin{pmatrix} a & b \\ c & d \end{pmatrix}.$$

We indicate the determinant by vertical lines:

$$\begin{vmatrix} a & b \\ c & d \end{vmatrix} = ad - bc.$$

When the cross product is zero, we say that there is no association between the two variables.

In this case, the cross product is positive,

$$(ad - bc)/n^2 = (260 \cdot 360 - 140 \cdot 240)/1000^2 = 0.06.$$

The magazines thus have some common appeal to readers, although they are far from identical in their readership. Analyzing this result further, we seek to explain why they are related.

Suppose that the auxiliary data on the 1,000 respondents includes information on the amount of education each has had, dichotomized as High-Ed and Low-Ed. When our hypothetical population is divided into these two groups, readership of the two magazines is observed as in Table 2.

---

[3]A much more extensive discussion of the analysis of dichotomous items is found in Paul Lazarsfeld, "The Algebra of Dichotomous Systems," *Studies in Item Analysis and Prediction*, Herbert Solomon, ed. (Stanford, Stanford University Press, 1961).

TABLE 2

Readership of Two Magazines, Controlling for Education

	High-Ed			Low-Ed		
	Read A	Do not read A		Read A	Do not read A	
Read B	240	60	300	20	80	100
Do not read B	160	40	200	80	320	400
	400	100	500	100	400	500

In each of the 2×2 tables where education is held constant it appears that there is no association between the two magazines. The two cross products vanish:

$$240 \cdot 40 - 160 \cdot 60 = 0; \qquad\qquad 20 \cdot 320 - 80 \cdot 80 = 0.$$

This lack of association is exemplified by the fact that among the High-Ed people, 4/5 read magazine A, whether or not they also read B. That is,

$$240/300 = 4/5 = 160/200.$$

Since there is no association between A and B when the population is stratified according to education, we say that education "explains" the original association between the magazines. The observed connection between reading A and reading B turns out to be due to the common appeal they both make to higher educated people.

Table 1 was the starting point of the analysis. The question "Why does the association exist?" was formulated in terms of the two items, reading A and reading B. Presumably, other factors beside education were considered as explanatory variables, but, when examined, were found not sufficient to account for the association. We can imagine a generalization of this problem, where the aim of the analysis is to explain not merely the association among two items, A and B, but the mutual association of a set of several items. This is, of course, a much more difficult problem.

It may not be clear just how the items are related; and even if we have a fairly good idea of how they are related, it is very unlikely that we shall find a single indicator variable (e.g., years of education) which is equivalent to the underlying concept (e.g., intelligence, sophistication). That is to say, the relating *concept* will usually be a *latent variable*, one which is not directly observable. In order to locate this latent variable, we formalize mathematically our procedure in analyzing the simple, two-item problem.

2.2 *Use of Probability*

The first step in the formalization is the introduction of probability theory. We assign a number, a probability, to an item as a quantitative measure of how people of a certain type react to the item. We may interpret this probability in several ways. When we say that the "probability of a highly educated person reading magazine A is 3/5," we might mean either:

(a) Three-fifths of all the High-Ed people have read A.
(b) The actual behavior of people is probabilistic: i.e., one decides *randomly*, by the flip of a suitably biased coin, whether or not to read magazine A each month. For the High-Ed people, this "coin" will tend to come up "read" three times out of five.

Often, especially in situations where psychological mechanisms are involved, interpretation (b) is followed. It is not necessary to assume always that actual behavior is random, however. Following (a) and not assuming that any random process of behavior is at work, we can say simply that some people read and others do not: the class of High-Ed people is characterized by the fact that if we *choose* any one member of the class at random there is a chance of 3/5 that he will have read A.

Before we can go any further, we must introduce some algebraic notation. Let:

$$p_A^H = \text{Probability of a High-Ed person reading magazine } A,$$
$$p_B^L = \text{Probability of a Low-Ed person reading magazine } B.$$

Similarly defined are p_A^L and p_B^H. We shall adopt the convention of letting subscripts refer to the items under investigation (magazines A, B), while the superscripts will refer to the independent variable which is separating the population. We also need to refer to the probability that someone will read both magazines, and these are given by p_{AB}^H and p_{AB}^L for the subgroups.

If we look at Table 2, we find that these probabilities are as follows:

$$p_A^H = 400/500 = 4/5, \qquad p_A^L = 100/500 = 1/5,$$
$$p_B^H = 300/500 = 3/5, \qquad p_B^L = 100/500 = 1/5,$$
$$p_{AB}^H = 240/500 = 12/25, \qquad p_{AB}^L = 20/500 = 1/25.$$

If we write $\overline{A}$ and $\overline{B}$ to stand for "do not read A" and "do not read B," respectively, the 2×2 table of probabilities may be symbolized as follows:

TABLE 3

Readership of Two Magazines

	Read A	Do not read A	Total
Read B	p_{AB}	$p_{\overline{A}B}$	p_B
Do not read B	$p_{A\overline{B}}$	$p_{\overline{A}\,\overline{B}}$	$p_{\overline{B}}$
Total	p_A	$p_{\overline{A}}$	1

This is, of course, obtained from Table 1 by dividing through by n. The condition that we required of the High-Ed — Low-Ed division before accepting education as the explanatory variable was that the cross product be zero in both tables of Table 2. This cross product, written in terms of probabilities, and symbolized by $[AB]$, is

$$[AB] = p_{AB}p_{\overline{A}\overline{B}} - p_{\overline{A}B}p_{A\overline{B}}$$
$$= p_{AB} - p_{A}p_{B}$$

which is the form we shall find most convenient to use.

ASIDE: The equality

$$p_{AB}p_{\overline{A}\overline{B}} - p_{\overline{A}B}p_{A\overline{B}} = p_{AB} - p_{A}p_{B}$$

is one that we shall use over and over again. It is most easily proven as an application of the following obvious equality:

given numbers a, b, c, and d,
$ad - bc = (a + b + c + d)a - (a + b)(a + c).$

In the special case where $a + b + c + d = 1$, we have the probability statement given above. ∎

For the cross product to be equal to zero, the probability of A and B both occurring must be equal to the product of their individual probabilities. So, in our example,

$$p_{AB}^{H} = p_{A}^{H}p_{B}^{H} \quad \text{and} \quad p_{AB}^{L} = p_{A}^{L}p_{B}^{L}.$$

This condition is known as *statistical independence* and in the future, instead of speaking of the association between two items vanishing, we shall say that the two items are independent.

2.3 *The Assumptions of Latent Structure Models*

We have already remarked that the basic use of latent structure is to *define* latent variables which will account for an association among observed items, in a fashion similar to the way education accounted for the relationship found between reading A and reading B in our hypothetical example. Let us see how our thinking would proceed in applying a two-class latent dichotomy.

First, we have some data, several items (let us say four) which are dichotomous and related in some way. Our motivation is a feeling that this relation among the items can be explained by a dichotomous latent variable, say S. If we could divide our respondents into those who are positive on S (class 1) and those who are negative on S (class 2) all association among the observed items would vanish: the items would be independent of each other within each of the two classes. Mathematically, as we have seen, this condition of within-class in-dependence is given by

$$p_{ij}^1 = p_i^1 p_j^1 \quad \text{and} \quad p_{ij}^2 = p_i^2 p_j^2,$$

where i and j stand for any two of our items.

The problem here, of course, is that we do not know what these *latent probabilities* or *latent marginals* p_i^α are ($\alpha = 1$ or $\alpha = 2$). Nor do we know what the proportions of people falling into the two categories of S (symbolized by v^1 and v^2) are. We have *at most* a vague idea of the nature of S, and a model. It is this *model* of the *underlying structure* which will eventually define the latent variable S. In order to specify the model, the latent marginals and the class frequencies must be related mathematically to the observable data. This observable data consists of the manifest responses to the items, marginal proportions p_1, p_2, p_3, p_4; joint proportions p_{12}, p_{13}, etc., standing for the proportion who respond positively to items 1 and 2, to items 1 and 3, etc. The equations which relate the latent parameters (p_i^α, v^1, v^2) to the manifest data (p_i, p_{ij}, etc.) are called *accounting equations*. In this chapter, we shall see how these equations are derived in the two-class model, and shall also show how the latent parameters can be derived from the observed frequencies.

The defining characteristic of the latent structure models is the *axiom of local independence*, stated here for the case of discrete latent classes.

AXIOM OF LOCAL INDEPENDENCE. *Within a latent class, α, responses to different items are independent. The within class probability of any pattern of response to any set of items is the product of the appropriate marginal probabilities. Stated algebraically:*

$$p_{ij}^\alpha = p_i^\alpha p_j^\alpha,$$

$$p_{i\bar{j}}^\alpha = p_i^\alpha p_{\bar{j}}^\alpha = (1 - p_i^\alpha) p_j^\alpha,$$

$$p_{ijk}^\alpha = p_i^\alpha p_j^\alpha p_k^\alpha, \textit{ etc., for any class } \alpha.$$

Notice that our definition applies to any set of items, no matter how large. Unless otherwise stated, the term "independence" will always mean complete independence, and not merely pair-wise independence.

Local independence is the essential unifying characteristic of all the models discussed in this book (Lazarsfeld, 1954, 1959).[4] As we shall see, the use of this assumption has not been restricted to what is usually called latent structure analysis. It is a common statistical assumption which often seems to make sense from a substantive point of view, although it is sometimes overlooked that justification for making the assumption rests more on the substantive, theoretical aspects of the problem than on empirical, statistical grounds.

---

[4]See bibliography at end of text for complete information about parenthetical references.

3. The Accounting Equations and Their Solutions

Let us suppose that we are working with a set of n dichotomous items. For the two-class model there are the following latent parameters:

The latent marginals, or item probabilities,

$$p_1^1, p_2^1, p_3^1, \cdots, p_n^1,$$
$$p_1^2, p_2^2, p_3^2, \cdots, p_n^2,$$

usually indicated by (p_i^α), $i = 1, 2, \ldots, n$; $\alpha = 1, 2$.

The relative frequencies of the two classes,

$$v^1, v^2,$$

usually indicated by (v^α), $\alpha = 1, 2$.

We shall always use a superscript to refer to a latent class, and a subscript to refer to an item. Whenever we refer to the "two-class model," or the "hypothesized latent structure," we are speaking of these $2n + 2$ parameters, along with the basic assumption of local independence. By *identification* of the model, we mean the specification of these parameters.

A barred subscript, e.g. $\bar{\imath}$, will always indicate the negative response to the item. Thus, as noted previously,

$$p_{\bar{1}} = 1 - p_1$$

is the probability of a negative response to item 1. The algebra of these barred terms is examined in the Exercises. In general, we can see that if s stands for any combination of subscripts, then

$$p_{s\bar{\imath}} = p_s - p_{si}.$$

(For instance, $p_{1\bar{2}} = p_1 - p_{12}$.)

The rationale for this is simply the fact that

$$p_s = p_{si} + p_{s\bar{\imath}}.$$

The set of those who give response s is made up of two subsets: one is positive on item i (p_{si}) and the other is negative on item i ($p_{s\bar{\imath}}$). Ultimately, any quantity which refers to one or more barred subscripts can be written in terms of positive responses only.

Since the model requires that the entire population be accounted for by the two classes, the sum of the class frequencies must be 1, and so the first equation we derive from the model is

$$1 = v^1 + v^2. \tag{1}$$

Next, we ask what the proportion of positive responses to a single item, 1, say, is in the entire population. This is simply a weighted sum of the marginals p_1^1 and p_1^2 within the two classes; the weights are the relative sizes of the classes,

v^1 and v^2. Letting p_1 stand for the population marginal of item 1, we have

$$p_1 = v^1 p_1^1 + v^2 p_1^2. \tag{2}$$

Equation (2) says that the probability of someone chosen at random giving a positive response to item 1 is equal to the probability that he belongs to class 1 times the conditional probability of a positive response within class 1, plus the probability that he belongs to class 2 times the conditional probability of a positive response within class 2.

> ASIDE: For instance, suppose that the population consists of two types of people who have different tendencies to have red hair. 1/4 have a 0.50 chance of being red-headed, while the other 3/4 have only a 0.02 chance. Then, by Equation (2),
>
> 1/4 (0.50) + 3/4 (0.02) = 1/4 (0.50 + 0.06) = 0.56/4 = 0.14
>
> is the probability of picking a red-haired person from the population at large. ▌

Equation (2) indicates the relationship between the *manifest* probability of a positive response to item 1, p_1, and the latent probabilities. The argument extends to any item i in our list and we have

$$p_i = v^1 p_i^1 + v^2 p_i^2. \tag{3}$$

Now, let us consider the joint probability of positive response to a pair of items, i and j. As with the marginals, the manifest probability p_{ij} is the weighted sum of probabilities p_{ij}^1 and p_{ij}^2, the weights being v^1 and v^2, respectively. The indicated equation is, therefore,

$$p_{ij} = v^1 p_{ij}^1 + v^2 p_{ij}^2. \tag{4}$$

It is a straightforward matter to write p_{ij}^1 and p_{ij}^2 in terms of the latent probabilities, (p_i^α). The axiom of local independence tells us that within any latent class, the probability of a positive response to any item is independent of the response to any other item. More simply, within a latent class, probabilities multiply. Thus,

$$p_{ij}^1 = p_i^1 p_j^1 \quad \text{and} \quad p_{ij}^2 = p_i^2 p_j^2 \tag{5}$$

and Equation (4) becomes

$$p_{ij} = v^1 p_i^1 p_j^1 + v^2 p_i^2 p_j^2. \tag{6}$$

> ASIDE: Continuing our example, suppose that the group that has the greater tendency for red hair also has a tendency to be left-handed. Specifically, suppose that in the smaller group there is a 0.50 chance of having red hair and a 0.40 chance of being left-handed, while in the rest of the population the chances are 0.02 for red hair and 0.04 for being left-handed. We saw that
>
> $$p_1 = \text{Prob (red hair)} = 0.16.$$

Similarly, using Equation (3) we have

$$p_2 = \text{Prob (left-handed)} = 1/4(0.40) + 3/4(0.04) = 0.10 + 0.03 = 0.13.$$

Assuming also that the axiom of local independence holds (i.e., that the two items are independent within each subpopulation), Equation (6) tells us that the probability of having red hair *and* being left-handed is

$$p_{12} = 1/4(0.50)(0.04) + 3/4(0.02)(0.04) = 0.05 + 0.0006 = 0.0506.$$

TABLE 4

Joint Distribution of Hair Color and Dexterity
in Two Subgroups (hypothetical)

	Group 1 ($\frac{1}{4}$)				Group 2 ($\frac{3}{4}$)				Total (1)		
	Hair				Hair				Hair		
	Red	Other			Red	Other			Red	Other	
Left-Handed	0.20	0.20	0.40	*L*	0.0008	0.0292	0.04	*L*	0.0506	0.0794	0.13
Right-Handed	0.30	0.30	0.60	*R*	0.0192	0.9408	0.96	*R*	0.1094	0.7606	0.87
	0.50	0.50	1.0		0.02	0.98	1.0		0.16	0.84	1.0

Notice that a positive association between having red hair and being left-handed appears in the total population: the cross product for the total table is $p_{12} - p_1 p_2 = 0.0506 - (0.13)(0.16) = 0.0298$, although in the two sub-tables the cross product is zero. ∎

The third-order probability, the probability of positive responses to three items, is computed in a similar fashion. First, by the addition rule for probabilities:

$$p_{ijk} = v^1 p_{ijk}^1 + v^2 p_{ijk}^2,$$

and second, by the local independence assumption,

$$p_{ijk}^\alpha = p_i^\alpha p_j^\alpha p_k^\alpha, \quad \alpha = 1, 2.$$

Hence, the appropriate accounting equation of third order is:

$$p_{ijk} = v^1 p_i^1 p_j^1 p_k^1 + v^2 p_i^2 p_j^2 p_k^2. \tag{7}$$

We can now summarize and generalize these results. Let s stand for a certain pattern of responses of any length whatsoever: we call s a *response pattern*. Let p_s^α stand for the conditional probability of response s within class α ($\alpha = 1, 2$), and p_s for the unconditional probability in the whole population.

25

We have at once

$$p_s = v^1 p_s^1 + v^2 p_s^2,$$

since the probability of s equals the probability of being in class 1 and responding s plus the probability of being in class 2 and responding s. Equation (4) is, of course, a special case of the above equation, in which s is taken to be (i, j). By local independence, p_s can always be written as the product of the appropriate marginals, e.g., if $s = (i, j, k)$,

$$p_{ijk}^\alpha = p_i^\alpha p_j^\alpha p_k^\alpha.$$

The accounting equations of the two class model are:

$$
\begin{aligned}
1 &= v^1 + v^2, & & \\
p_i &= v^1 p_i^1 + v^2 p_i^2, & i &= 1, 2, \ldots, n, \\
p_{ij} &= v^1 p_i^1 p_j^1 + v^2 p_i^2 p_j^2, & i, j &= 1, 2, \ldots, n, \qquad (8) \\
p_{ijk} &= v^1 p_i^1 p_j^1 p_k^1 + v^2 p_i^2 p_j^2 p_k^2, & i, j, k &= 1, 2, \ldots, n,
\end{aligned}
$$

etc. for any combinations of subscripts.

If negative responses occur in the response pattern s, the appropriate barred symbols are carried over to the right side of Equations 8, with the understanding that

$$p_{\bar{\imath}} = 1 - p_i.$$

For instance, if $s = (1, 2, \bar{3})$, we see that

$$p_{12\bar{3}} = v^1 p_1^1 p_2^1 p_{\bar{3}}{}^1 + v^2 p_1^2 p_2^2 p_{\bar{3}}{}^2.$$

The probabilities on the left-hand side of the Equations (8) are properties of the complete, undivided population. As such, they may be estimated directly by drawing a random sample from this population and calculating the appropriate proportions of positive responses in this sample. It is also conceivable that this population might be small enough so that a complete count could be made; in such a case, we would know these manifest probabilities exactly. Unless we have repeated observations of the same population, probabilities with repeated subscripts such as p_{11} or p_{22j} cannot be estimated. Therefore, we shall always assume when writing such equations that subscripts are not repeated. We call p_i, p_{ij}, etc. *manifest* probabilities, indicating that they are characteristics of the entire population.

At this point, however, we assume two things: (i) we are in a situation where the particular latent structure model (i.e., the latent dichotomy) truly applies, and (ii) the manifest probabilities p_i, p_{ij}, etc. are known exactly. In this idealized situation, our problem is strictly algebraic, i.e., it is to solve the system of Equations (8) for the unknown latent parameters. Later, we shall consider the *statistical* problems of estimating the latent parameters when we have only estimates of the manifest probabilities, and of examining the "fit" of the latent structure model to the observed data.

3.1 *The Solution for Three Items*

If we have n dichotomous items, there are $2n + 2$ latent parameters: n marginal probabilities in each class, and two class frequencies. On the other hand, the accounting equations include n first-order equations (p_i), $n(n - 1)/2$ of second order (p_{ij}), and, in general, $\binom{n}{m} = \dfrac{n!}{m!(n - m)!}$ of order m. If we agree to call the first equation of (8) the "zero-order" equation, then there are a total of

$$1 + \binom{n}{1} + \binom{n}{2} + \binom{n}{3} + \cdots + \binom{n}{n} = \sum_{m=0}^{n} \binom{n}{m} = 2^n$$

accounting equations.

From the above it follows that if $n = 2$, the accounting equations cannot be solved. For in that case there are six unknown latent parameters, and only four derived equations, $1 = v^1 + v^2$, p_1, p_2, and p_{12}. Since these equations summarize all the information we have available to us, there is no way to find a unique solution unless we have made some restrictions on these latent parameters.

When $n = 3$, on the other hand, there are $2 \cdot 3 + 2 = 8$ latent parameters and $2^3 = 8$ manifest parameters, and, with exactly as many equations as unknowns, we can at least hope for a unique solution.

For the moment, suppose that we have only three items. We shall show later how the solution here derived can be extended to more than three items. Let $[ij] = p_{ij} - p_i p_j$ denote the *cross product* of items i and j. Also, define the *stratified cross product* $[ij;k]$ of items i and j, given k, as follows:

$$[ij;k] = p_{ijk}p_k - p_{ik}p_{jk}. \tag{9}$$

Use of these particular combinations of the positive frequencies will simplify computations at times.

ASIDE: Earlier we noted that the ordinary cross product was related to the *determinant* of a 2×2 table,

$$\begin{vmatrix} a & b \\ c & d \end{vmatrix}$$

and derived the equality

$$ad - bc = (a)(a + b + c + d) - (a + b)(a + c).$$

Thus, in the case of two variables we had:

$$p_{12}p_{\bar{1}\bar{2}} - p_{\bar{1}2}p_{1\bar{2}} = p_{12} - p_1 p_2 = [12].$$

When a third variable is considered, two fourfold tables can be constructed, indicating the relationship between variables 1 and 2 for positive and negative values, respectively, of variable 3.

p_{123}	$p_{1\bar{2}3}$	p_{13}	$p_{12\bar{3}}$	$p_{1\bar{2}\bar{3}}$	$p_{1\bar{3}}$
$p_{\bar{1}23}$	$p_{\bar{1}\bar{2}3}$	$p_{\bar{1}3}$	$p_{\bar{1}2\bar{3}}$	$p_{\bar{1}\bar{2}\bar{3}}$	$p_{\bar{1}\bar{3}}$
p_{23}	$p_{\bar{2}3}$	p_3	$p_{2\bar{3}}$	$p_{\bar{2}\bar{3}}$	$p_{\bar{3}}$

The stratified cross product, as defined in Equation (9) is the cross product of the first table, where the response to item 3 is positive:

$$p_{123}p_{\bar{1}\bar{2}3} - p_{1\bar{2}3}p_{\bar{1}23} = p_3p_{123} - p_{13}p_{23} = [12;3].$$

This follows from the previous result. In exactly the same way, [12;$\bar{3}$] is defined as the cross product of the right-hand table, and is obtained by barring the appropriate subscripts:

$$[12;\bar{3}] = p_{\bar{3}}p_{12\bar{3}} - p_{1\bar{3}}p_{2\bar{3}}.$$

An interesting equality among these cross products is

$$[12] = [12;3]/p_3 + [12;\bar{3}]/p_{\bar{3}} + [13][23]/p_3p_{\bar{3}}. \qquad (10)$$

The proof is left as an exercise. ∎

We are trying to solve these equations for the latent probabilities. The kind of technique that is often useful is illustrated below, for the case of the cross product $[ij] = p_{ij} - p_ip_j$. This is a function of the manifest probabilities: we ask for its relation to the latent quantities. Using the definition of a 2×2 determinant, we see that, in this model:

$$[ij] = \begin{vmatrix} 1 & p_i \\ p_j & p_{ij} \end{vmatrix} = \begin{vmatrix} v^1 + v^2 & v^1p_i^1 + v^2p_i^2 \\ v^1p_j^1 + v^2p_j^2 & v^1p_i^1p_j^1 + v^2p_i^2p_j^2 \end{vmatrix}.$$

Although it is possible to multiply out the determinant on the right, collecting terms and simplifying in a straightforward fashion, we shall proceed to evaluate it by a more circuitous path.

That expression can be written as the product of two matrices:[5]

$$\begin{pmatrix} v^1 + v^2 & v^1p_i^1 + v^2p_i^2 \\ v^1p_j^1 + v^2p_j^2 & v^1p_i^1p_j^1 + v_i^2p_i^2p_j^2 \end{pmatrix} = \begin{pmatrix} v^1 & v^2 \\ v^1p_j^1 & v_j^2p_j^2 \end{pmatrix}\begin{pmatrix} 1 & p_i^1 \\ 1 & p_i^2 \end{pmatrix}.$$

Since the determinant of the product of two matrices is equal to the product of the determinants, we have

$$[ij] = \begin{vmatrix} v^1 & v^2 \\ v^1p_j^1 & v^2p_j^2 \end{vmatrix}\begin{vmatrix} 1 & p_i^1 \\ 1 & p_i^2 \end{vmatrix}$$

$$= (p_i^2 - p_i^1)\begin{vmatrix} 1 & 1 \\ p_j^1 & p_j^2 \end{vmatrix}\begin{vmatrix} v^1 & 0 \\ 0 & v^2 \end{vmatrix}.$$

$$[ij] = (p_i^2 - p_i^1)(p_j^2 - p_j^1)v^1v^2 \qquad (11)$$

[5]Those unfamiliar with the operations of matrix algebra should read Appendix A before proceeding.

where, in the intermediate step, we again "factored" a matrix into the product of two other matrices whose determinants were easier to write down.

Thus the cross product is equal to a product of latent probabilities. We define

$$\delta_1 = p_i^2 - p_i^1$$

for each item i, and can write

$$[ij] = v^1 v^2 \delta_i \delta_j,$$
$$[ik] = v^1 v^2 \delta_i \delta_k,$$
$$[jk] = v^1 v^2 \delta_j \delta_k.$$

These facts imply that the ratio:

$$\frac{[ij][ik]}{[jk]} = v^1 v^2 (\delta_i)^2$$

does not depend on our choice of j and k (as long as $[jk] \neq 0$). A certain combination of manifest quantities has resulted in a fairly simple latent form.

The simple form of this result leads us to examine the *conditional* cross product $[12;3]$ in a similar way. Writing

$$[ij;k] = \begin{vmatrix} p_k & p_{ik} \\ p_{jk} & p_{ijk} \end{vmatrix} = \begin{vmatrix} v^1 p_k^1 + v^2 p_k^2 & v^1 p_i^1 p_k^1 + v^2 p_i^2 p_k^2 \\ v^1 p_j^1 p_k^1 + v^2 p_j^2 p_k^2 & v^1 p_i^1 p_j^1 p_k^1 + v^2 p_i^2 p_j^2 p_k^2 \end{vmatrix}.$$

It takes only a little calculation to show that an analogous decomposition of this table can be applied:

$$[ij;k] = \begin{vmatrix} v^1 & v^2 \\ v^1 p_j^1 & v^2 p_j^2 \end{vmatrix} \begin{vmatrix} p_k^1 & p_i^1 p_k^1 \\ p_k^2 & p_i^2 p_k^2 \end{vmatrix}$$

$$= \begin{vmatrix} 1 & 1 \\ p_j^1 & p_j^2 \end{vmatrix} \begin{vmatrix} v^1 & 0 \\ 0 & v^2 \end{vmatrix} \begin{vmatrix} p_k^1 & 0 \\ 0 & p_k^2 \end{vmatrix} \begin{vmatrix} 1 & p_i^1 \\ 1 & p_i^2 \end{vmatrix}$$

$$= (p_j^2 - p_j^1)(v^1 v^2)(p_k^1 p_k^2)(p_i^2 - p_i^1)$$

$$= v^1 v^2 (p_i^2 - p_i^1)(p_j^2 - p_j^1) p_k^1 p_k^2.$$

By now comparing this expression with Equation (11), we see that

$$[ij;k] = [ij] p_k^1 p_k^2. \tag{12}$$

These two results:

$$[ij] = v^1 v^2 \delta_i \delta_j$$

and

$$[ij;k] = [ij] p_k^1 p_k^2$$

form the basis of our solution.

We use the fact, familiar from elementary algebra, that if the sum of two numbers, $x + y = b$, and their product, $xy = c$, are given, then the two numbers are the roots of the quadratic equation:

$$t^2 - bt + c = 0.$$

We can see from Equations (11) and (12) that

$$p_3^1 p_3^2 = [12;3]/[12], \tag{13}$$

so we only need to specify the sum of these quantities in order to solve for p_3^1 and p_3^2.

In Equation (12), we can let $k = \bar{3}$; that is, we can consider the cross product conditional on a negative response to item 3. The result is immediate:

$$[12;\bar{3}] = [12]p_{\bar{3}}^1 p_{\bar{3}}^2 = [12](1 - p_3^1)(1 - p_3^2).$$

Dividing by [12],

$$\frac{[12;3] - [12;\bar{3}]}{[12]} = p_3^1 p_3^2 - (1 - p_3^1)(1 - p_3^2)$$
$$= p_3^1 + p_3^2 - 1.$$

The sum of the two latent probabilities is thus:

$$p_3^1 + p_3^2 = 1 + \frac{[12;3] - [12;\bar{3}]}{[12]}, \tag{14}$$

which leads to the basic result:

THEOREM 1. *If* $[12] \neq 0$, *then* p_3^1 *and* p_3^2 *are the two roots of Equation* (15).

$$t^2 - t\left(1 + \frac{[12;3] - [12;\bar{3}]}{[12]}\right) + \frac{[12;3]}{[12]} = 0. \tag{15}$$

3.2 Identification of the Remaining Parameters

Once the latent item probabilities p_3^1 and p_3^2 are found as the roots of Equation (15), the other latent parameters can be found by solving linear equations, as long as $p_3^1 \neq p_3^2$. v^1 and v^2 can be derived from the equation for p_3:

$$p_3 = v^1 p_3^1 + v^2 p_3^2 = p_3^1 - v^2 p_3^1 + v^2 p_3^2,$$
$$v^2 = (p_3 - p_3^1)/(p_3^2 - p_3^1), \text{ since } v^1 = 1 - v^2.$$

If j stands for any item other than 3, p_j^1 and p_j^2 can be found by solving the two equations:

$$\begin{aligned}
p_j &= v^1 p_j^1 + v^2 p_j^2, \\
p_{3j} &= v^1 p_3^1 p_j^1 + v^2 p_3^2 p_j^2,
\end{aligned} \tag{16}$$

which are linear in the two unknowns. Notice that now we can solve for the latent probabilities of any other item j, not merely the items 1 and 2 used in the initial step (15).

We obtain p_j^1 and p_j^2 by solving the first equation for p_j^1, and substituting in the second equation. The result is

$$p_j^1 = (p_{j3} - p_j p_3^2)/(p_3 - p_3^2) \quad \text{and} \quad p_j^2 = (p_{j3} - p_j p_3^1)/(p_3 - p_3^1). \tag{17}$$

(As an exercise, verify that (17) is a solution to Equations (16).)

It is clear that if p_3^1 and p_3^2 are equal, these equations cannot be applied, since

$$p_3^1 - p_3^2 = 0$$

implies

$$p_3 - p_3^1 = 0 = p_3 - p_3^2,$$

and the equations would imply a division by zero.

Fortunately, it is not necessary to solve the quadratic equations to find out whether $p_3^1 = p_3^2$. By Equation (11),

$$[3j] = v^1 v^2 (p_3^1 - p_3^2)(p_j^1 - p_j^2).$$

Since we assumed that [12] was not zero, [13] and [23] are equal to zero if and only if $p_3^1 = p_3^2$; hence if [13] $\neq 0$, the two latent probabilities will be unequal.

The complete solution of the two-class model is summarized here for convenience. First, if we can find two items (1 and 2) so that

$$[12] = p_{12} - p_1 p_2 \neq 0,$$

we form the quadratic equation

$$t^2 - bt + c = 0, \tag{18}$$

where

$$b = (p_{123} + p_3 p_{12} - p_1 p_{23} - p_2 p_{13})/[12] \quad \text{and} \quad c = [12;3]/[12].$$

The two roots of (18) are p_3^1 and p_3^2. If these are distinct (a sufficient condition for this is that [13] and [23] be not zero), then we continue, obtaining v^1, v^2, p_j^1, and p_j^2 where j is any item other than 3:

$$v^1 = (p_3 - p_3^2)/(p_3^1 - p_3^2) \qquad v^2 = (p_3^1 - p_3)/(p_3^1 - p_3^2) \tag{19}$$

$$p_j^1 = (p_{j3} - p_j p_3^2)/(p_3 - p_3^2) \qquad p_j^2 = (p_{j3} - p_j p_3^1)/(p_3 - p_3^1). \tag{20}$$

We have said that sufficient conditions for the equations above to provide a solution are that there be three items, 1, 2, and 3, say, such that [12], [13], and [23] are all different from zero. (If all the cross products *were* equal to zero, we would not be considering a latent class model, since there would not appear to be any basic association among the items.) In such a case, the equations can be solved, and we obtain values of the "latent parameters." The reader is cautioned that nothing in the *algebra* requires that these values lie between 0 and 1. If any of the values of p_1^1, p_1^2, v^1, etc. lie outside the unit interval, or are complex numbers, it simply means that the two-class latent structure model is not really generating this particular set of manifest probabilities.

In order to illustrate these ideas, we shall work out two examples; in the first case the solution is an acceptable latent structure, while in the second, the solution is not acceptable.

3.3 *Examples*

Example A. Suppose that the positive responses to three items are as recorded in Table 5. The p_i and p_{ij} are entered in a table, the marginals appearing in the "zeroth" row and column, and the p_{ij} appearing in the appropriate spot, the row indicated by i and the column by j.

TABLE 5

Manifest Probabilities for Example A

Item	First and Second Order 1	2	3	Third order
0	0.6	0.5	0.4	$p_{123} = 0.22$
1	—	0.38	0.28	
2		—	0.28	

We note first that all three cross products are non-zero:

$$[12] = 0.38 - (0.5)(0.6) = 0.08; \quad [13] = 0.28 - (0.6)(0.4) = 0.04;$$
$$[23] = 0.28 - (0.5)(0.4) = 0.08.$$

$$[12;3] = \begin{vmatrix} 0.22 & 0.28 \\ 0.28 & 0.4 \end{vmatrix} = 0.0096.$$

$$[12;\bar{3}] = \begin{vmatrix} 0.16 & 0.32 \\ 0.22 & 0.6 \end{vmatrix} = 0.0256.$$

Thus the coefficients of Equation (18) are:

$$b = ([12;3] - [12;\bar{3}])/[12] + 1 = -0.016/0.08 + 1 = 0.8,$$
and
$$c = [12;3]/[12] = 0.0096/0.08 = 0.12.$$

We find that $p_3^1 = 0.6$ and $p_3^2 = 0.2$. (It is arbitrary which class we choose to call "1" and which we call "2".)

The remaining unknown parameters are found by applying Equations (19) and (20):

$$v^1 = (0.4 + 0.2)/(0.6 + 0.2) = 0.2/0.4 = 1/2, v^2 = 1/2,$$
$$p_1^1 = (0.28 + 0.6(0.2))/(0.4 + 0.2) = 0.16/0.2 = 0.8,$$
$$p_1^2 = (0.28 - 0.6(0.6))/(0.4 - 0.6) = 0.4,$$
$$p_2^1 = (0.28 - 0.2(0.5))/(0.4 - 0.2) = 0.9,$$
$$p_2^2 = (0.28 - 0.6(0.5))/(0.4 - 0.6) = 0.1.$$

The derived latent structure is, therefore,

TABLE 6

Latent Structure A

Class	Size	Item 1	Item 2	Item 3
1	0.5	0.8	0.9	0.6
2	0.5	0.4	0.1	0.2

(The reader should verify that these latent parameters do, in fact, give rise to the manifest probabilities of Table 5. Use the accounting Equations (8).)

Example B. Suppose that we have three items and that the manifest probabilities are as given in Table 7. Assuming a two-class structure, we apply the solution described previously.

TABLE 7

Manifest Probabilities for Example B

Item	First and Second Order 1	2	3	Third Order
0	0.38	0.40	0.26	$p_{123} = 0.1248$
1	—	0.264	0.166	
2	—	—	0.128	

All three cross products are non-zero: $[12] = 0.112$, $[13] = 0.0672$, and $[23] = 0.024$, so the solution can be applied.

The coefficients of the quadratic equation are:

$$b = 0.0784/0.112 = 0.7,$$
$$c = 0.0112/0.112 = 0.1,$$

and the roots of:

$$t^2 - 0.7t + 0.1 = 0$$

are 0.2 and 0.5.

Applying Equations (19) and (20), we find that the complete solution is

Class	Size	Item 1	Item 2	Item 3
1	0.8	0.1	0.3	0.2
2	0.2	1.5	0.8	0.5

This result is not acceptable, however, since the value indicated for p_1^2 is not a valid "probability," lying outside the interval [0,1].

We have introduced this example in order to emphasize the rather obvious point that there are sets of data which are not compatible with a latent structure model. In this case, the manifest probabilities are certainly logically possible, and could be observations obtained in, say, a sample survey. The accounting equations of the two-class model can be solved uniquely, but the results of this analysis tell us that a latent dichotomy which explains the relations among the three items does not exist.

Of course, it is possible for us to state some conditions which the manifest probabilities must satisfy if a particular latent structure is to be inferred. Some of these "conditions of reducibility" for the two-class model have already been derived, although we did not explicitly discuss them as such. For instance, when there are more than 3 items, the ratio:

$$[ij][ik]/[jk]$$

does not depend on the choice of items j and k, if we are considering the true manifest probabilities of a two-class model. In a sample, where the cross products are only estimated by sample quantities, the ratio should vary around the true value if we change j and k.

All such conditions are *necessary:* if the model is appropriate they must hold. No single condition is *sufficient*, however, to imply that the model must apply. Some numerical conditions which must hold are the following:

   (i) $[ij;k]/[ij] \geq 0$,
   (ii) $[ij;\overline{k}]/[ij] \geq 0$.

These must hold since the ratios are, respectively, $p_k^1 p_k^2$ and $p_{\overline{k}}^1 p_{\overline{k}}^2$. These last two conditions can be restated in terms of the basic relation among the items. If the items i and j are positively associated, i.e., if $[ij]$ is positive, then controlling by a third item k will not modify the sign of this relation in any way. The two-class model thus requires that the items be *strongly related* to one another: both $[ij;k]$ and $[ij;\overline{k}]$ must have the same sign as $[ij]$. This condition is not satisfied by the items of Example B, where $[23;1] = 0.0026$ and $[23;\overline{1}] = -0.0108$.

3.4 *Symmetric Parameters*

In "The Algebra of Dichotomous Systems" (Lazarsfeld, 1961), there is an extensive discussion of associations between two items. In addition, the problem of defining the joint relationship among three items is discussed, leading to consideration of the *third-order symmetric parameter*. For any three dichotomous items i, j, and k, this parameter is defined to be:

$$[ijk] = p_{ijk} - p_i[jk] - p_j[ik] - p_k[ij] - p_i p_j p_k. \qquad (21)$$

Symmetric in the three items, $[ijk]$ will equal zero if the items are statistically independent of each other, for independence implies that all the cross products are zero, and also that $p_{ijk} = p_i p_j p_k$. It is possible for $[ijk]$ to be zero, indicating that there is no *third-order* relationship among the items, even when they are not independent. That is, if the cross products $[ij]$, $[ik]$, and $[jk]$ were not zero, but $[ijk]$ were zero, it would indicate that the pairwise relations describe the interaction of the three items completely. Also when all $[ij] = 0$, $[ijk]$ may $\neq 0$.

An important identity shows how the third-order symmetric parameter is related to the conditional cross products:

$$[ijk] = [ij;k] - [ij;\bar{k}] - [ij](p_k - p_{\bar{k}}).$$

(See Exercise 6 at the end of the Chapter.)
Notice that if $p_k = 1/2$, or if $[ij] = 0$, then the symmetric parameter is simply the difference of the two conditional relationships.

It is possible to extend the notion of symmetric parameter to any number of items. For instance, the fourth-order parameter is:

$$[1234] = p_{1234} - \sum p_i[jkm] - \sum p_i p_j[km] - p_1 p_2 p_3 p_4, \qquad (22)$$

where the two indicated summations are over all distinct combinations of the four items.

It is possible, when studying a non-numerical variable which can take on only two values, to let one of the two outcomes be associated with the number "0" and the other with the number "1." Thus, the qualitative responses "Yes" and "No" would be replaced by the values "1" and "0," respectively. The new, quantitative, variable effectively *counts* the number of positive responses. The cross products and other quantities which we have defined above can be regarded as *expected values* of certain functions of these two-valued variables.

Let X_i stand for the random variable which equals 1 if the response to item i is positive, and 0 if the response is negative. The expected value of X_i is equal to p_i:

$$E(X_i) = p_i(1) + (1 - p_i)(0) = p_i.$$

If we take two such variables, X_i and X_j, their product $X_i X_j$ can also take on only two values, 0 and 1. The probability that the product $X_i X_j$ equals 1 is the probability of a positive response to both items, namely p_{ij}. Thus,

$$E(X_i X_j) = p_{ij}(1) + (1 - p_{ij})(0) = p_{ij}.$$

Any joint positive probability, such as p_{123} or p_{12345}, can be expressed as the expected value of the appropriate product of random variables.

The *covariance* of two variables, X_i and X_j, is also an expected value, taking into account the means of the two variables:

$$\mathrm{Cov}(X_i, X_j) = E\big(X_i - E(X_i)\big)\big(X_j - E(X_j)\big)$$
$$= E(X_i - p_i)(X_j - p_j).$$

Multiplying out this expression,

$$\mathrm{Cov}(X_i, X_j) = E(X_i X_j - p_i X_j - p_j X_i + p_i p_j)$$
$$= p_{ij} - p_i p_j = [ij].$$

35

Thus, when we define the 0/1-valued variables X_i and X_j, their covariance is equal to what we have called the cross product of the items. The symmetric parameters of third and higher order have the analogous relation to the random variables(X_i):

$$[ijk] = E(X_i - p_i)(X_j - p_j)(X_k - p_k),$$
$$[ijkm] = E(X_i - p_i)(X_j - p_j)(X_k - p_k)(X_m - p_m),$$

and so forth.

The expected values of products of random variables are often referred to as *moments:*

$$E(X_i X_j X_k)$$

is a *moment of third order.* When the random variables are modified by subtracting their means, the term "moment" is qualified by the adjective *central:*

$$E(X_i - p_i)(X_j - p_j)$$

is a *central moment of second order.* Occasionally we shall make direct use of this parallel between the symmetric parameters and the central moments.

4. Recruitment Probabilities

One of the most valuable aspects of latent structure analysis is the fact that for every possible response pattern the probability of the responder's belonging to each latent class can be computed directly from the latent parameters. These *recruitment probabilities* are a means of *classifying respondents:* one way would be to assign a respondent to the class which he is most likely to belong to, given his responses to the entire set of items.

Let s range over all the ultimate (nth order) response patterns. The basic equation

$$p_s = v^1 p_s^1 + v^2 p_s^2$$

indicates how the proportion giving response s is "recruited" from the two classes. For example, let us consider the latent structure discussed previously, whose latent parameters are:

Class	Size	Item 1	Item 2	Item 3
1	0.5	0.8	0.9	0.6
2	0.5	0.4	0.1	0.2

If s is the pattern $+++$ (or, in the usual notation, 123), the manifest probability is

$$p_{123} = (0.5)(0.8)(0.9)(0.6) + (0.5)(0.4)(0.1)(0.2)$$
$$0.22 = 0.216 + 0.004.$$

We expect 22% of the sample to give this response; 21.6% recruited from class 1 and 0.4% from class 2. Since this response pattern is characteristic of class 1, the natural classification scheme would be to assign any respondent who answered all three items positively to class 1.

In Table 8 below, we elaborate these recruitment probabilities for each of the eight ultimate response patterns.

TABLE 8

*Recruitment Probabilities
for the Model of Example A*

Response Pattern s	Class 1 $v^1 p_s^1$	Class 2 $v^2 p_s^2$	Manifest Probability p_s
+ + +	0.216	0.004	0.220
+ + −	0.144	0.016	0.160
+ − +	0.024	0.036	0.060
− + +	0.054	0.006	0.060
+ − −	0.016	0.144	0.160
− + −	0.036	0.024	0.060
− − +	0.006	0.054	0.060
− − −	0.004	0.216	0.220
Totals:	0.500	0.500	1.000

Notice that the sum of the class 1 column is v^1 and the sum of the class 2 column is v^2.

The above table is quite sufficient for assigning response patterns to the most likely class: we simply go down the columns picking the class which contains the larger number. We can even calculate a measure of the total amount of misclassification to expect, on the average, by summing the lesser numbers in each row. That is, if we decide to always classify a + + + respondent as a "1", we shall *misclassify* those who actually belonged to class 2; this amounts to 0.004 of the population. Referring to the above table, then, we find that the probability of a correct classification is

$$0.216 + 0.144 + 0.036 + 0.054 + 0.144 + 0.036 + 0.054 + 0.216 = 0.900,$$

and the probable misclassification amounts to

$$0.004 + 0.016 + 0.024 + 0.006 + 0.016 + 0.024 + 0.006 + 0.004 = 0.100.$$

It is important to realize that the misclassification mentioned here is a function of the probabilistic nature of the model, not of any uncertainty or lack of fit in the estimation of the parameters. Even if we are certain that the model as given applies to the population, with the given set of latent probabilities, we cannot assert with certainty that someone who gives three positive responses does belong to class 1. There will always be some expected proportion of misclassifications, and this proportion serves as a measure of the usefulness of the model as a classificatory instrument. If it is quite large, we may prefer not to use the items in question, even if we are sure that the latent class model does serve to describe the behavior of the population in question.

It may be more useful, in some cases, to compute and present the reverse probabilities, i.e., the probability of being in class 1 (or 2), given a certain response pattern s. These are computed by means of the basic probability identity called Bayes Theorem. If we denote these probabilities by $P(1|s)$ and $P(2|s)$, respectively (read "probability of class 1, given s"), the identity is

$$P(\alpha|s) = v^\alpha p_s^\alpha / p_s.$$

Thus these are obtained by dividing through the class columns in the previous table by the last column. Continuing our example, we give these probabilities in Table 9 below.

TABLE 9

Reverse Probabilities
for the Model of Example A

Response Pattern s	Class 1 $P(1|s)$	Class 2 $P(2|s)$	Manifest Probability p_s
+++	0.982	0.018	0.220
++−	0.900	0.100	0.160
+−+	0.400	0.600	0.060
−++	0.900	0.100	0.060
+−−	0.100	0.900	0.160
−+−	0.600	0.400	0.060
−−+	0.100	0.900	0.060
−−−	0.018	0.982	0.220

Notice that the use of these reverse probabilities permits us to define a numerical scale, or to order the respondents, as to how closely they come to falling into class 1. The larger $P(1|s)$ is, the surer we are that that individual came from class 1; the smaller it is, the less sure we are. In situations where the latent structure analysis is done in order to define a new variate, we could choose to use the values of $P(1|s)$ as this variate, rather than the dichotomy that arises if we classify the respondents into "most likely class."

38

In this example, the ordering of the response patterns that develops from the latent structure model does not correspond to an ordering based on "number of positive items." The pattern $-+-$, with only one positive item, is higher than $+-+$, which has two. The complete ordering is

$$+++, \; ++-, \; -++, \; -+-, \; +-+, \; +--, \; --+, \; ---.$$

(Patterns with the same value of $P(1|s)$ have been ordered arbitrarily.)

5. The Problem of Fitting Real Data

The solution that has been presented for the two-class latent structure answers the following question: Given a set of numbers p_i, p_{ij}, p_{ijk} which are known to satisfy the accounting Equations (8) for some *unknown choice of parameters* (v^1, v^2, p_i^1, p_i^2), determine those latent parameters.

Since latent structure models are *probability models*, we can be *quite sure* that the positive proportions we observe in a sample will *not* be exactly equal to the probabilities p_i, p_{ij}, etc., and thus that these sample quantities will *not* exactly satisfy the accounting equations. Therefore, even assuming that a latent structure model is generating the observed responses, the *true* latent parameters cannot be determined exactly, since the true (or perfect, a term often used to refer to these data) manifest probabilities are not known exactly.

The course we take, faced with this problem of estimation, is to use the observed positive proportions, and use the solution of the accounting equations to obtain an estimate of the latent structure, figuring that small errors in the estimates of the p_i, p_{ij}, and p_{ijk} will lead to only small errors in the latent parameters.

5.1 A Sampling Experiment

For example, let us see what happens when we draw a sample of size 1,000 from the population described in Example A. Our procedure was to assume that responses to the three items were governed by a two-class latent structure

TABLE 10

Underlying Latent Structure: Example A

		Item		
Class	Size	1	2	3
1	0.5	0.8	0.9	0.6
2	0.5	0.4	0.1	0.2

process, and to generate the "sample" on an electronic computer with the help of a random number generator. The resulting manifest proportions are shown in Table 11 and should be compared with the "perfect" manifest probabilities given in Table 5.

TABLE 11

Manifest Data: Random Sample of 1000

Item	First and Second Order 1	2	3	Third Order
0	0.608	0.490	0.388 (marginals)	$p_{123} = 0.201$
1	—	0.355	0.274	
2		—	0.263	

The latent parameters are estimated by solving the accounting equations, as before. Using item 3 as the stratifier, we obtain the equation

$$t^2 - 0.7809\ t + 0.1038 = 0,$$

the roots of which, 0.611 and 0.170, are estimates of p_3^1 and p_3^2. The complete solution is given below, and may be compared with the true parameters shown in Table 10.

TABLE 12

Estimates of the Latent Parameters
From Data of Table 11

Class	Size	Item 1	2	3
1	0.494	0.783	0.824	0.611
2	0.506	0.437	0.163	0.170

If we had increased our sample size, the estimates here would tend to approach the true parameters. This fact follows from a two-step argument. The sample estimates of the manifest probabilities will surely approach the true values of these parameters, as the sample size increases, and solving the accounting equations will lead to better estimates of the latent parameters.

As we shall see in the next section, the estimation procedure is not quite as simple when there are more than three items.

5.2 More than Three Items

When we have more than three items, and the manifest data only approximate the true manifest probabilities, we may obtain more than one estimate of the latent probabilities by varying the stratifier item. If item 3 were the stratifier, the only third-order data used in the solution are of the form p_{ij3}, while if item 4 were the stratifier, the third-order data would be p_{ij4}. Usually two such solutions would lead to different estimates of the latent parameters, due to the difference in the accuracy of the estimation of p_{ij3} and p_{ij4}.

Another way of introducing variations is to let item 3 be the stratifier, but in one case use items 1 and 2, and in another case use items 4 and 5 to form the quadratic Equation (20). In the first case, our solution tells us that the latent probabilities of item 3 are the two roots of the equation

$$[12]t^2 - ([12;3] - [12;\bar{3}] + [12])t + [12;3] = 0,$$

while in the second case, they are the roots of:

$$[45]t^2 - ([45;3] - [45;\bar{3}] + [45])t + [45;3] = 0.$$

If the true manifest probabilities were used as coefficients of these equations, they would have the same two roots, i.e., p_3^1 and p_3^2. In practice, however, they will not have the same roots: each solution will be an approximation to the true latent probabilities, but, of course, not necessarily the *same approximation!* Note carefully that these differences are not due to questions of rounding, or of inaccurate solving of the two quadratic equations; they are caused by the fallibility of the observed responses, which only provide *estimates* of the manifest probabilities.

Ideally, a "good" solution is one that gives estimates that are very close to the true underlying latent structure. Practically, a good solution is one which fits all the observed data as well as possible, since the observed responses are the only information we have about the population. One way of resolving the problem of having several different estimates, therefore, is to compute all possible solutions and then average them. For instance, we might form all possible quadratic equations that arise using item 3 as stratifier, and average their solutions to get estimates of p_3^1 and p_3^2. We can also try to find some simple criterion to restrict our attention to a subset of all possible solutions, in order to save a great deal of computational labor. Aspects of this approach will be discussed in Chapter 4.

Another procedure is to use some arbitrary criteria such as chi-square to measure how well a given solution fits *all* the data, not merely the p_i, p_{ij}, p_{ijk} used in solving for the latent parameters. A way of doing this, and of improving the estimates of the latent parameters so that the overall fit is improved has been developed. This is an iterative program for obtaining best, asymptotically normal (BAN) estimates of the latent structure, and it is also discussed in Chapter 4.

5.3 *The Direct Computation of Latent Class Frequencies*

In this section, we derive an alternative solution of the two-class model, in which the class frequencies, v^1 and v^2, are computed as the first step. Because no single item has to be singled out as the stratifier, this approach is more symmetric with respect to the items than the previously derived solution.

The main result is most easily given in terms of the symmetric parameters of second and third order, as stated in the following theorem.

THEOREM 2. *If i, j, and k are three items in a two-class latent structure for which* [ij], [ik], *and* [jk] *are non-zero, then* v^1 *and* v^2 *are the roots of the quadratic equation*

$$t^2 - t + 1/(4 + M^2) = 0, \tag{23}$$

where

$$M^2 = [ijk]^2/[ij][ik][jk]. \tag{24}$$

PROOF: The sum of the two frequencies is 1, of course, so that it is only necessary to show that the product $v^1 v^2$ must equal the constant term in the equation $1/(4 + M^2)$.

In Section 3.4, we defined the third-order symmetric parameter, and noted the important identity

$$[ijk] = [ij;k] - [ij;\bar{k}] - [ij](p_k - p_{\bar{k}}). \tag{25}$$

We have also shown, in Equation (12), how to express the conditional cross products in terms of the latent parameters of the two-class model. From these we have

$$[ij;k] = [ij]p_k^1 p_k^2 \tag{26}$$

and

$$[ij;\bar{k}] = [ij]p_{\bar{k}}^1 p_{\bar{k}}^2. \tag{27}$$

Substituting (26) and (27) into Equation (25),

$$[ijk] = [ij](p_k^1 p_k^2 - 1 + p_k^1 + p_k^2 - p_{\bar{k}}^1 p_{\bar{k}}^2 - p_k + 1 - p_k)$$
$$= [ij](p_k^1 + p_k^2 - 2p_k).$$

Since

$$p_k = v^1 p_k^1 + v^2 p_k^2,$$

we find that

$$[ijk] = [ij](p_k^1 - p_k^2)(v^2 - v^1). \tag{28}$$

From Equation (11) we know that

$$[ij] = v^1 v^2 \delta_i \delta_j, \tag{29}$$

where $\delta_i = p_i^1 - p_i^2$, for any i. Substituting this value into (28), we obtain an expression for [ijk] that is indeed symmetric in the latent parameters of the three items:

$$[ijk] = \delta_i \delta_j \delta_k v^1 v^2 (v^2 - v^1). \tag{30}$$

Now, we can compute the ratio

$$M^2 = [ijk]^2/[ij][ik][jk]$$

by combining (29) and (30).

$$M^2 = (\delta_i \delta_j \delta_k)^2 (v^1 v^2)^2 (v^2 - v^1)^2 / (\delta_i \delta_j \delta_k)^2 (v^1 v^2)^3$$
$$= (v^2 - v^1)^2 / v^1 v^2.$$

From this point, it is easy to see that $1/(M^2 + 4)$ does equal $v^1 v^2$:

$$M^2 + 4 = [(v^2 - v^1)^2 + 4v^1 v^2]/v^1 v^2$$
$$= (v^1 + v^2)^2 / v^1 v^2 = 1/v^1 v^2.$$

The only condition required is that the three cross products be different from zero.

ASIDE: The expression M has an interesting interpretation in terms of the distribution of the population into the two classes. If we imagined drawing persons from the total population, the expected proportion from class 2 would be v^2 and the variance would be $v^2 v^1$. If we standardized by subtracting the mean and dividing by the standard deviation, the third moment of the binomial distribution is

$$M = (v^2 - v^1)/(v^1 v^2)^{1/2}.$$

Another way of saying this would be to suppose that class 1 is located at the point $v^2/(v^1 v^2)^{1/2}$ on a scale, and that class 2 is located at the point $-v^1/(v^1 v^2)^{1/2}$. The first moment of this distribution is zero:

$$v^1(\text{location 1}) + v^2(\text{location 2}) = 0;$$

the second moment is one:

$$v^1(\text{location 1})^2 + v^2(\text{location 2})^2$$
$$= [v^1(v^2)^2 + v^2(v^1)^2]/v^1 v^2 = v^2 + v^1 = 1;$$

and the third moment is M:

$$v^1(\text{location 1})^3 + v^2(\text{location 2})^3$$
$$= [v^1(v^2)^3 - v^2(v^1)^3]/(v^1 v^2)^{3/2}$$
$$= [(v^2)^2 - (v^1)^2]/(v^1 v^2)^{1/2}$$
$$= (v^2 - v^1)/(v^1 v^2)^{1/2}. \ \blacksquare$$

The true value of M depends only on the latent class frequencies and not on the particular items i, j, and k that are used in the derivation. This important fact suggests a way of averaging data in order to obtain more accurate estimates in an analysis of real data. That is, we could consider all possible triples of items, compute the value of M (or of M^2 or of $1/(M^2 + 4)$), for each triple, and average these values before setting up the quadratic equation and solving for v^1 and v^2. (Of course, we could also solve the quadratic equation defined by each triple, and average the results.) The relative efficiency of these procedures has not been studied in great detail, and we shall not carry the discussion further at this point.

Once the class frequencies have been determined, the item parameters may be obtained in a variety of ways. For instance, the equations:

$$p_i = v^1 p_i^1 + v^2 p_i^2,$$

$$\sqrt{[ij][ik]/[jk]} = \delta_i (v^1 v^2)^{1/2} = (p_i^1 - p_i^2)(v^1 v^2)^{1/2},$$

are linear in the two unknowns p_i^1 and p_i^2, and can easily be solved as long as neither class frequency is zero and there exists a non-zero cross product $[jk]$. Again, for estimation purposes, these estimates could be averaged over all choices of the items j and k, in order to attain a degree of reliability and to utilize as much of the data as possible.

6. Summary

The development of the two-class model in this chapter has followed a general pattern, which is summarized as follows. First we *define* the model: in this case we specified that the population was divided into two latent classes, and that the responses to the various dichotomous items were governed by the rule of local independence. This specification of the model gives rise to the *accounting equations*, which relate the latent probabilities to the manifest probabilities. Second, we investigate the conditions under which the model is *identifiable*. For instance, we noted that if only two items are available, it is not possible to determine the resulting latent probabilities from the available manifest probabilities. With more than two items, the solution presented as applicable under *certain conditions* which were spelled out in the process of obtaining the solution (e.g., there be three items 1, 2 and 3, such that [12], [13] and [23] not be zero). Third, we want to be able to classify individuals according to their responses into one or the other of the latent classes. We saw how to do this by computing the recruitment probabilities of each response pattern. Fourth, there is the problem of *estimating* the latent parameters when the manifest probabilities are not known exactly, and of deciding whether the model fits the observed data well enough.

When presenting new models in later chapters, we shall generally follow the above pattern in our analysis. Note that the various steps will be relevant to different types of analysis. For instance, the sociologist who wants to apply an already developed model (say, the latent dichotomy of this chapter) will be interested in step four, the estimation of parameters, and in step three, the classification of respondents, once he is assured that there are no problems of specification and identification of the model. On the other hand, any new latent structure model that is introduced must be analyzed for identifiability, before it can be applied to actual data. This is the mathematical aspect, which is our principal topic in this book.

Exercises

1. Using the identity $p_s = p_{si} + p_{s\bar{i}}$ for any response pattern s, show that

$$p_{\bar{1}\bar{2}\bar{3}} = 1 - p_1 - p_2 - p_3 + p_{12} + p_{13} + p_{23} - p_{123}.$$

2. Show that $[i\bar{j}] = -[ij]$ for any two items i and j.
3. What is $[\bar{i}\bar{j}]$?
4. Show that $[12] = [12;3]/p_3 + [12;\bar{3}]/p_{\bar{3}} + [13][23]/p_3 p_{\bar{3}}$.
   Hint: Note that the third-order terms will drop out on the right side:

$$[12;3]/p_3 + [12;\bar{3}]/p_{\bar{3}} = p_{123} + p_{12\bar{3}} - p_{13}p_{23}/p_3 - p_{1\bar{3}}p_{2\bar{3}}/p_{\bar{3}}$$
$$= p_{12} - p_{13}p_{23}/p_3 - (p_1 - p_{13})(p_2 - p_{23})/p_{\bar{3}}.$$

5. Show that $[ij\bar{k}] = -[ijk]$.
6. Show that $[ijk] = [ij;k] - [ij;\bar{k}] - [ij](p_k - p_{\bar{k}})$.
   Hint: Using the identity $p_{ik} = [ik] + p_i p_k$, show that

$$[ij;k] = p_k([ijk] + [ij]) - [ik][jk].$$

The desired result follows immediately, remembering that

$$[i\bar{k}] = -[ik] \text{ and } [ij\bar{k}] = -[ijk].$$

45

3

General Latent Class Models

1. Specifying the Model

In this chapter, we generalize the two-class model of the previous chapter. We now assume that there are m latent classes ($m > 1$) with all the items being independent of one another within each of the classes. The notation is similar to that used before: the latent parameters will consist of the relative frequencies of the m classes, and p_i^α, the probabilities of a positive response (marginals) for each item within each class.

TABLE 1

The Latent Parameters: m Latent Classes

Class Frequencies:	v^1	v^2	$\cdots$	v^m
Marginals for item 1	p_1^1	p_1^2	$\cdots$	p_1^m
Marginals for item 2	p_2^1	p_2^2	$\cdots$	p_2^m
$\cdots$	$\vdots$	$\vdots$	$\cdot \vdots \cdot$	$\vdots$
Marginals for item n	p_n^1	p_n^2	$\cdots$	p_n^m

Local independence, as in the two-class case, implies that higher-order probabilities, within a class, are always simple products of the appropriate within-class marginals. For instance, the probability of responding positively to items i and j, when the respondent belongs to class 3, is $p_{ij}^3 = p_i^3 p_j^3$.

As usual, we shall begin our analysis of this latent structure model by seeing how the latent probabilities are related to the unconditional or manifest probabilities of positive response to one or more of the items. We know, of course, that the m class frequencies must sum to 1:

$$v^1 + v^2 + \cdots + v^m = 1.$$

And, by the same argument used in the previous chapter, we have

$$p_i^1 v^1 + p_i^2 v^2 + \cdots + p_i^m v^m = p_i.$$

Instead of continuing to use this awkward way of indicating the sum of m terms, we shall use the usual notation, $\sum\limits_{\alpha=1}^{m}$ to indicate the sum of m terms.

The above two equations thus become

and

$$1 = \sum_{\alpha=1}^{m} v^\alpha,$$

$$(1)$$

$$p_i = \sum_{\alpha=1}^{m} v^\alpha p_i^\alpha.$$

Equations for second-, third-, or higher-order manifest probabilities follow from the within-class independence assumptions.

$$p_{ij} = \sum v^\alpha p_i^\alpha p_j^\alpha,$$

$$(2)$$

$$p_{ijk} = \sum v^\alpha p_i^\alpha p_j^\alpha p_k^\alpha.$$

(For convenience, we shall simply write $\sum$ instead of $\sum\limits_{\alpha=1}^{m}$ whenever it is clear that the summation is over all m classes.)

Once a latent structure model has been specified, with accounting equations such as (1) and (2) relating the latent probabilities to the manifest probabilities, we must ask whether those equations can be solved uniquely. That is, if the manifest probabilities are known exactly, is it possible to determine exactly the latent probabilities? We shall present one solution to this problem that was developed by Lazarsfeld (1951), Anderson (1954), and Gibson (1955); in addition we shall note a generalization due to Madansky (1960) which places less restrictive conditions on the parameters.

As a start, by comparing the number of latent and manifest probabilities we can arrive at a necessary condition on the number of items which must be present. There are 2^n manifest probabilities (n is the number of items), and $mn + m = m(n + 1)$ latent probabilities (m is the number of classes). Since there must be at least as many equations as unknowns if there is to be a solution, $m(n + 1)$ must not be greater than 2^n. This is a necessary condition, but not a sufficient condition. That is, if there is to be a solution the condition must hold, but sometimes there may be no solution even though this condition is satisfied.

ASIDE: For example, in the two-class case, $m = 2$, and the above condition implies that n must be at least 3. But we saw in the previous chapter that in certain cases there is no solution even though n is 3; e.g., when $p_1^1 = p_1^2$. ∎

The general scheme for developing the solution of the accounting equations has three parts. First of all we introduce a matrix notation to supplement the ordinary algebraic notation of Equations (1) and (2). Matrix notation enables us to consider many different equations of first, second, and third order at the same time, and, as we shall see, the particular form which we propose makes very visible the structure of the latent part of those equations. Second, we manipulate the matrix equations in such a way as to reduce the number of latent parameters. While the manifest probabilities in these derived equations are combined into quite complicated functions, the latent probabilities on the other side of the equations take on much simpler forms. Finally we reach a point at which the latent probabilities can be computed by some standard computational techniques of matrix algebra.

2. Combining the Accounting Equations in Matrix Form

The use of matrix notation in a purely descriptive manner does not need to be justified at all in the case of the second order manifest probabilities, (p_{ij}). The notation "p_{ij}" already indicates that the natural way of presenting these quantities is in a two dimensional array, the rows and columns varying over the n items. The ambiguous diagonal terms, p_{ii}, of such an array must be left out, however, for they are not observable quantities. For this reason we shall restrict our attention to non-symmetric submatrices of the entire $m \times m$ array which do not include any of the symbols p_{ii}, $i = 1, 2, \ldots, m$. Such a matrix is defined by specifying the set of items which make up the *row indices*, and the set of items making up the *column indices*, and requiring that these sets do not overlap.

Precisely, we define a *signature* to be *an ordered set of items*. Then, if s is a signature and r is a signature, the symbol P_{rs} will stand for the matrix (p_{ij}), where i belongs to r, and j belongs to s . r and s should be non-overlapping sets of items, in order that P_{rs} be entirely made up of manifest probabilities. We refer to r as the *horizontal* (or row) *signature* of P_{rs}; and to s as the *vertical* (or column) *signature* of P_{rs}.

It is equally natural to present the latent probabilities in a two dimensional array, one dimension specified by items, and the other by classes. That is, given a signature s, we define a matrix L_s which has in row k and column α the probability p_i^α, where i is the kth item in the signature s. Since all classes will be represented in such a matrix, it will have m columns. The number of rows will equal the number of items in the signature s.

For example, if $m = 3$, and $s = (3, 5)$,

$$L_s = \begin{pmatrix} p_3^1 & p_3^2 & p_3^3 \\ p_5^1 & p_5^2 & p_5^3 \end{pmatrix}.$$

Column α of L_s consists of the latent probabilities of the items in s within class α. Such a column will be denoted by

$$L_s^{(\alpha)};$$

the superscript reminding us that the column is formed by specifying a latent class.

With this much matrix notation at hand, we turn back to the accounting equations of second order:

$$p_{ij} = \sum_{\alpha=1}^{m} v^{\alpha} p_i^{\alpha} p_j^{\alpha}, \quad i \neq j.$$

This is one of the most common types of equation in matrix algebra. The left-hand side can be represented as the product of a row vector, times a diagonal matrix, times a column vector:

$$p_{ij} = (p_i^1, p_i^2, \ldots, p_i^m) \begin{pmatrix} v^1 & 0 & 0 & 0 \\ 0 & v^2 & \cdots & 0 \\ \vdots & \vdots & & \vdots \\ 0 & 0 & \cdots & v^m \end{pmatrix} \begin{pmatrix} p_j^1 \\ p_j^2 \\ \vdots \\ p_j^m \end{pmatrix},$$

as the reader can easily verify.

Let V be defined to be the diagonal matrix of order m whose diagonal entries are the class frequencies v^{α}. The latent structure of a second order matrix P_{rs} can now be expressed in terms of the matrices L_s, L_r, and V, as follows:

Let s and r be any two non-overlapping signatures. Then

$$P_{rs} = L_r V L_s'.$$

(L_s' is the *transpose* of L_s.)

This very simple result forms the basis for a solution of the accounting equations, primarily by directing our thoughts into certain channels which do turn out to be fruitful.

The first extension of the result comes by noticing that the equations for the marginal probabilities, p_i, can be fitted into this same matrix framework. For instance, the accounting equation (1) can be expressed:

$$p_i = (p_i^1, p_i^2, \ldots, p_i^m) V \begin{pmatrix} 1 \\ 1 \\ \vdots \\ 1 \end{pmatrix}.$$

Formally, therefore, we define a dummy item which has all of its latent probabilities equal to 1. We number this dummy item "0", and shall refer to it as the zero-item. With this notation, it is clear that the above equation for p_i could be written:

$$p_i = (p_i^1, p_i^2, \ldots, p_i^m) V \begin{pmatrix} p_0^1 \\ p_0^2 \\ \vdots \\ p_0^m \end{pmatrix}.$$

49

The marginals can thus be included in the matrix P_{rs} by using the natural notation:

$$p_i = p_{i0}, p_i = p_{0i} \text{ and } 1 = p_{00}.$$

Thus the matrix equation which was derived in a natural way to take care of the accounting equations of second order can include first order equations as well. We state this as follows: Let s and r be any two non-overlapping signatures. Let $h = (0, r)$, and $v = (0, s)$ be augmented signatures whose first element is the dummy item zero. The latent matrices L_h and L_v will therefore always contain an initial row of 1's. P_{hv}, the matrix of second order manifest probabilities bordered by marginal probabilities, satisfies the matrix equation:

$$P_{hv} = L_h V L_v'.$$

We specifically reserve the use of the symbols h and v so that they always include the zero item as leading item, and are otherwise non-overlapping.

Notice that in this single matrix equation we have summarized all of these accounting equations:

$$1 \quad = \sum v^{\alpha};$$
$$p_i = \sum v^{\alpha} p_i^{\alpha} \quad \text{for } i \text{ contained in } r;$$
$$p_j = \sum v^{\alpha} p_j^{\alpha} \quad \text{for } j \text{ contained in } s;$$
$$p_{ij} = \sum v^{\alpha} p_i^{\alpha} p_j^{\alpha} \quad \text{for } i \text{ contained in } r \text{ and } j \text{ contained in } s.$$

Thus far we have not specified how many items are included in the signatures h and v: P_{hv} could have any number of rows and columns, restricted only by n, the number of items available. Because V is an $m \times m$ matrix, however, the most important situation turns out to be the one in which P_{hv} is square, and of order m. We shall refer to such a matrix as a *basic matrix*, and use a special notation for it.

DEFINITION. B_{hv} is a *basic matrix* if h and v each contain item 0 as their leading element, and otherwise consist of two non-overlapping sets of $m - 1$ items each, and $B_{hv} = P_{hv}$, as defined above.

(The reason for specifying the square matrix of order m is that in developing the solution in the next section we need to use the *inverse* of this matrix. If it were of order larger than m the inverse would not exist, owing to the fact that the *rank* of the matrix cannot exceed m. This will be discussed in more detail later in this chapter.)

Next we turn to the accounting equations of third order. There is apparently no natural matrix notation for the probabilities p_{ijk}: a "natural" formulation would require a three dimensional array, so that each subscript could refer to a different dimension. The choice that is made is to fix one of the three subscripts, and to let the other two vary over the rows and columns of a matrix, a procedure we have already used in Chapter 2.

Specifically, we proceed to *stratify* the basic matrix B_{hv} by replacing each entry p_{ij} of B_{hv} by p_{ijk}, k being some item different from those appearing in h and v.

50

DEFINITION. If B_{hv} is a basic matrix, and if k is an item not included in the signatures h and v, the matrix formed by replacing the p_{ij} of B_{hv} by p_{ijk} is called the *stratified basic matrix*, and denoted by $B_{hv;k}$.

For example, in the $m = 3$ case, let $h = (0, 2, 3)$ and $v = (0, 4, 5)$. Then

$$B_{hv} = \begin{pmatrix} 1 & p_4 & p_5 \\ p_2 & p_{24} & p_{25} \\ p_3 & p_{34} & p_{35} \end{pmatrix},$$

and

$$B_{hv;k} = \begin{pmatrix} p_k & p_{4k} & p_{5k} \\ p_{2k} & p_{24k} & p_{25k} \\ p_{3k} & p_{34k} & p_{35k} \end{pmatrix},$$

as long as k does not equal 2, 3, 4, or 5. (Of course it would be trivial to let $k = 0$: by definition $B_{hv;0} = B_{hv}$.) k is called the *stratifier item*, or simply the stratifier.

It is convenient to arrange manifest probabilities of third order in the form of $B_{hv;k}$, but the critical question that has to be asked is whether that matrix has a particularly useful form in terms of the equations that link manifest and latent probabilities. In fact, the equation can be derived quite simply, and will prove very convenient in our search for a solution to the equations of the model.

In Table 2 we compare the accounting equations for the elements of B_{hv} and of $B_{hv;k}$. The corresponding terms are identical, except that wherever

TABLE 2

The Latent Expressions for
Corresponding Entries of Basic and
Stratified Matrices

Entries of B_{hv}	Entries of $B_{hv;k}$
$\sum v^\alpha$	$\sum v^\alpha p_k^\alpha$
$\sum v^\alpha p_i^\alpha$	$\sum v^\alpha p_k^\alpha p_i^\alpha$
$\sum v^\alpha p_i^\alpha p_j^\alpha$	$\sum v^\alpha p_k^\alpha p_i^\alpha p_j^\alpha$

v^α appears in B_{hv}, $v^\alpha p_k^\alpha$ appears in $B_{hv;k}$. The equation

$$B_{hv} = L_h V L_v'$$

suggests that the proper equation for $B_{hv;k}$ would be obtained if we substituted for the diagonal matrix V another diagonal matrix whose $\alpha\alpha$th entry were $v^\alpha p_k^\alpha$. The result is easily expressed by defining D_k to be the diagonal matrix, of order m, whose entries are the latent probabilities of item k, i.e., p_k^α. Then it follows from the above discussion that

$$B_{hv;k} = L_h V D_k L_v'.$$

In the next section we shall show how a solution for the latent probabilities can be derived fairly easily by manipulating these matrix equations. For convenience of notation we shall specify that the stratifier item, k, is 1; that the horizontal signature, h, is $(0, 2, 3, \ldots, m)$; and the vertical signature, v, is $(0, m + 1, m + 2, \ldots, 2m - 1)$. Furthermore, we drop the h and v from the symbols for the basic matrices, as below:

$$B = B_{hv} = L_h V L_v' \tag{3}$$

$$B_1 = B_{hv;1} = L_h V D_1 L_v'. \tag{4}$$

3. A Solution of the Accounting Equations

We have chosen to write certain combinations of the accounting equations in matrix form, and seen that they lead to the equations (3) and (4). In this section we show how the latent parameters can be found by manipulating the manifest matrices B and B_1 in certain ways. As we point out in Section 4, this is not the *only* way of solving the accounting equations: it is *a* solution, which can be applied under certain general conditions. Because of the important role played by this solution, it will be referred to throughout the book as the *basic solution* of the latent class model.

In Equations (3) and (4) the unknown latent parameters appear as the matrices L_h, L_v, V, and D_1. It is apparent that if these quantities were representing ordinary numbers (i.e., were *scalars*) rather than matrices, a division of B_1 by B would give us D_1. The matrix analog of such a division is the multiplication of B_1 by the inverse of B. Since the inverse of a product equals the product of the inverses, in reversed order, we have

$$B^{-1} = (L_h V L_v')^{-1} = (L_v')^{-1} V^{-1} L_h^{-1}. \tag{5}$$

Defining a new matrix,

$$G = B_1 B^{-1},$$

we find that

$$G = L_h D_1 V L_v' L_v'^{-1} V^{-1} L_h^{-1} = L_h D_1 L_h^{-1}. \tag{6}$$

G is easily computed from the matrices B and B_1 of manifest probabilities, and Equation (6) shows that the unknowns V and L_v have been eliminated. We next show that the m probabilities (p_i^α) which make up the diagonal matrix D_1 can be uniquely computed from G.

ASIDE: The general form of the matrix G will appear many times throughout the text. The entries of a product TS^{-1} have an interesting property, which is derived in Appendix A. This is that the entry in row i and column j of the product TS^{-1} equals the determinant of the matrix formed by substituting row i of T for row j of S, divided by the determinant of S. Thus the entries of G equal determinants of matrices formed by replacing a row of the *unstratified* matrix, B, with a row of the *stratified* matrix, B_1, and dividing through by the determinant of B. ∎

Consider the *determinantal equation*

$$|G - tI| = 0 \tag{7}$$

where I is the identity matrix and t is an unknown, real-valued variable. Substituting for G, we have:

$$|L_h D_1 L_h^{-1} - tI| = 0,$$
$$|L_h(D_1 - tI)L_h^{-1}| = 0,$$
$$|L_h| \, |D_1 - tI| \, |L_h^{-1}| = 0.$$

If L_h has an inverse, its determinant cannot equal zero, and therefore

$$|D_1 - tI| = 0. \tag{8}$$

Since D_1 is a diagonal matrix, and since we know that the determinant of a diagonal matrix is equal to the product of its diagonal entries we must have:

$$(p_1^1 - t)(p_1^2 - t) \cdots (p_1^m - t) = 0. \tag{9}$$

Therefore t is a root of equation (7) if and only if t equals one of the m latent probabilities p_1^α.

ASIDE: Equation (7) is a polynomial of degree m in t. For example, when $m = 2$:

$$|G - tI| = \begin{vmatrix} g_{11} - t & g_{12} \\ g_{21} & g_{22} - t \end{vmatrix} = (g_{11} - t)(g_{22} - t) - g_{12}g_{21}.$$

Thus the quadratic equation is:

$$t^2 - t(g_{11} + g_{22}) + g_{11}g_{22} - g_{12}g_{21} = 0.$$

The reader should work out the determinantal equation for the case $m = 3$. We note two facts about the general equation

$$t^m - a_1 t^{m-1} + a_2 t^{m-2} - \cdots \pm a_m = 0.$$

(The signs alternate throughout the equation.) First, a_1 equals the sum of the diagonal entries of G; and, second, a_m equals the determinant of G. This is evident in the $m = 2$ case cited above, and should be checked directly in the case $m = 3$ by the reader. ∎

The latent probabilities of the stratifier item can be found by solving the polynomial equation of degree m, Equation (7). One way of finding the latent probabilities for other items is to vary the stratifier, thus getting other equations of degree m. This method has two drawbacks, however. First, it requires that we solve many of these rather complicated higher-degree equations. Second, each solution results in m numbers: the within-class latent probabilities of the specified item. These numbers do *not* possess "tags" telling us which class they refer to, so it is difficult to match the numbers for one item with those of another item, class by class. For instance, if we found (in a three-class model) that the solution of (7) with stratifier "1" gave (.5, .3, .1), while with stratifier "6" the solution gave (.7, .4, .2), we would not be able to decide without additional evidence whether the .5 for item 1 and the .7 for item 6 referred to the same or to different classes.

Fortunately there is a simpler way to extend the solution to more items. Return to Equation (6):

$$G = L_h D_1 L_h^{-1}.$$

By multiplying both sides of the equation by L_h, on the right, we find that a very simple type of equation results:

$$GL_h = D_1 L_h. \tag{10}$$

D_1 is the diagonal matrix whose non-zero entries are the latent probabilities of the stratifier item, "1". Once these have been found, Equation (10) is entirely linear in the unknown elements of L_h. Thus, the entry in row i and column α of the products (10) is:

$$\sum_j g_{ij} p_j^\alpha = p_1^\alpha p_i^\alpha.$$

Recall that column α of L_h consists of the latent probabilities within class α, and that we use the notation $L_h^{(\alpha)}$ to stand for that column vector. Thus, the equation

$$GL_h^{(\alpha)} = p_1^\alpha L_h^{(\alpha)}$$

holds, for any choice of class α. With G consisting of manifest information, and the p_1^α known for all α, the column vector $L_h^{(\alpha)}$ is found by solving the homogeneous linear equation:

$$(G - I p_1^\alpha) L_h^{(\alpha)} = 0. \tag{11}$$

A homogeneous equation such as (11) does not have a unique solution, in general, for the unknown vector is determined only up to multiplication by a constant. Here, however, we know that the first element of $L_h^{(\alpha)}$ equals one, because the dummy item "0" has been included in the signature h. The vector contains only $m - 1$ unknowns:

$$L_h^{(\alpha)} = \begin{pmatrix} 1 \\ p_2^\alpha \\ \vdots \\ p_m^\alpha \end{pmatrix}.$$

Thus by solving in turn for $L_h^{(1)}, L_h^{(2)} \ldots L_h^{(m)}$ we determine L_h, the latent probabilities of the items in the signature h.

Now the remaining latent probabilities can be found by straightforward manipulations of manifest matrices and L_h. For instance,

$$B = L_h V L_v'$$

implies that

$$L_h^{-1} B = V L_v'. \tag{12}$$

Since V is a diagonal matrix, and L_v' has a first column of ones, the first column of the product $V L_v'$ consists of the class frequencies, (v^α). (The reader can verify this directly.) Therefore the v's can be determined, since they make up the first column of $L_h^{-1} B$, by Equation (12). Then, when V has been found,

$$L_v' = V^{-1} L_h^{-1} B. \tag{13}$$

Finally, if there are more than $2m - 1$ items (the number included in the signatures h and v, plus the stratifier), the latent probabilities of the remaining items can be found by constructing a matrix of second order manifest probabilities. Let r denote the set of additional items. Let P_{hr} be the matrix (not necessarily square) of probabilities p_{ij}, where i belongs to h and j to r. As we have already shown,

$$P_{hr} = L_h V L_r',$$

and therefore

$$L_r' = V^{-1} L_h^{-1} P_{hr}. \tag{14}$$

3.1 Conditions and Summary of Basic Solution

Let us now review the solution of the accounting equations described above, pointing out what conditions must hold if it is to be applied.

First of all, it is necessary to have at least $2m - 1$ items available, in order to make up the horizontal and vertical signatures, and the stratifier item. Then the unstratified basic matrix, B_{hv}, must have an inverse. This is equivalent to saying that L_h, L_v, and V have inverses (the latter condition, in turn, means that there are no empty classes).

When these conditions are satisfied we can construct G and solve the determinantal equation (7) for the stratifier item probabilities.

Finally, in order to solve Equation (11) for the columns of L_h, one by one, it is necessary that the m probabilities, $p_1^1, p_1^2, \ldots, p_1^m$ all be distinct. This condition is, perhaps, less obvious than the others, but is easy to understand intuitively. Suppose that $p_1^1 = p_1^2 = \tau$, say. Then, substituting into (11), both

$$(G - \tau I) L_h^{(1)} = 0,$$

and

$$(G - \tau I) L_h^{(2)} = 0.$$

If there were a unique solution for the first vector, $L_h^{(1)}$, it would have to be true that $L_h^{(1)} = L_h^{(2)}$. Since it is quite possible to think of situations in which $p_1^1 = p_1^2$, but $p_j^1 \neq p_j^2$ for j belonging to h, we must conclude that columns 1 and 2 of L_h cannot be uniquely determined by Equation (11) in this case.

What we are doing when we solve the equation

$$G = L_h D_1 L_h^{-1}$$

55

as described above is finding what is called the *diagonal form* of G. In general, when an equation

$$G = AEA^{-1}$$

can be written, with E a diagonal matrix, we call the entries of E the *character-istic roots*, or eigenvalues, of G. When the e_{ii} are distinct, the columns of A are called the *characteristic column vectors* of G, and are unique up to multiplica-tion by a constant. As we point out in Appendix A, there are several different numerical methods for computing the characteristic roots and vectors of a given matrix. (See Hohn, 1964, Chapter 8, and Faddeeva, 1959.) The point we wish to emphasize here is that when we are given a manifest matrix G, the equation involving unknowns D_1 and L_h:

$$G = L_h D_1 L_h^{-1}$$

can be solved by standard mathematical methods as long as no two elements on the diagonal of D_1 are identical.

We summarize by stating the following theorem.

THEOREM 1. *The accounting equations of an n-item, m-class latent structure model can be solved uniquely by application of the basic solution if* (i) $n \geq 2m - 1$; (ii) *all classes are non-empty;* (iii) *there is at least one item which has distinct latent probabilities: let one such item be chosen and designated item 1;* (iv) *there are two sets of m − 1 items each, non-overlapping and not including the item "1", such that the matrices L_h and L_v have inverses, h and v indicating the two sets of items, with the "zero item" added to each.*

The basic solution consists of constructing the basic matrices B_{hv} and $B_{hv;\,1}$; finding the characteristic roots and corresponding characteristic column vectors of $B_{hv;\,1} B_{hv}^{-1}$, which equal D_1 and L_h, respectively; and completing the solution as indicated in Equations 12, 13, and 14.

Example. Suppose that we have a five-item, three-class, latent structure with latent probabilities as given in Table 3 below.

TABLE 3

Example A
Latent Probabilities

Class	Size	Item 1	2	3	4	5
1	0.3	0.9	0.9	0.8	0.6	0.5
2	0.5	0.5	0.7	0.4	0.5	0.9
3	0.2	0.1	0.1	0.3	0.4	0.1

The manifest probabilities can be computed from these latent probabilities, and the entire set is given in Table 4.

TABLE 4

Example A
Manifest Probabilities

p_1	p_2	p_3	p_4	p_5
0.54	0.64	0.50	0.51	0.62
p_{12}	p_{13}	p_{14}	p_{15}	p_{23}
0.420	0.322	0.295	0.362	0.362
p_{24}	p_{25}	p_{34}	p_{35}	p_{45}
0.345	0.452	0.268	0.306	0.323
p_{123}	p_{124}	p_{125}	p_{134}	p_{135}
0.265	0.2341	0.2792	0.182	0.1986
p_{145}	p_{234}	p_{235}	p_{245}	p_{345}
0.1943	0.202	0.2346	0.2393	0.1644
p_{1234}	p_{1235}	p_{1245}	p_{1345}	p_{2345}
0.15188	0.16026	0.15173	0.09004	0.12804
p_{12345}				
0.089844				

It is left as an exercise for the reader to check these manifest probabilities by carrying out the necessary calculations, using the accounting equations (1) and (2) of Section 1.

We shall now apply our solution to these manifest probabilities. The matrices B and B_1 are:

$$B_{23,45} = \begin{pmatrix} 1.0 & 0.51 & 0.62 \\ 0.64 & 0.345 & 0.452 \\ 0.50 & 0.268 & 0.306 \end{pmatrix} \quad B_{1;23,45} = \begin{pmatrix} 0.54 & 0.277 & 0.362 \\ 0.420 & 0.2341 & 0.2792 \\ 0.322 & 0.1820 & 0.1986 \end{pmatrix}.$$

The inverse of B, B^{-1}, is:

$$B^{-1} = \tfrac{1}{792} \begin{pmatrix} 15,566 & -10,100 & -16,620 \\ -30,160 & 4,000 & 55,200 \\ 980 & 13,000 & -18,600 \end{pmatrix}.$$

Multiplying B_1 and B^{-1}, we have:

$$G = B_1 B^{-1} = \tfrac{1}{792} \begin{pmatrix} -136.8 & 432 & 576 \\ -249.12 & 324 & 748.8 \\ -282.24 & 57.6 & 1000.8 \end{pmatrix},$$

57

which is

$$G = \begin{pmatrix} -0.172 & 0.545 & 0.727 \\ -0.3145 & 0.409 & 0.945 \\ -0.3563 & 0.072 & 1.263 \end{pmatrix}$$

where the underlined numerals indicate repeating digits.

We must now determine the characteristic values and vectors of G. That is, we must find numbers t and column vectors x such that

$$Gx = tx. \qquad (15)$$

As noted above, the three characteristic values are the three roots of the determinantal equation,

$$|G - tI| = 0.$$

Here we have

$$|G - tI| = \begin{vmatrix} -0.172727 - t & 0.545454 & 0.727272 \\ -0.314545 & 0.409090 - t & 0.945454 \\ -0.356363 & 0.072727 & 1.263636 - t \end{vmatrix}.$$

Calculation of coefficients leads to the equation:

$$t^3 - 1.500t^2 + 0.590t - 0.045 = 0,$$

and

$$(t - 0.9)(t - 0.5)(t - 0.1) = 0.$$

Substituting, in turn, these three values of t, we solve for the three columns of L_h

$$(G - tI)x = 0, \qquad (16)$$

subject to the condition that the first element of each vector is 1. For instance, when $t = 0.9$, Equation (16) is:

$$\begin{pmatrix} -1.072 & 0.54 & 0.72 \\ -0.3145 & -0.490 & 0.945 \\ -0.3563 & 0.072 & 0.36 \end{pmatrix} \begin{pmatrix} 1.0 \\ x_1 \\ x_2 \end{pmatrix} = \begin{pmatrix} 0 \\ 0 \\ 0 \end{pmatrix},$$

and any two of the three equations can be used to solve for the two unknowns, giving $x_1 = 0.90 = p_2^1$ and $x_2 = 0.80 = p_3^1$.

The other two vectors are found to be $(1, 0.7, 0.4)$ and $(1, 0.1, 0.3)$. (As an exercise, verify that these two vectors satisfy Equation (16) when t is 0.5 and 0.1, respectively.)

These three vectors are the three columns of L_h, so that we can write:

$$L_h = \begin{pmatrix} 1 & 1 & 1 \\ 0.9 & 0.7 & 0.1 \\ 0.8 & 0.4 & 0.3 \end{pmatrix} \begin{matrix} \text{Item:} \\ 2 \\ 3 \end{matrix}$$

Then

$$L_h^{-1} = \tfrac{1}{22} \begin{pmatrix} -17 & -10 & 60 \\ 19 & 50 & -80 \\ 20 & -40 & 20 \end{pmatrix},$$

and the product $L_h^{-1}B$ is, therefore,

$$L_h^{-1}B = \begin{pmatrix} 0.3 & 0.18 & 0.15 \\ 0.5 & 0.25 & 0.45 \\ 0.2 & 0.08 & 0.02 \end{pmatrix}.$$

We conclude, therefore, that $v^1 = 0.3$, $v^2 = 0.5$, $v^3 = 0.2$. And, finally, dividing each row by its first entry, we have:

$$L_v' = \begin{pmatrix} 1 & 0.6 & 0.5 \\ 1 & 0.5 & 0.9 \\ 1 & 0.4 & 0.1 \end{pmatrix}.$$
$$\text{Item:} \quad 4 \quad\quad 5$$

We have recovered the original parameters, given in Table 3.

4. Identification of a Model

Formally, we may describe what was done in the previous section as "deriving conditions under which the m-class model is identifiable." Identification has a very specific meaning. In short, a model is identifiable if there is a *unique* latent structure which generates the manifest probabilities.

DEFINITION. Let θ be a set of latent parameters of a particular model, M. Let $S = S(\theta)$ be the set of manifest probabilities generated by θ and the assumptions of the model. We say that the model is *identifiable* if and only if

$$S(\theta_1) = S(\theta_2)$$

implies that

$$\theta_1 = \theta_2.$$

Thus, in showing that under the conditions of Theorem 1, the latent probabilities of the m-class model were uniquely determined by the manifest probabilities, we proved that the m-class model is identifiable when those conditions are satisfied.

In this section, we shall examine some extensions of Theorem 1, by which the conditions for identifiability of the latent class model can be weakened. First, however, we digress somewhat in order to define the notion of an *ascending* matrix.

4.1 *Ascending Matrices*

There are two aspects of the solution of Section 4 which are particularly important methodologically. On the one hand, the only manifest probabilities used in the solution are of first-, second-, or third-order; higher-order probabilities do not enter. On the other hand, the arrangement of these probabilities in a simple basic matrix and its stratified analog was vital to the derivation of a solution. In this section we look at higher-order manifest probabilities, hoping to reduce, if possible, the minimum number of items needed for a solution. At the same time, the notion of stratified and unstratified matrix will be exploited to the fullest.

To define a basic matrix, we had to specify two sets of items which did not overlap (except for the dummy item zero). Given one set s and another set r, the matrix

$$P_{sr}$$

was defined as the matrix (p_{ij}) with i in the set s, and j in the set r. Let us now generalize the concept of "signature" from a set of *items* to a set of response patterns.

DEFINITION. A *generalized signature* is a vector

$$s = (s_1, s_2, \ldots, s_k)$$

each of whose entries represent some possible pattern of response.

For example, if $k = 3$, and $s_1 = 2$, $s_2 = 3$, and $s_3 = 23$, the vector

$$s = (2, 3, 23)$$

is a *generalized signature*. (The "23" could, of course, be read as "twenty-three," but we are using it to refer to the positive response to items 2 and 3, in keeping with our usual notation, e.g., p_{23}. Whenever there are more than 9 items present, we shall be very careful to indicate the meaning of such subscripts.)

Now, any two such generalized signatures can be used to generate a matrix of manifest probabilities, as long as no item appears in both signatures (in any form).

For example, if

$$s = (2, 3, 23) \quad \text{and} \quad r = (4, 5, 45),$$

the matrix

$$P_{sr} = (p_{s_i r_j})$$

would be

r s	4	5	45
2	p_{24}	p_{25}	p_{245}
3	p_{34}	p_{35}	p_{345}
23	p_{234}	p_{235}	p_{2345}

In order that no repeated subscripts appear in the matrix P_{sr}, we have to require that any item that appears in s, in any form, cannot appear in r at all, and vice versa. (Again, we note that this is true "except for item zero.")

When either signature s or r contains response patterns of different order, we call the matrix so generated an *ascending* matrix. The term is used descriptively, since we shall usually order the elements of the signatures so that their lengths increase from left to right, and so the subscripts within the matrix P_{sr} get longer as we move down and to the right. (This, we emphasize, is a convention, not a prescription!)

The usefulness of these ascending matrices is seen when we express them in terms of the parameters of the latent class model. It is always true that, given two response patterns a and b,

$$p_{ab} = \sum v^\alpha p_a^\alpha p_b^\alpha. \tag{17}$$

Of course, when a or b represent more than the response to a single item, we can reduce the expressions p_a^α and p_b^α, since they will be products of appropriate latent marginals, p_i^α. For the moment, however, we shall *not* carry out this symbolic reduction. Equation (17) implies that

$$P_{sr} = L_s V L_r', \tag{18}$$

where we shall define L_s and L_r in the obvious way:

If $s = (s_1, s_2, \ldots, s_k)$, then $(L_s)_{ij} = p_{s_i}^j$.

For example, letting $s = (2, 3, 23)$, we would have

$$L_s = \begin{pmatrix} p_2^1 & p_2^2 & \cdots & p_2^m \\ p_3^1 & p_3^2 & \cdots & p_3^m \\ p_2^1 p_3^1 & p_2^2 p_3^2 & \cdots & p_2^m p_3^m \end{pmatrix}.$$

A stratified matrix will be defined as before, but with the obvious generalization that the stratifier need not be a single item: it, like the elements of the generalized signatures, may be any response pattern.

DEFINITION. Let s and r be generalized signatures, having no common item. Let t be any response pattern containing no item that is present in either s or r. Then, the *stratified matrix* is:

$$P_{s,r;t} = (p_{s_i, r_j; t}).$$

61

THEOREM 2. *In the case of m latent classes,*

$$P_{s,r;t} = L_s V D_t L_r',$$

where D_t is a diagonal matrix with $(D_t)_{jj} = p_t^j$.

4.2 A Solution Using Higher-Order Probabilities

We shall now use the results of Section 4.1 to indicate how the solution of Section 3 can be extended.

Define two signatures, h and v, which contain exactly m elements. Suppose, also, that they both have the zero item as their first element, but that no other item appears in both. Then

$$P_{hv} = L_h V L_v' \qquad (19)$$

is a square, $m \times m$ matrix, m being the number of latent classes. The first row of L_h consists of ones, as does the first row of L_v.

If t is a response pattern which contains no item in common with h or v, then the stratified matrix:

$$P_{hv;t} = L_h V D_t L_v' \qquad (20)$$

can also be written down.

Explicitly, we note that t does not have to be a single item; h and v may include elements that are not single items.

However, since the Equations (19) and (20) are algebraically identical to the Equations (3) and (5) of Section 2, the same theorem dealing with their solution still applies.

THEOREM 3. *If, as defined above, the inverses of L_h, L_v and V exist; and if the entries of D_t are all distinct; then L_h, L_v, V, and D_t can be uniquely determined if P_{hv} and $P_{hv;t}$ are known. Specifically:*

(i) *Since $P_{hv;t}P_{hv}^{-1} = L_h D_t L_h^{-1}$, D_t and L_h are determined uniquely as the characteristic roots and column vectors of $P_{hv;t}P_{hv}^{-1}$.*
(ii) *$V L_v' = L_h^{-1} P_{hv}$, and hence V is the first column of $L_h^{-1} P_{hv}$.*
(iii) *$L_v' = V^{-1} L_h^{-1} P_{hv}$.*

The proof of this theorem was, essentially, given in Section 3. We have only removed the restriction that h and v consist of individual items, and that the stratifier also be an item.

It is particularly important to note how the use of these ascending matrices in a solution decreases the number of items required. For example, consider the case $m = 4$. Each signature h and v must contain 3 elements besides 0. If the solution uses basic matrices, each of these 6 elements must be a distinct item, and so, adding one more item to be the stratifier, we see that at least 7 items are needed in order to identify the latent probabilities. On the other hand, an ascending matrix can be constructed which involves only 4 items by letting

$$h = (0, 2, 3, 23),$$
$$v = (0, 4, 5, 45).$$

Letting the stratifier be item 1, we find that only 5 items are required for a solution.

Note that $1 + 2(m - 1) = 2m - 1$ items are needed for the basic solution. The minimum number of items which are needed to apply the general solution is $1 + 2k$, where k is the smallest integer greater than $\log_2 m$. The proof that this is so is quite straightforward. Suppose that $n = 1 + 2k$. Then one item must be the stratifier, and k items must generate the $m - 1$ elements of each signature. The maximum number of distinct response patterns generated by k items would be

$$\binom{k}{1} + \binom{k}{2} + \binom{k}{3} + \cdots + \binom{k}{k} = 2^k - 1.$$

Thus

$$m - 1 \leq 2^k - 1,$$
$$m \leq 2^k.$$

By taking logarithms to base 2,

$$k \geq \log_2 m,$$

and so

$$n = 1 + 2k \geq 1 + 2 \log_2 m.$$

The following table contrasts the minimum number of items needed for the basic and ascending solutions.

TABLE 5

Minimum Number of Items for Classes 2 to 10

Number of classes	Minimum n using ascending solution	Minimum n using basic solution
2	3	3
3	5	5
4	5	7
5	7	9
6	7	11
7	7	13
8	7	15
9	9	17
10	9	19

The next question we must ask, however, is this: Given L_h, L_v, D_t, and V, is it possible to calculate the marginal probabilities p_i^α for each item? This will actually depend on what h and v are; however, we can see at once that t must be a single item; if, say, t consists of items 1 and 2, $t = 12$, then $p_t^\alpha = p_{12}^\alpha = p_1^\alpha p_2^\alpha$ is known, but p_1^α and p_2^α remain unknown.

If, for instance, $m = 4$, and $h = (0, 2, 3, 23)$ while $v = (0, 4, 5, 45)$, it is clear that the fourth row of L_h and L_v gives redundant information. On the other hand, if $h = (0, 2, 36, 26)$, the individual item probabilities could be recovered and there is no redundancy:

$$p_6^\alpha = p_{26}^\alpha/p_2^\alpha, \text{ and then } p_3^\alpha = p_{36}^\alpha/p_6^\alpha.$$

Even if no marginals at all were known, to begin with, they might all be recoverable: if $h = (0, 26, 36, 236)$ then,

$$p_2^\alpha = p_{236}^\alpha/p_{36}^\alpha,$$
$$p_3^\alpha = p_{236}^\alpha/p_{26}^\alpha,$$
$$p_6^\alpha = p_{26}^\alpha/p_2^\alpha.$$

However, if $h = (0, 23, 26, 27)$, the individual item probabilities could not be found. We would not expect to determine more than $m - 1$ item probabilities from a matrix L_h, while we would expect to be able to determine them all if $m - 1$, or fewer items were involved in the $m - 1$ non-zero elements of the signature.

Thus we have the following corollary to Theorem 3.

COROLLARY. *If $m - 1$ items or fewer appear in the signature h, and likewise for the signature v, and if t is a single item; then all item probabilities p_i^α can be determined.*

4.3 *Remarks on Identifiability*

The previous sections provided a constructive approach to the problem of identifying the parameters of a latent class model. That is, they give rise to theorems which allow us to say "if there are m classes, and if certain conditions are satisfied, then the latent parameters can be uniquely determined by carrying out such-and-such operations on the given manifest probabilities."

If we do not know the value of m, however, we must consider the problem of determining it, given the manifest probabilities. Consider the complete, symmetric array of second-order manifest probabilities, p_{ij}, where i and j go from 1 to n. The diagonal entries we leave blank, since they are not manifest. Except for these diagonal entries, this matrix, call it P, is equal to the product of an $n \times m$ latent matrix L, times V, times L transpose. The ith row of L consists of the m latent probabilities of item i. This equation,

$$P = LVL' \tag{21}$$

is simply the complete, symmetric analog of the basic matrices defined earlier. We *define* p_{ii} to mean $\sum v^\alpha p_i^\alpha p_i^\alpha$, even though these quantities are *not* manifest probabilities, as are the p_{ij}.

Because V, one of the factors of P, is an $m \times m$ matrix, and m is less than n, P cannot have an inverse. Indeed, the *rank* of P cannot be any greater than m. This means that any *square submatrix of P that is larger than $m \times m$ will have a determinant equal to zero* (see Appendix A). Examining the manifest entries of P would thus be a way of testing the hypothesis that there were no more than *m* classes: we would just have to see whether all determinants of submatrices bigger than $m \times m$ were zero.

The following theorem generalizes this statement. It concerns the identifiability, not of the *parameters* of a latent class model, but of the model itself.

THEOREM 4. *If there is an m-class latent structure model generating the manifest probabilities, then any basic or ascending matrix of manifest probabilities larger than* $m \times m$ *must have determinant zero, i.e., is a singular matrix.*

PROOF: Let *h* and *v* be the horizontal and vertical signatures of a matrix, and suppose that there are more than *m* elements in each signature. Then

$$P_{hv} = L_h V L_v',$$

whether *h* and *v* are basic or ascending signatures. Likewise, if the matrix is stratified by any item or *combination of items*, *t*, then

$$P_{hv;t} = L_h V D_t L_v'.$$

The rank of *P* cannot be greater than *m*, since *V* is $m \times m$. Since the order of *P* is greater than its rank, $|P| = 0$. Likewise, $|P_t| = 0$. ∎

Use of Theorem 4 permits us to determine a lower bound for the number of classes, namely that number m^* such that all basic matrices of order $m^* + 1$ or larger have zero determinants, while there exists at least one such matrix, of order m^*, which has a non-zero determinant. Since we nearly always feel that the number of classes ought to be as small as possible, it is natural to agree to let $m = m^*$, the smallest number of classes consistent with the manifest probabilities. It is easy to see how the number of "classes" could be increased without limit: by asserting the existence of classes for which $v^\alpha = 0$ (empty classes) although the item probabilities are well defined; or by artificially splitting a non-empty class into two subclasses which have identical item probabilities for all the items. Obviously, no information about the manifest probabilities could prove or disprove the existence of such "classes."

We shall also use Theorem 4 in the analysis of the following problem. Suppose that there are 3 latent classes and only 4 items ($m = 3, n = 4$). There are $m(n + 1) - 1 = 15$ latent probabilities, and $2^n - 1 = 15$ manifest probabilities (leaving out one of the class sizes and the condition that the v^α all add to 1). However, neither of the solutions presented earlier can apply; 5 is the minimum number of items using either basic or ascending matrices. We cannot rule out *a priori*, however, the chance that a solution does exist, since there are the same number of manifest probabilities as unknown, latent probabilities. Of course, the 15 unknowns would have to be independent of one another if a solution were to exist. They are not, however, and here is one way of showing it.

Consider the 4×4 matrix

$$P_{hv} = \begin{pmatrix} 1 & p_1 & p_2 & p_{12} \\ p_3 & p_{13} & p_{23} & p_{123} \\ p_4 & p_{14} & p_{24} & p_{124} \\ p_{34} & p_{134} & p_{234} & p_{1234} \end{pmatrix}$$

generated by the signatures

$$h = (0, 3, 4, 34),$$

and

$$v = (0, 1, 2, 12).$$

As shown above, $P_{hv} = L_h V L'_v$ where, for instance,

$$L_h = \begin{pmatrix} 1 & 1 & 1 \\ p_3^1 & p_3^2 & p_3^3 \\ p_4^1 & p_4^2 & p_4^2 \\ p_3^1 p_4^1 & p_3^2 p_4^2 & p_3^3 p_4^3 \end{pmatrix}.$$

Since P_{hv} is 4×4, while V is only 3×3, Theorem 4 implies that the *determinant of P_{hv} must be zero*. The equation $|P_{hv}| = 0$ thus constitutes a relation among the manifest probabilities. For instance, we could solve explicitly for p_{1234} in terms of the lower-order probabilities. Since there are 15 unknowns, and *no more* than $15 - 1 = 14$ independent equations, the parameters cannot be identified.

4.4 Equivalent Items

Special cases of the latent class model can be defined by placing restrictions on the items. For instance, we might require that the items all be *equivalent*, that is, that they all have exactly the same latent characteristics. This particular assumption does have some usefulness, especially in connection with intelligence tests. A homogeneous test, in which the items are all interchangeable, is sometimes considered a desirable goal of test construction.

For simplicity, suppose that there are 5 items and 3 classes. Equivalent items means that

$$p_i^\alpha = p_j^\alpha$$

for each pair of items i and j. We assume that

$$p_i^\alpha \neq p_i^\beta$$

when $\alpha \neq \beta$. For ease of notation, let

$$x = p_i^1, \; y = p_i^2, \; z = p_i^3.$$

We see at once that

$$p_i = p_j, \, p_{ij} = p_{kn},$$

and so forth.

The basic solution cannot be applied to this model, since, for any signature $h = (0, i, j)$, the latent matrix would be:

$$L_h = \begin{pmatrix} 1 & 1 & 1 \\ p_i^1 & p_i^2 & p_i^3 \\ p_j^1 & p_j^2 & p_j^3 \end{pmatrix} = \begin{pmatrix} 1 & 1 & 1 \\ x & y & z \\ x & y & z \end{pmatrix}.$$

This matrix does not have an inverse, and thus the basic solution, Theorem 1, cannot be used.

On the other hand, the use of ascending matrices will allow the model to be solved. Define two signatures $h = (0, 2, 23)$ and $v = (0, 4, 45)$. Then L_h and L_v will be invertible as long as x, y, and z are distinct:

$$L_h = \begin{pmatrix} 1 & 1 & 1 \\ p_2^1 & p_2^2 & p_2^3 \\ p_2^1 p_3^1 & p_2^2 p_3^2 & p_2^3 p_3^3 \end{pmatrix} = \begin{pmatrix} 1 & 1 & 1 \\ x & y & z \\ x^2 & y^2 & z^2 \end{pmatrix}.$$

The determinant of L_h is of a very simple form:

$$L_h = (x - y)(y - z)(z - x)$$

which can be zero only if (at least) two of the three numbers are equal.

ASIDE: We shall meet this determinant again in a later chapter. It is called the Vandermonde determinant, and in most general form, where $x_{ij} = (x_i)^{j-1}$,

$$|X| = \begin{vmatrix} 1 & 1 & \cdots & 1 \\ x_1 & x_2 & \cdots & x_m \\ x_1^2 & x_2^2 & \cdots & x_m^2 \\ \vdots & \vdots & & \vdots \\ x_1^m & x_2^m & \cdots & x_m^m \end{vmatrix}$$

is equal to $(x_1 - x_2)(x_2 - x_3) \cdots (x_m - x_1)$.
The easiest proof is by an inductive argument. ∎

Continuing the derivation, it becomes clear that the ascending solution does work, since both L_h and L_v will have inverses, and stratifying by item 1 completes the solution.

The manifest matrices used are

$$P = \begin{pmatrix} 1 & p_4 & p_{45} \\ p_2 & p_{24} & p_{245} \\ p_{23} & p_{234} & p_{2345} \end{pmatrix},$$

$$P_1 = \begin{pmatrix} p_1 & p_{14} & p_{145} \\ p_{12} & p_{124} & p_{1245} \\ p_{123} & p_{1234} & p_{12345} \end{pmatrix}.$$

Since all p_i are the same, as are all p_{ij}, and all p_{ijk}, etc., we would not use the above solution in a problem involving real data which was obtained by random sampling. It would be more reasonable to combine all marginal information to estimate *the* marginal; all second-order information to estimate *the* second-order manifest probability; etc. If the data frequencies were

$$n_1, n_2, n_3, n_4, n_5, n_{12}, n_{13}, \ldots, n_{12345},$$

and the total sample were N, we would let

$$
\begin{aligned}
P_{(1)} &= \sum n_i/5N, \\
P_{(2)} &= \sum n_{ij}/10N, \\
P_{(3)} &= \sum n_{ijk}/10N, \\
P_{(4)} &= \sum n_{ijkl}/5N, \\
P_{(5)} &= n_{12345}/N,
\end{aligned}
$$

and use the estimated manifest probabilities on P and P_1:

$$
P = \begin{pmatrix} 1 & P_{(1)} & P_{(2)} \\ P_{(1)} & P_{(2)} & P_{(3)} \\ P_{(2)} & P_{(3)} & P_{(4)} \end{pmatrix},
$$

$$
P_1 = \begin{pmatrix} P_{(1)} & P_{(2)} & P_{(3)} \\ P_{(2)} & P_{(3)} & P_{(4)} \\ P_{(3)} & P_{(4)} & P_{(5)} \end{pmatrix}
$$

to solve for the unknown latent probabilities

$$p_i^1 = x, \; p_i^2 = y, \; p_i^3 = z, \; v^1, v^2, \text{ and } v^3.$$

The generalization of this approach to any number of classes and to any number of items (above the minimum required for m classes) ought to be clear. The important point to remember is that all elements in the signature h must be of different order, and the same for v.

5. Classification of Respondents

The problem of assigning respondents to one of the latent classes, once the latent parameters are known, was discussed in the preceding chapter. We emphasize here the idea that as much information as possible should be utilized in making this classification. This means that we should, if possible, examine the complete response pattern of an individual before assigning him to a class. This nth-order, or ultimate response pattern, s, is usually represented by a sequence of n binary digits, a 1 standing for a positive response and a 0 for a negative response.

Assuming the latent structure is known, there is a certain probability $P(\alpha|s)$, that the respondent came from class α, $(\alpha = 1, 2, \ldots, m)$, if he gave response s.

This is equal, by Bayes' theorem, to

$$P(\alpha|s) = p_s^{\alpha}v^{\alpha}/p_s,$$

where p_s^{α} is the conditional probability of response s *within class* α, and $p_s = \sum v^{\alpha}p_s^{\alpha}$ is the *unconditional* probability of response s. Because of within-class independence of items, p_s^{α} is simply a product of the item probabilities p_i^{α} and $1 - p_j^{\alpha}$, according as item i appears positively in s and item j appears negatively in s.

The following Table 6 illustrates the necessary calculations for the hypothetical example discussed in Section 3.

TABLE 6

Analysis for Class Assignment, Example A

Response Patterns	Latent Class Probabilities			Manifest Probability	Probability of Belonging to a Class, Given s		
(s)	p_s^1	p_s^2	p_s^3	p_s	$P(1|s)$	$P(2|s)$	$P(3|s)$
1 1 1 1 1	0.1944	0.0630	0.0001	0.0898	0.649*	0.351	0.000
1 1 1 1 0	0.1944	0.0070	0.0011	0.0620	0.940*	0.056	0.004
1 1 1 0 1	0.1296	0.0630	0.0002	0.0704	0.552*	0.447	0.001
1 1 1 0 0	0.1296	0.0070	0.0016	0.0427	0.910*	0.082	0.008
1 1 0 1 1	0.0486	0.0945	0.0003	0.0619	0.236	0.763*	0.001
1 1 0 1 0	0.0486	0.0105	0.0025	0.0203	0.717*	0.258	0.002
1 1 0 0 1	0.0324	0.0945	0.0004	0.0571	0.170	0.828*	0.002
1 1 0 0 0	0.0324	0.0105	0.0038	0.0157	0.618*	0.334	0.048
1 0 1 1 1	0.0216	0.0270	0.0011	0.0202	0.321	0.668*	0.011
1 0 1 1 0	0.0216	0.0030	0.0097	0.0099	0.653*	0.151	0.196
1 0 1 0 1	0.0144	0.0270	0.0016	0.0181	0.238	0.744*	0.018
1 0 1 0 0	0.0144	0.0030	0.0146	0.0087	0.494*	0.172	0.334
1 0 0 1 1	0.0054	0.0405	0.0025	0.0224	0.072	0.905*	0.023
1 0 0 1 0	0.0054	0.0045	0.0227	0.0084	0.193	0.268	0.541*
1 0 0 0 1	0.0036	0.0405	0.0038	0.0221	0.049	0.917*	0.034
1 0 0 0 0	0.0036	0.0045	0.0340	0.0101	0.107	0.222	0.671*
0 1 1 1 1	0.0216	0.0630	0.0011	0.0382	0.170	0.825*	0.006
0 1 1 1 0	0.0216	0.0070	0.0097	0.0119	0.543*	0.294	0.163
0 1 1 0 1	0.0144	0.0630	0.0016	0.0361	0.119	0.872*	0.009
0 1 1 0 0	0.0144	0.0070	0.0146	0.0107	0.402*	0.326	0.272
0 1 0 1 1	0.0054	0.0945	0.0025	0.0494	0.033	0.957*	0.010
0 1 0 1 0	0.0054	0.0105	0.0227	0.0114	0.142	0.460*	0.398
0 1 0 0 1	0.0036	0.0945	0.0038	0.0491	0.022	0.963*	0.015
0 1 0 0 0	0.0036	0.0105	0.0340	0.0131	0.082	0.400	0.518*
0 0 1 1 1	0.0021	0.0270	0.0097	0.0162	0.045	0.835*	0.120
0 0 1 1 0	0.0024	0.0030	0.0875	0.0197	0.037	0.076	0.887*
0 0 1 0 1	0.0016	0.0270	0.0146	0.0169	0.028	0.799*	0.172
0 0 1 0 0	0.0016	0.0030	0.1312	0.0282	0.017	0.053	0.930*
0 0 0 1 1	0.0006	0.0405	0.0227	0.0250	0.007	0.811*	0.182
0 0 0 1 0	0.0006	0.0045	0.2041	0.0433	0.004	0.052	0.944*
0 0 0 0 1	0.0004	0.0405	0.0340	0.0272	0.004	0.745*	0.250
0 0 0 0 0	0.0004	0.0045	0.3062	0.0636	0.002	0.035	0.953*

*Indicates the largest value of $P(\alpha|s)$, for each response s.

For example, consider the response pattern $s = (1, 1, 1, 0, 1)$ which represents positive responses to items 1, 2, 3, and 5; and negative response to item 4.

$$p_s^1 = (0.9)(0.9)(0.8)(1 - 0.6)(0.5) = 0.1296,$$
$$p_s^2 = (0.5)(0.7)(0.4)(1 - 0.5)(0.9) = 0.0630,$$
$$p_s^3 = (0.1)(0.1)(0.3)(1 - 0.4)(0.1) = 0.0002.$$

Since $v^1 = 0.3$, $v^2 = 0.5$, and $v^3 = 0.2$,

$$p_s = \sum v^\alpha p_s^\alpha = 0.3(0.1296) + 0.5(0.0630) + 0.2(0.0002) = 0.1704.$$

Notice that this response is quite likely to have come from either class 1 or class 2:

$$P(1|s) = 0.552 \text{ and } P(2|s) = 0.447.$$

While some responses can be typed fairly clearly as coming from one particular class, others (such as this one here) are not clear cut in their implications.

The best assignment rule, in the sense of minimizing the total expected error, is to always assign a respondent to the *most likely* class. In Table 6, the largest probabilities $P(\alpha|s)$ have been marked with an asterisk. The total expected error under this maximum likelihood assignment procedure will be

$$E = 1 - \sum p_s P(*|s),$$

where $P(*|s)$ is the asterisked number in row s.

In this case, we find that E is approximately 0.20; we could, therefore, hope to be about 80% accurate in assigning respondents to classes with this particular model, once the latent probabilities were known.

4

The Latent Class Model:
Estimation of Parameters

A number of different techniques have been proposed for dealing with the statistical problems associated with the latent class models. We shall, in this chapter, discuss four different approaches. First, there is the straightforward estimation procedure of replacing the manifest probabilities, p_i, p_{ij}, etc., by their sample analogues, n_i/N, n_{ij}/N, etc., and applying the basic Theorem 1 of Chapter 3 to solve the accounting equations. Some statistical properties of this estimation procedure have been studied by T. W. Anderson, and his paper is included as Appendix B to this book.

Second, we shall report on some studies of the usefulness of maximum likelihood estimation in latent class analysis. The theoretical results of this section were derived by McHugh (1956), and the practicality of the method has been studied through use of a computer program.

A third estimation procedure is due to W. A. Gibson, and has been described by him in two articles (Gibson, 1951 and 1956). This involves using only sample frequencies of first and second order, and adapting factoring and rotation methods usually associated with factor analysis. We include an example which Gibson had worked out in illustration of these methods.

Finally, there is an empirical sorting method, proposed by Madansky (1959), which has some utility when a high-speed computer is available. The process consists of trying to discover what assignment of respondents to classes will lead to the best fit of the principle of local independence.

1. Estimation Involving the Solution of Chapter 3

1.1 *Discussion and Example*

As mentioned above, it is quite reasonable to use the solutions of the accounting equations presented in Chapter 3 to estimate the latent parameters of the latent class model. Given data from a random sample of N individuals, we replace the manifest probabilities by their sample analogues, and proceed to solve for the latent probabilities.

Problems arise in several different ways due to the fact that the frequencies n_{ij}/N are only estimates of the true manifest probabilities.

Recall how the basic solution, described in Theorem 1, operated. Item 1, say, is the stratifier item. Two signatures, h, and v, specify the items which make up the basic matrices. The data which would be used in the solution are:

$$n_i \quad \text{for all items } i;$$
$$n_{ij} \quad \text{for } i \text{ in } h \text{ and } j \text{ in } v;$$
$$n_{1j} \quad \text{for all } j;$$
$$n_{1ij} \quad \text{for } i \text{ in } h \text{ and } j \text{ in } v.$$

Not only are we restricted to the use of data of third order and less, but in addition, only certain of the second- and third-order frequencies are used. For instance, no third-order frequency that does not involve the stratifier item, 1, is used. If the same set of data is analyzed twice, using a different stratifier each time, the resulting estimates will probably vary. (The only exception to this statement is in the trivial case for which all available data are used in the solution, e.g., the case of three items and two classes.) The example we chose to illustrate these estimation problems is a two-class, four-item model, which appears in Table 1. The model consisting of the first three items was presented in Chapter 2, where we discussed the computation of manifest probabilities, given a set of latent parameters.

TABLE 1

The Latent Probabilities of a
Hypothetical Two-Class Structure

Class	Size	Item			
		1	2	3	4
1	0.5	0.8	0.9	0.6	0.7
2	0.5	0.4	0.1	0.2	0.5

Using a computer, we generated a random sample of size 1,000, based on the latent probabilities of Table 1. Using a subroutine which generates "pseudo-random" numbers, a number between 0 and 1 is chosen. If it is less than v^1, an individual from class 1 enters our sample; if not, an individual from class 2 enters the sample. Next, this individual's responses to the four items are observed: a response to each item is, according to the model, independent of responses to other items, and so four independent random numbers, between 0 and 1, determine whether the responses are $+$ or $-$. For instance, if the first of the four random numbers is less than p_1^α, where α is the proper class already specified, the response to item 1 is positive; otherwise it is negative. This procedure is repeated until 1,000 "individuals" have been sampled.

The sample frequencies, n_s/N, where s is a positive response pattern, are shown in Table 2. For comparison, we also include the true values of the manifest

TABLE 2

Manifest Probabilities (p_s) Derived
from the Model of Table 1, and Relative
Frequencies (n_s/N) in a Random Sample,
N = 1,000

Item Pattern s	True Manifest Probability p_s	Sample Relative Frequency n_s/N
1	0.6	0.599
2	0.5	0.487
3	0.4	0.414
4	0.6	0.602
12	0.38	0.370
13	0.28	0.287
14	0.38	0.373
23	0.28	0.284
24	0.34	0.339
34	0.26	0.277
123	0.220	0.220
124	0.262	0.259
134	0.188	0.200
234	0.194	0.202
1234	0.1532	0.157

probabilities, p_s, calculated according to the accounting equations of the two-class model. There are twelve different ways of obtaining estimates of the set of latent parameters, using basic matrices, as shown in Table 3 below. Any three items may be chosen to construct the basic matrices, and the latent probabilities

TABLE 3

Effectively Different Solutions
Two Classes, Four Items

Basic Items	Item used in calculation of remaining parameters		
1, 2, 3	1	2	3
1, 2, 4	1	2	4
1, 3, 4	1	3	4
2, 3, 4	2	3	4

of these items calculated.[1] Then, any one of the three items, call it item i, can be chosen and n_{ir}/N used, along with n_r/N, to calculate the latent probabilities of the remaining item, r.

Of the four possible choices of basic items, only two led to estimates which consisted of acceptable probabilities between 0 and 1. These were the solutions beginning with items 1, 2, 3 and items 2, 3, 4. The six complete sets of estimates which were thus obtained are given in Table 4, and the true latent structure is included there for comparison.

TABLE 4

Six Estimates of the Latent Structure

Estimate No.	Class	Size	Item 1	Item 2	Item 3	Item 4	Basic Items
1	1	0.52	0.78	0.87	0.61	0.71	
	2	0.48	0.40	0.06	0.20	0.48	
2	1	0.52	0.78	0.87	0.61	0.73	(1, 2, 3)
	2	0.48	0.40	0.06	0.20	0.46	
3	1	0.52	0.78	0.87	0.61	0.66	
	2	0.48	0.40	0.06	0.20	0.53	
4	1	0.54	0.76	0.83	0.62	0.72	
	2	0.46	0.41	0.09	0.17	0.47	
5	1	0.54	0.69	0.83	0.62	0.72	(2, 3, 4)
	2	0.46	0.49	0.09	0.17	0.47	
6	1	0.54	0.80	0.83	0.62	0.72	
	2	0.46	0.37	0.09	0.17	0.47	
True Parameters	1	0.5	0.8	0.9	0.6	0.7	
	2	0.5	0.4	0.1	0.2	0.5	

None of these estimates is very far from the actual latent structure, with the first estimate being the most accurate, perhaps. In actual practice, the true latent structure is unknown, however, and thus it is of no *practical* use to speak of the "estimate which is closest to the true structure." A criterion for choosing one or another of these estimates, or an average of two or more of the estimates, has to be formulated without reference to the true values of the latent probabilities. One obvious criterion is to choose that estimate which provides the best

[1]All twelve of these possible solutions were calculated, using a program prepared for the 7094 computer. This program, LASY, is written in the FORTRAN IV language, and permits the computation of many different solutions using different arrangements of the same data. All of the first-, second-, and third-order relative frequencies are read into the computer. Then, for each solution, the stratifier item and the items which are to make up the signatures h and v are specified. The proper basic matrices are constructed within the computer, and the algebra of Theorem 1, Chapter 3, is carried out. After printing one set of estimates, the program continues as long as alternate solutions are requested.

TABLE 5

Comparison of Sample Frequencies (n_s/N) and Pseudo-Manifest
Probabilities Generated by Estimates of the Latent Parameters

Response Patterns s	Sample Frequencies n_s/N	Probability of s: Estimate 1	Probability of s: Estimate 2
0000	0.104	0.114	0.119
0001	0.117	0.108	0.104
0010	0.031	0.031	0.032
0011	0.032	0.032	0.031
0100	0.018	0.018	0.018
0101	0.035	0.034	0.035
0110	0.019	0.019	0.018
0111	0.045	0.045	0.046
1000	0.091	0.081	0.084
1001	0.071	0.084	0.081
1010	0.024	0.028	0.028
1011	0.043	0.040	0.040
1100	0.048	0.045	0.042
1101	0.102	0.102	0.105
1110	0.063	0.064	0.059
1111	0.157	0.154	0.158

overall fit to all the data. In Table 5, we have set forth the sample relative frequencies of each nth-order response pattern s, and the "pseudo-manifest" probabilities of the response patterns computed from the estimated latent probabilities in the first and second estimates. Clearly, it is an impossible task to evaluate by eye the fit of the probabilities generated by the two estimates to the data, even in this very simple four-item case.

1.2 *Goodness of Fit*

There are many different ways of defining a single number that will measure the similarity of two columns of numbers. The simplest is probably the sum of the absolute values of the differences:

$$\sum_s |p_s - n_s/N|.$$

Another common measure is the sum of squared differences:

$$\sum_s (p_s - n_s/N)^2.$$

Both these measures would equal zero if there were perfect fit, i.e., if all the sample frequencies n_s/N equaled exactly the pseudo-manifest probabilities p_s computed from the estimated latent parameters. The information function:

$$-\sum_s n_s \log p_s$$

may also be used, and it too has its minimum value (for a given set of p_s) when $n_s/N = p_s$. Later, we shall study this function in more detail, for it is equivalent, except for sign, to the logarithm of the *likelihood* of the sample frequencies.

At this point, however, we choose to use the well-known chi-square statistic to measure the relative fit of different estimates to the data:

$$\chi^2 = \sum_s (n_s - Np_s)^2/Np_s.$$

Two things must be emphasized before continuing this discussion. First, the "p_s" in the formula for χ^2 is a "pseudo-manifest" probability, which is calculated not from the true latent probabilities (which would be unknown in practice), but from some particular estimate of those latent probabilities. Second, although we use the familiar term "chi-square statistic" to describe χ^2, we do not imply that any chi-square test or distribution should be referred to. We merely propose that this function is a reasonable measure of how well the data agree with probabilities generated by an estimate of a latent structure, and that it is also reasonable to accept estimate "A" as better than estimate "B" if the value of χ^2 computed for "A" is smaller than that computed for "B."

We computed the statistic χ^2 for each of the six estimates in Table 4. The results are given in Table 6. By this standard, the first estimate appears to be the best, with $\chi^2 = 6.03$. It is gratifying to note that the estimate which fits

TABLE 6

Values of χ^2
for Six Estimates

Estimate No.	χ^2
1	6.03
2	7.47
3	13.30
4	10.11
5	35.27
6	8.85

the data best was also closest to the true latent structure, which, in this artificial example, was known.

It is not difficult to program a computer to carry out the analytic scheme presented above. In brief, the instructions would be:

(i) Using as data the first-, second-, and third-order positive proportions, compute *all or some* of the solutions possible by changing stratifier and signature items.

(ii) Discard all solutions involving estimates of probabilities that do not lie between 0 and 1.

(iii) Calculate x^2 for each acceptable estimate, comparing the nth-order frequencies with the manifest probabilities generated by the estimates.

(iv) Use that estimate which has the smallest value of x^2.

What are some of the difficulties with such a scheme? With regard to step (i), the number of possible basic solutions gets very large very quickly as n and m increase. In the two-class case, three items are chosen initially, and then one of these three must be selected in the sequel if there are more than three items. Thus:

$$\binom{n}{3}\binom{3}{1} = n(n-1)(n-2)/2$$

different arrangements are possible. With $n = 10$, this number is already equal to 360. When there are more classes, the rate of increase is even faster. Even with fast computers available, it will not be practical to calculate *all* solutions to every problem: some selection will have to be made.

In step (ii), the problem is the reverse. As the number of classes goes up, the chances become greater that very few of the estimates obtained in this way will be completely acceptable. There is a kind of law of propagation of error at work: each sample frequency may be within 0.01, say, of the true manifest probability associated with it, but in the process of combining all these estimates in the determinantal equation and solving for the m roots of that equation, these small deviations become magnified. It becomes unlikely that all roots of that equation will be between 0 and 1, especially if m is large and/or some of the true values of p_i^α are near the limits of 0 and 1.

Finally, we ask two questions concerning the x^2 criterion itself. First, is there perhaps some estimate of the latent parameters which we have not calculated which would have a lower x^2 than those of the estimates we did compute? The answer is yes, and we shall suggest how this "best" or "minimum x^2" estimate can be found. Second, is there a good reason for using the x^2 measure rather than one of the others mentioned? To answer this question, we need to introduce a few statistical concepts involved in making a "best" estimate, which is now done in Section 2.

Readers who are not familiar with mathematical statistics, particularly with maximum likelihood estimation ideas, should be prepared to skip around freely in this chapter. In Section 3, and again in Section 5, there is discussion of some analysis of real data that may be of substantive interest. Section 4 is quite technical, and may be skipped at a first reading. Section 3, with its presentation of examples and experiments, ought to be read in order to get the feel of what effects sampling error will have on the estimation of latent class parameters.

2. Some Statistical Theory

In this section, we shall briefly talk about some of the important aspects of large-sample statistical theory which are applicable to the latent class model and to other models of latent structure analysis. Anyone who has taken even the simplest of statistics courses has been introduced to large-sample theory in the form of the law of large numbers and the central limit theorem, applied to the traditional problem of coin-tossing.

If N independent tosses of a coin are made, and the probability of a head is always p, the law of large numbers says that the number of heads, divided by N, will approach p as N gets very large. The idea of the estimator n_h/N approaching p can be made rigorous in several ways, and one of the ways is by the definition of *consistency*.

DEFINITION. Let p be a parameter, and let $T(N)$ be an *estimator* of p, based on a sample of N independent observations. $T(N)$ is said to be a *consistent estimator* of p if, for any chosen positive number δ,

$$Pr\ (|T(N) - p| > \delta)$$

approaches 0 as N approaches infinity.

That is, the probability that the estimator is more than a fixed distance away from the true value of the parameter gets small as N gets large.

The most important property of consistent estimators from our point of view is this: if $q = f(p)$ is a continuous function of p, and if T is a consistent estimator of p, then $f(T)$ is a consistent estimator of q.

This theorem is true not only in the univariate case, but in the multivariate case as well. The application to the latent structure models is, of course, in the multivariate form. The sample frequencies, n_s/N, will always be consistent estimators of the manifest probabilities p_s if the sample is a simple random sample, since the model on the manifest level is just a gigantic coin-tossing process (or, in more proper language, a multinomial process). But the accounting equations of the model are, in functional terms:

$$p_s = p_s((v^\alpha), (p_i^\alpha)).$$

When we solve these equations for the latent parameters, and show that the model is identifiable, we are demonstrating the existence of continuous functions g_α and $h_{i\alpha}$ such that:

$$v^\alpha = g_\alpha(p_s), \ p_i^\alpha = h_{i\alpha}(p_s).$$

Thus, when the p_s are replaced by the consistent estimators n_s/N, $g_\alpha(n_s/N)$ and $h_{i\alpha}(n_s/N)$ are consistent estimators of v^α and p_i^α, according to the very general theorem cited above.

In the simple coin-tossing experiment, the central limit theorem says that the quantity:

$$\sqrt{N}\,(n_h/N - p)$$

will tend to have a normal distribution as N gets large, with mean 0 and variance $p(1 - p)$. We usually say that for large values of N, n_h/N is approximately normally distributed with mean p and variance $p(1 - p)/N$, which makes clear the fact that the variance of the sample estimate, n_h/N, is approaching zero as N gets large.

When a random variable has a distribution that tends to be normal as N gets large, we say that it is *asymptotically normally distributed*.

The definition for the univariate case can be stated as follows.

DEFINITION. An estimator $T(N)$ is said to have an *asymptotic normal distribution*, with mean p and variance σ^2 if

$$\sqrt{N}\,(T(N) - p)/\sigma$$

has a distribution which tends to the unit normal distribution (mean 0, variance 1) as N approaches infinity.

In the multivariate case, the same kind of definition applies, but in describing a multivariate normal distribution it is necessary to specify *covariances* as well as variances. Thus, we speak of a normal distribution with mean vector θ, say, and variance-covariance matrix C.

Just as when dealing with simple binomial experiments, the fact that some estimate-vector is known to have an asymptotic distribution that is normal, with a known mean and variance, permits us to calculate approximate confidence intervals for the estimates and, perhaps, to test some hypotheses involving the parameters.

In Appendix B, T. W. Anderson has proven that the estimates of the latent parameters of the latent class models obtained by applying the basic solution to the sample data are asymptotically normally distributed. Since he also derives the functional form of the asymptotic covariance matrix, we could investigate the probable accuracy of these estimates, given certain values of the latent probabilities.

When there is only a single parameter being estimated, the size of the asymptotic variance of an estimator is a measure of how fast the estimate will converge to the true value of the parameter as N gets large. Thus, if there are two estimators of the same parameter, it will be logical to choose to use that one which has the smaller asymptotic variance. Generally speaking, there always exists some lower bound to the asymptotic variance which an estimator of a particular parameter can have, and an estimator which actually attains this lower bound is called asymptotically *efficient*. The use of the method of maximum likelihood to get estimates of a parameter is based, in part, on the fact that whenever asymptotically efficient estimates of a parameter exist, the maximum likelihood estimator will be asymptotically efficient. (See, for instance, Cramér (1946), p. 477, and Rao (1952), pp. 157–161.)

79

The concept of asymptotic efficiency can also be carried over to the multi-variate situation, but since it then refers not to a single variance being as small as possible, but to a covariance matrix having a "smallness" property, it is somewhat harder to explain briefly, and we only state the definition: we say that a covariance matrix (σ_{ij}) is "smallest" if the quadratic form:

$$\sum_i \sum_j \sigma_{ij} x_i x_j$$

is a minimum for any choice of $x_1, \ldots, x_k$ subject to the condition $\sum_i x_i^2 = 1$. (See Anderson (1958), p. 57.)

McHugh, in his paper on the maximum likelihood estimation of latent class parameters, showed that the latent class model satisfied the requirements of a general theorem of Neyman's which implied that the estimates obtained as the solution of the likelihood equations would, in fact, be asymptotically normally distributed, and would be "best" estimators in the sense of having a smallest covariance matrix.

Neyman (1949) had defined a whole class of estimators which, in the limit as the sample size goes to infinity, are equivalent to each other and have the two properties of:

(i) an asymptotically normal distribution,
(ii) "smallest" covariance matrix.

Such estimators are called "Best Asymptotically Normal," BAN. In many situations, both the maximum likelihood estimator and the minimum chi-square estimator are BAN, that is, equivalent in the large-sample theory.

In Section 4 below, we give the details of computations which will give us BAN estimates of the latent parameters for the m-class model. The procedure used there is an iterative one. That is, we begin with an initial estimate of the latent parameters and then, by comparing the data with the manifest probabilities generated by this initial estimate, compute a new estimate. The method of "comparing" and computing a new estimate is summarized by the following matrix equation:

$$\theta^1 = \theta^0 + H_0^{-1} A_0. \tag{1}$$

Here θ^0 and θ^1 are column vectors containing the initial and derived estimate of the latent parameters, respectively; H_0 is a square matrix whose entries depend on the data and on the estimate θ^0 (hence the use of the subscript "0"); and A_0 is a column vector which also depends on the data and on θ^0.

In Section 4, we show exactly how H and A are constructed. Here we merely mention that the procedure is an approximation to maximum likelihood estimation. Equation (1) implies that the derived estimate-vector θ^1 could be put in place of θ^0, new H matrix and A vector computed, and a second derived estimate obtained. In theory, this could be repeated until the series of vectors (θ^t) converged to a limit. If it did so converge, that limit-vector would be very close to being a maximum likelihood estimate of the latent parameters, due to the way the equations for H and A are derived.

However, it follows from the work of Neyman that we have already cited that if θ^0, the initial estimate, is *consistent*, then θ^1 will be a BAN estimate of the parameters. Thus, if we obtained the initial estimate by an application of the basic solution of the accounting equations, knowing that this is consistent, we would be able to say that θ^1 has the same large-sample characteristics as the maximum likelihood estimate or the minimum chi-square estimate of the parameters. Of course, this means that θ^2, θ^3, or θ^t, for any t, would also have these same asymptotic characteristics. Furthermore, if the series (θ^t) did turn out to converge, the limiting estimate usually will have a better fit to the data, as measured by chi-square, than does θ^1.

We raise these points to emphasize that there are many different ways to get estimates of the latent class parameters. In the examples discussed in the next section, we have used a computer program (called BAN) which follows this iterative procedure. Most of the estimates reported as "BAN estimates" were limiting estimates, after anywhere from 5 to 20 iterations of the program. The cost of obtaining them is quite high, however, and it would usually be necessary to balance the cost of running many iterations in order to reduce the chi-square and improve the fit of the estimate against the value of such a best-fitting estimate.

A further important result has to do with testing the hypothesis that the data actually come from a specified model. If the estimates used are BAN estimates, the statistic χ^2 actually does have, approximately, a chi-square distribution when the hypothesis of m latent classes is true and N is large. The degrees of freedom equal $2^n - n(m + 1)$, the number of response patterns minus the number of latent parameters estimated.

3. Some Examples and Experiments

In this section, we shall give three examples of the use of the BAN estimation procedure. The first two examples involve randomly generated data which was analyzed in order to test the computer routines and also to learn more about the usefulness and the accuracy of the method. The third example formed part of an actual study.

Before looking at these analyses, we summarize some of the important aspects of the estimation procedure. First, it is necessary to have an initial estimate of the latent parameters, θ^0, say. This estimate ought to be consistent so that some of the large-sample theory can be applied, but it is possible to use "fit" as the only criterion and to try completely arbitrary initial estimates.

Next, a series of estimates $\theta^1, \ldots, \theta^t$ are generated according to the scheme of Equation (1). It is possible, as we noted, to let $t = 1$; the estimate θ^1 will be consistent and "best asymptotically normal," if the initial estimate is consistent. (Of course, any estimate in the series will have these same large-sample properties.) At the other extreme, we may compute the entire sequence and take the final estimate, θ^t; if the sequence turns out to be convergent and θ^t is very close to θ^{t-1}, then θ^t is very near the limit of the sequence and to the maximum likelihood estimate.

Third, once a BAN estimate has been obtained, we can look at the approximate variances of the estimates to get an idea of the accuracy of the estimates. The matrix $H^{-1}(\theta^t)$ is the estimate of the covariance matrix, and its diagonal entries provide the estimated variances.

To test the hypothesis that the assumed model actually applies, the chi-square distribution with $2^n - n(m + 1)$ degrees of freedom is used, for this is the approximate distribution of χ^2 when N is large. When the number of degrees of freedom is very large, reference may be made to a table of the normal distribution, for the square root of $2\chi^2$ is approximately normal, with mean $2(\text{df}) - 1$ and standard deviation 1. (Cramér (1946), p. 251.)

We found in our experiments with the BAN computational procedure that the sequence of estimates did not always converge to a limit. This non-convergence was most likely to occur when one of the item parameters, p_i^α, was very close to the limits of 0 and 1, for it was impossible for the iterative procedure to move back within the $(0, 1)$ bounds once it had taken on some values outside this interval. In nearly all of the examples studied that involved randomly generated data that actually came from a latent class population, there was fairly quick convergence to a good estimate. On the other hand, many attempts to fit a latent structure to real data failed because of non-convergence of the estimates. This suggests that when the sequence fails to converge it is less a matter of a poor choice of an initial estimate than a poor fit to the data.

One further point has to do with sample sizes. As we shall see, even with sample sizes of 1,000 the standard errors of the estimates are quite large. Many times latent class analysis has been applied to samples of only a few hundred: in those cases, even if the model did apply, the sampling error would cause the final estimates to be no more accurate than to the nearest 0.1, and often even less accurate. Under such small-sample conditions the various bits of large-sample theory which lead to the use of BAN estimates would not be of much use. The best that could be said of the resulting estimates would probably be that they fit the first-, second-, and third-order data fairly well (if in fact they do!), without ruling out the possibility that some other model or theory was indeed at work.

3.1 A Two-Class Example

In Section 1 of this chapter, we presented as an example a two-class, four-item latent structure. A random sample of size 1,000 was generated, several different estimates were computed, and we used the χ^2 statistic to measure the degree of fit of the estimates to the data (Table 6).

When the data were analyzed by the BAN method, the limiting estimate we now present in Table 7 was obtained. Two points should be noted. First, it did not matter which of the six estimates in Table 4 were used as the initial estimate in the iteration. Convergence to the estimate of Table 7 occurred in each case. Second, the χ^2 value associated with the limiting estimate is smaller than any of the values previously calculated for the original six estimates. The large-sample theory tells us that the maximum likelihood estimate and the minimum χ^2 estimate should be very close to each other, and the limiting BAN estimate is close to both.

TABLE 7

Limiting BAN Estimates
True Values in Parentheses

Class	Size	Item			
		1	2	3	4
1	0.52	0.78	0.88	0.61	0.71
	(0.5)	(0.8)	(0.9)	(0.6)	(0.7)
2	0.48	0.40	0.06	0.20	0.48
	(0.5)	(0.4)	(0.1)	(0.2)	(0.5)
		$\chi^2 = 5.91$			

The number of degrees of freedom is $2^4 - 4 \cdot 3 = 4$, and the value observed, 5.91, would not usually be considered significantly large (the 0.10 significance level of chi-square, with d.f. $= 4$, is 6.25).

An idea of the sampling variation that is present can be gained by looking at Table 8, which gives the asymptotic standard deviations of the estimates of Table 7. Those estimates of the latent parameters can be considered to be approximately normally distributed, with the standard deviations as given in Table 8. (The numbers in Table 8 were obtained as described in Section 4: the estimates of the asymptotic variances are the diagonal entries of H^{-1}, and the standard deviations are the corresponding square roots.)

TABLE 8

Standard Deviations of Estimates
of the Latent Probabilities

Class	Size	Item			
		1	2	3	4
1	0.044	0.027	0.045	0.031	0.024
2	0.044	0.032	0.047	0.030	0.028

The largest entry in Table 8 is 0.047, for p_2^2. The estimate of p_2^2 is 0.06. If we apply the normal theory, we would say that these figures tell us that we are

90% confident that the true value of p_2^2 lies in the interval

$$0.06 \pm (1.96)(0.047) = 0.06 \pm 0.09.$$

Roughly, then, the sample of 1,000 allows us to say that p_2^2 is pretty surely between 0 and 0.15. Of course, there are many things that will get in the way of accurate confidence statements. One is the usual problem of applying the normal distribution to a finite sample; another is that we know that this particular number surely is greater than 0; finally, the estimates of the ten latent parameters are correlated one with the other, so that independent confidence intervals for each parameter cannot be constructed without some adjustment in the confidence levels.

On the other hand, it is probably wise not to "believe" in a point estimate without considering the possible effects of a variation of 1 or 1.5 standard deviations. Here, in this very simple structure, with only four degrees of freedom, and with an N of 1,000, these rough limits of accuracy are found to range from ± 0.04 to ± 0.07. Some experiments which systematically analyzed a large number of samples generated from the same structure would help us to comprehend the actual confidence levels of these intervals.

3.2 A Three-Class Example

A three-class latent structure, given in Table 9, was postulated, and a random sample of 1,000 was generated in the same way as explained earlier for the two-class example. The resulting sample frequences of positive responses, $n_s/1000$, are given in Table 10 along with the true manifest probabilities calculated from the actual latent probabilities.

TABLE 9

A Three-Class Latent Structure

Class	Size	Item				
		1	2	3	4	5
1	0.3	0.9	0.9	0.8	0.5	0.2
2	0.5	0.5	0.7	0.4	0.9	0.9
3	0.2	0.1	0.1	0.3	0.1	0.1

We estimated the latent parameters just as we did in the previous example, by applying the basic solution of the accounting equations to the sample proportions. Any of the five items can be the stratifier, and the reader can verify that, given a stratifier item, there are *three* different ways to construct the basic matrix *B*. There are, therefore, fifteen possible algebraic solutions, different ways of getting estimates of the latent probabilities.

TABLE 10

*True Manifest Probabilities Computed from the Model of Table 9,
and Relative Frequencies in a Random Sample of 1,000*

Item Pattern	Manifest Probability p_s	Sample Relative Frequency $n_s/1000$
1	0.54	0.551
2	0.64	0.654
3	0.50	0.491
4	0.62	0.617
5	0.53	0.516
12	0.420	0.439
13	0.322	0.321
14	0.362	0.365
15	0.281	0.287
23	0.362	0.374
24	0.452	0.465
25	0.371	0.379
34	0.306	0.295
35	0.234	0.213
45	0.437	0.439
123	0.265	0.277
124	0.279	0.295
125	0.206	0.220
134	0.182	0.195
135	0.134	0.129
145	0.230	0.239
234	0.235	0.248
235	0.170	0.178
245	0.311	0.321
345	0.187	0.180
1234	0.160	0.172
1235	0.102	0.110
1245	0.166	0.181
1345	0.103	0.105
2345	0.135	0.149
12345	0.076	0.088

ASIDE: In deciding whether two arrangements are the same or different, we just have to check whether the same probabilities occur in each. Thus the basic matrices

$$\begin{pmatrix} 1 & p_1 & p_2 \\ p_3 & p_{31} & p_{32} \\ p_4 & p_{41} & p_{42} \end{pmatrix} \text{ and } \begin{pmatrix} 1 & p_2 & p_3 \\ p_1 & p_{12} & p_{13} \\ p_4 & p_{24} & p_{34} \end{pmatrix}$$

will lead to different solutions, since p_{32} and p_{41} appear in the first, but not in the second. ∎

All fifteen possible solutions were computed, using the computer program LASY. Of these, only two were completely acceptable, that is, had all estimates between 0 and 1. These are shown in Table 11 along with three other solutions which were almost acceptable, having only one or two improper estimates. We include these in our table in order to show how similar the different estimates of the probabilities p_i^α are, even when one or two of them fall outside the unit interval. We would have a fairly good idea of the latent structure of these items even if for some reason we had only estimates 3 or 5 available.

TABLE 11

Five Estimates of the Latent Structure
Computed Using Basic Solution

Estimate No.	Class	Size	Item				
			1	2	3	4	5
	1	0.34	0.85	0.95	0.80	0.51	0.23
1	2	0.44	0.52	0.72	0.36	0.94	0.96
	3	0.22	0.16	0.08	0.29	0.14	0.07
	1	0.35	0.84	0.95	0.80	0.52	0.23
2	2	0.43	0.52	0.73	0.34	0.93	0.99
	3	0.23	0.17	0.07	0.29	0.16	0.06
	1	0.39	0.81	0.96	0.78	0.52	0.23
3	2	0.38	0.51	0.71	0.34	1.01	1.09
	3	0.24	0.20	0.26	0.15	0.15	0.07
	1	0.53	0.76	0.91	0.73	0.57	0.47
4	2	0.22	0.45	0.66	0.08	1.28	1.04
	3	0.25	0.18	0.10	0.34	0.12	0.16
	1	0.52	0.77	0.91	0.75	0.67	0.28
5	2	0.22	0.49	0.69	0.08	0.94	1.61
	3	0.26	0.18	0.12	0.33	0.24	0.05

Estimates 1 and 2 are practically identical (both were obtained using item 1 as the stratifier). If we had no other machinery available for the analysis of the data, we would probably have been satisfied with either one, or perhaps the average of the two, or we might have checked the χ^2 goodness of fit of the two estimates. We were able to use the BAN method of determining the maximum likelihood estimates, however, and so both estimates 1 and 2 were used as initial estimates θ^0 for the iterative procedure.

In both cases the series converged fairly quickly to the limiting solution which is given in Table 12. The standard deviations of these estimates are also included in Table 12. Notice that the range of these s.d.'s is from 0.018 to 0.050; the ± 1.5 standard deviation rule would give a confidence interval of between ± 0.04 and ± 0.06, for most of the item probabilities.

TABLE 12

Limiting BAN Estimates of the Latent Probabilities

Class	Size	Item 1	2	3	4	5
1	0.28	0.90	0.95	0.81	0.50	0.19
2	0.51	0.51	0.72	0.37	0.89	0.90
3	0.21	0.15	0.09	0.36	0.09	0.02

$$\chi^2 = 20.8$$
$$\text{d.f.} = 14$$

Standard Deviations of the Limiting BAN Estimates

Class	Size	Item 1	2	3	4	5
1	0.034	0.036	0.032	0.036	0.040	0.050
2	0.035	0.027	0.023	0.027	0.022	0.033
3	0.018	0.037	0.035	0.038	0.032	0.025

It is impossible to use an initial estimate which has values of probabilities outside the required range (0, 1), and, for this reason, the last three estimates in Table 11 cannot be used to begin the BAN iterations. When those values were arbitrarily set less than 1 the iteration occasionally converged, but usually the initial estimate was so far away from the limiting value that the process diverged. Non-convergence is usually characterized by the production of estimates which are improper, that lie outside the unit interval. As soon as this occurs, we are sure that further iterations will not succeed in the task of finding a maximum likelihood estimate. Unfortunately, there is no way of telling whether an initial estimate is "good" or "bad" before beginning the process.

The one important *empirical* fact that we have noted in our research with this estimation method is that different initial estimates never converge to different limiting estimates. One may converge and the other may not, but if both converge, it is to the same value. A satisfactory proof that this *must* always be the case has *not* been given, as far as we know, although appeal can be made to the fact that under fairly general conditions, the maximum likelihood estimate is the unique solution of the likelihood equations.

3.3 *An Example Using Real Data*

The following example will illustrate some of the steps that are taken in the course of a latent structure analysis of a number of items. In particular, we shall see how the BAN estimation procedure enables us to make a rational decision as to how many latent classes are necessary to explain the data.

The data studied here are from a study by Charles Kadushin of the Bureau of Applied Social Research of persons who have decided to undertake psychotherapy (Kadushin, 1966). Kadushin considered nine items which seemed to be indicators of sophistication. He wanted to combine these into an index of sophistication so that comparisons of reasons for seeking psychiatric help could be made, as well as comparisons of persons applying to the various clinics under study.

These items are given below, along with the proportion giving the positive response ($N = 1089$).

Item No.	Description	n_i/N
1	Go to plays several times a year.	0.569
2	Go to concerts several times a year.	0.411
3	Go to cocktail parties several times a year.	0.299
4	Go to museums several times a year.	0.597
5	Read psychology books and articles.	0.280
6	Know others with similar problems.	0.438
7	Know close friends or relatives who went to psychiatrist.	0.679
8	Told a few persons about coming (for therapy).	0.553
9	Asked friends for referral.	0.421

As the first step in the analysis a simple latent dichotomy was hypothesized: sophisticated vs. unsophisticated. By using methods similar to the basic solution of the accounting equations, estimates of the two-class latent parameters were obtained, using only the first-, second-, and third-order positive proportions (n_i, n_{ij}, n_{ijk}). This estimate is given in Table 13.

In order to improve the estimate, and to make use of all the data available to us, we entered the above estimate as the initial estimate for the BAN procedure (i.e., θ^0), and generated a sequence of estimates that converged to the estimate in Table 14. We include in that table the value of the goodness of fit statistic χ^2 and also the degrees of freedom, $2^9 - (10)(2)$.

TABLE 13

Estimate of Two-Class Latent Structure
(from determinantal solution)

Class	Size	Item								
		1	2	3	4	5	6	7	8	9
1	0.54	0.83	0.56	0.43	0.81	0.35	0.61	0.92	0.75	0.68
2	0.46	0.27	0.23	0.14	0.35	0.21	0.23	0.39	0.53	0.11

TABLE 14

Limiting BAN Estimate of the Two-Class Latent Structure

Class	Size	Item								
		1	2	3	4	5	6	7	8	9
1	0.53	0.88	0.66	0.44	0.86	0.39	0.58	0.87	0.71	0.62
2	0.47	0.22	0.13	0.14	0.31	0.15	0.28	0.47	0.38	0.20

$$\chi^2 = 772$$
$$\text{d.f.} = 492$$

In this case, we were discouraged by the size of χ^2 from continuing to hold the assumption that there are two latent classes. (If Y is a chi-square variable with a degrees of freedom, then $\sqrt{2Y} - \sqrt{2a - 1}$ is approximately normal, mean 0 and variance 1, for large a; here $\sqrt{1540} - \sqrt{983}$ is quite substantial.)

Several alternatives now presented themselves. We might have kept the nine items and tried a three-class latent structure. We might have analyzed the data more closely to see whether the fit might be significantly improved by discarding one or two of the items. Or, we might even have turned to a more thorough analysis of the content of the items.

Indeed, all of these approaches were investigated. The first proved impossible. We could not obtain *any* acceptable three-class latent structure at all. Restricted to the first four items alone, a two-class structure was obtained that did not fit well, but better than the nine-item structure above. The same was true of the two-class structure of the last four items. It seemed clear from the content of the items that this separation of the items into a set related to "cultural" sophistication (1–4) and another set related specifically to sophistication in matters pertaining to psychotherapy (6–9) would be valuable. Item 5 fell somewhere between the two sets, both conceptually and statistically, and was discarded from the analysis.

Working from this point, it was hypothesized that there should be four latent classes, corresponding to the double dichotomy of "cultural" sophistication and "psychiatric" sophistication, as illustrated below.

Sophistication About Psychotherapy
(Items 6–9)

		High	Low
Cultural Sophistication (Items 1–4)	High	Class 1	Class 2
	Low	Class 3	Class 4

We tested the hypothesis by using, for the initial estimate, the appropriate item probabilities from the two-class, four-item analyses. The class sizes were then obtained by a least-squares fit of the marginals. This initial estimate is given in Table 15; the limiting estimate generated by the BAN procedure is in Table 16.

TABLE 15

Initial Four-Class, Eight-Item Estimate

Class	Size	Item							
		1	2	3	4	6	7	8	9
1	0.436	0.901	0.685	0.421	0.854	0.628	0.919	0.783	0.691
2	0.111	0.901	0.685	0.421	0.854	0.222	0.406	0.292	0.114
3	0.108	0.167	0.080	0.151	0.286	0.628	0.919	0.783	0.691
4	0.245	0.167	0.080	0.151	0.286	0.222	0.406	0.292	0.114

TABLE 16

Limiting BAN Estimate of Four-Class Latent Structure
(Eight Items Only)

Class	Size	Item							
		1	2	3	4	6	7	8	9
1	0.38	0.91	0.73	0.45	0.92	0.63	0.92	0.79	0.72
2	0.19	0.82	0.55	0.30	0.67	0.25	0.45	0.28	0.14
3	0.16	0.34	0.06	0.30	0.28	0.59	0.90	0.72	0.59
4	0.27	0.03	0.07	0.07	0.25	0.25	0.35	0.28	0.09

$$\chi^2 = 232$$
$$\text{d.f.} = 220$$

The last four items stay quite close to the pattern that we started with. The largest difference is 0.13, between p_9^1 and p_9^3. The first four, on the other hand, tend to have a High-Medium-Low pattern, which varies from item to item as shown below.

	Item			
Class	1	2	3	4
1	H	H	H	H
2	H	M	M	M
3	M	L	M	L
4	L	L	L	L

We leave explanations of these relationships to the reader, who can refer to Kadushin's book, but we offer one idea: That the so-called sophistication about psychotherapy may be *prior to* the cultural sophistication. In other words, the former is more closely tied to intrinsic psychological states of the individual, which in turn lead him to go or not to go to plays, cocktail parties, etc. We say this because the expected High-Low, High-Low pattern of items 6–9 has not been affected by the concurrent analysis of items 1–4, while the opposite is not the case. The low values for items 6–9 have *pulled down* items 2, 3, and 4 within class 2, while the high values of items 6–9 for the people of class 3 have *pulled up* the values of items 1 and 3. Going to cocktail parties (3) is thus particularly sensitive to whatever items 6–9 are measuring. Going to concerts (2) is relatively unaffected, while going to plays (1) and going to museums (4) are affected *in different ways*.

Notice that this four-class model provides a good fit of the data. With 220 degrees of freedom, a chi-square of 232 is not significant. For a more visible comparison of the fit of the model to the data, we note that the marginals and the second-order proportions agree with the probabilities computed from this estimate very closely, almost always agreeing in the second decimal. These are given in Table 17.

This study did not end with the calculation of the parameters of a four-class latent structure. Kadushin went on to assign each respondent to the most likely class on the basis of his response to the eight items. As we noted in Chapter 3, this involves calculating for a given nth order response pattern s:

$$v^\alpha p_s^\alpha$$

for $\alpha = 1, 2, 3,$ and 4. The most likely class is the one for which this quantity is the largest.

The expected error involved in an assignment of this kind cannot be calculated with certainty. If the latent parameters were known exactly, the error would be:

$$\sum_s (p_s - \max_\alpha v^\alpha p_s^\alpha).$$

TABLE 17

Observed First- and Second-Order Proportions, and Probabilities
Computed From Four-Class Estimate
(Observed *above* main diagonal, Computed *below*)

Item*	0	1	2	3	4	6	7	8	9
0	—	0.562	0.408	0.296	0.586	0.447	0.676	0.542	0.420
1	0.561	—	0.34	0.23	0.44	0.29	0.44	0.36	0.30
2	0.407	0.34	—	0.16	0.33	0.21	0.31	0.26	0.22
3	0.295	0.22	0.16	—	0.21	0.16	0.23	0.19	0.16
4	0.585	0.44	0.33	0.21	—	0.29	0.45	0.35	0.30
6	0.447	0.29	0.21	0.16	0.29	—	0.36	0.29	0.23
7	0.675	0.44	0.31	0.23	0.44	0.35	—	0.43	0.36
8	0.541	0.35	0.26	0.19	0.36	0.29	0.43	—	0.30
9	0.491	0.30	0.22	0.16	0.30	0.24	0.36	0.30	—

*The marginals are in the 0 row and column.

Since error is present in the estimates of the parameters, and we are using the same data for assignment as we are for estimation of the parameters, no 100% accurate probability statement can be made about the probability of mis-classification. It is clear, nevertheless, that this is the best possible technique, given the data at hand.

Once the four-class division of the sample was available, it was used as an independent variable, characteristic of the individuals, in analysis of the rest of the data.

3.4 A Sampling Experiment

A number of years ago, T. W. Anderson and R. O. Carleton carried out a systematic analysis of some data that had been generated from a three-class

TABLE 18

Hypothetical Latent Class Structure

Class	Size	Item							
		1	2	3	4	5	6	7	8
1	0.3	0.9	0.9	0.8	0.6	0.5	0.2	0.4	0.5
2	0.5	0.5	0.7	0.4	0.5	0.9	0.9	0.8	0.6
3	0.2	0.1	0.1	0.3	0.4	0.1	0.1	0.3	0.4

latent structure model by the Rand Corporation (Anderson and Carleton, n.d.) The analysis dealt primarily with the estimation of the latent probabilities of the *stratifier item* using the basic solution of the accounting equations.

There were eight items in all, with the latent structure as given in Table 18. The sample consisted of 4,000 respondents which were divided into four sub-samples of 1,000 each.

The sample was randomly generated according to a procedure similar to that described in Section 3.2. For each item probability, p_i^α, 280 different estimates were calculated out of the total of 420 which are possible. This total is obtained as follows: each basic matrix, in the three-class case, involves four items. With the stratified item specified, there are $\binom{7}{4} = 35$ ways of choosing the four items. Then, there are three distinct arrangements of the chosen items in the basic matrix form, illustrated below for items 1–4:

$$(i) \begin{pmatrix} 1 & P_1 & P_2 \\ P_3 & P_{13} & P_{23} \\ P_4 & P_{14} & P_{24} \end{pmatrix}$$

$$(ii) \begin{pmatrix} 1 & P_1 & P_4 \\ P_3 & P_{13} & P_{34} \\ P_2 & P_{12} & P_{24} \end{pmatrix}$$

$$(iii) \begin{pmatrix} 1 & P_1 & P_3 \\ P_2 & P_{12} & P_{23} \\ P_4 & P_{14} & P_{34} \end{pmatrix}$$

Since there were four samples of size 1,000, the total number of possible estimates is $4 \cdot 3 \cdot 35 = 420$. In the experiment, only two of the three arrangements of four items were used, leaving $4 \cdot 2 \cdot 35 = 280$. With eight items, there were $8 \cdot 280 = 2240$ determinantal equations, and 6,720 estimates of latent item probabilities. We shall summarize a few of the important findings of the analysis.

3.4.1 *Accuracy of Estimation.* Not only were the estimates obtained disappointingly inaccurate, but a large proportion of the "estimates" were not even acceptable as probabilities.

Of the 2,240 cubic equations, only 754 had all three roots between 0 and 1, and in only 312 cases were all three of the estimates within 0.1 of the true values. If the stratifier item and the two signatures of the basic matrix were picked at random, therefore, there would be only about 1 chance in 3 of beginning the estimation procedure with acceptable values for all three latent probabilities of the stratifier, and less than 1 chance in 7 of having estimates which were accurate to within 0.1.

Table 19 gives a detailed breakdown of these percentages for each item.

TABLE 19

Accuracy of Estimates Summarized by Stratifying Item

	Item								All Items
	1	2	3	4	5	6	7	8	
All Roots within 0.1 of true value Percent of all Equations	42 15.0%	33 11.8%	26 9.3%	60 21.4%	46 16.4%	26 9.3%	38 13.6%	41 14.6%	312 13.9%
All Roots Between 0 and 1 Percent of all Equations	78 27.9%	63 22.5%	86 30.7%	132 47.1%	105 37.5%	65 23.2%	118 42.1%	107 38.2%	754 33.7%
Not All Roots Between 0 and 1 Percent of all Equations	202 72.1%	217 77.5%	194 69.3%	148 52.9%	175 62.5%	215 76.8%	162 57.9%	173 61.8%	1,486 66.3%
Total Number of Equations	280	280	280	280	280	280	280	280	2,240

TABLE 20

Accuracy of Estimates Restricted to Fourteen Largest Population Determinants by Stratifier Item

	Item								All Items
	1	2	3	4	5	6	7	8	
All Roots within 0.1 of true value Percent of all Equations	31 55.4%	23 41.1%	22 39.3%	35 62.5%	31 55.4%	21 37.5%	26 46.4%	21 37.5%	210 46.9%
All Roots between 0 and 1 Percent of all equations	37 66.1%	30 53.6%	38 67.9%	44 78.6%	44 78.6%	30 53.6%	48 82.1%	41 73.2%	310 69.2%
Not All Roots between 0 and 1 Percent of all equations	19 33.9%	26 46.4%	18 32.1%	12 21.4%	12 21.4%	26 46.4%	10 17.9%	15 26.8%	138 30.8%
Total Number of Equations	56	56	56	56	56	56	56	56	448

95

The most important finding in this analysis was that the size of the determinant of the basic matrix, B_{hv}, was directly related to the accuracy of estimation. Table 20 shows this striking relationship: When only those equations which derive from the fourteen basic matrices with largest population determinants for each choice of stratifier item are considered, 46.9% give three roots accurate to within 0.1. Even in the worst case, for items 6 and 8 where only 37.5% are this accurate, we note the improvement over 9.3% and 14.6%, the corresponding figures in Table 19.

Of course, in practice we cannot use the *population* determinant as a criterion, but must settle for the *sample* quantity. Computations exactly analogous to those involved in Table 20 were not reported by Anderson and Carleton, except for item 1; when the 56 (out of 280) configurations with the largest sample determinants were utilized[2] the results were even better than those of Table 20:

All Roots between 0 and 1: 76.8%.
All Roots within 0.1 of true values: 53.6%.

Table 21 compares the percentage of equations for which all three roots were between 0 and 1 in the unrestricted case and when restricted to the largest 56 (of 280) sample determinants. It is clear that such a restrictive criterion is very helpful in obtaining useful and accurate estimates.

TABLE 21

Equations with all Roots in Probability Range:
Comparison of Configurations with Highest-Valued
Sample Unstratified Determinants
Number of Equations with all Roots Between 0 and 1

	All Configurations	Configurations with Highest 20% of Sample Determinants
Item 1	78(27.9%)	43(76.8%)
Item 2	63(22.5%)	33(58.9%)
Item 3	86(30.7%)	37(66.1%)
Item 4	132(47.1%)	44(78.6%)
Item 5	105(37.5%)	47(83.9%)
Item 6	65(23.2%)	33(58.9%)
Item 7	118(42.1%)	46(82.1%)
Item 8	107(38.2%)	44(78.6%)
Number of Configurations used for each item	280	56

[2]With item 1 as the stratifier.

Using configurations with large values of B_{hv} helps guard against the possibility that the population matrix, B_{hv}, is singular, i.e., that $|B_{hv}| = 0$. In the latent structure studied here, any basic matrix with a signature containing items 1 and 4, or 5 and 8, will have a zero determinant. This is easy to see, since

$$|L_{0,1,4}| = \begin{vmatrix} 1 & 1 & 1 \\ 0.9 & 0.5 & 0.1 \\ 0.6 & 0.5 & 0.4 \end{vmatrix} = \begin{vmatrix} 1 & 0 & 0 \\ 0.9 & -0.4 & -0.8 \\ 0.6 & -0.1 & -0.2 \end{vmatrix} = 0,$$

and

$$|L_{0,5,8}| = \begin{vmatrix} 1 & 1 & 1 \\ 0.5 & 0.9 & 0.1 \\ 0.5 & 0.6 & 0.4 \end{vmatrix} = \begin{vmatrix} 1 & 0 & 0 \\ 0.5 & 0.4 & -0.4 \\ 0.5 & 0.1 & -0.1 \end{vmatrix} = 0,$$

and we know that

$$|B_{hv}| = |L_h|\,|V|\,|L'_v|.$$

Thus, if we had been given the manifest probabilities exactly, we would not be able to use a solution that involved these two pairs of items in one of the basic signatures. However, given sample data, we do not *know* that the structure is of this kind, because the sample matrices will *not* have determinants that are exactly zero. What happens, of course, is that we are trying to analyze sampling error when these particular configurations are used. The restriction to large values of the sample determinants helps us to avoid this likelihood unless, of course, *all* of the population matrices happen to be singular.

3.4.2 *A Procedure for Estimating Parameters.* Referring back to the estimation scheme proposed in Section 1.2 of this chapter, we see how important this result is: instead of several hundred different estimates of the same parameters being computed and presented for examination to the researcher, we could proceed to calculate determinants of all possible basic matrices (for a chosen stratifier item) and then compute only those estimates corresponding to the largest 10% or 20% of these determinants. Many of these estimates would have values outside the unit interval, but the results reported by Anderson and Carleton suggest that a high proportion would be acceptable. If all three roots of the determinantal equation were between 0 and 1, then we would proceed to find the estimates of the remaining latent parameters, using the methods implicit in Theorem 4 of Chapter 3.

This would probably not be an inefficient procedure because it is not a difficult job for the computer to evaluate determinants of small matrices. "Small" is a relative term, but $m = 10$ is certainly a reasonable upper limit to the number of latent classes that should be considered at one time, and we doubt that any more than about six classes could be meaningfully analyzed unless some additional structural assumptions are made (such as described in Chapter 5). An outline of the computations suggested here is given below.

Outline of Proposed Estimation Procedure

1. Input Data: $(n_i, n_{ij}, n_{ijk}, N, m, n)$, m = no. of classes; n = no. of items; N = sample size.
2. Systematically construct all possible basic matrices, B_{hv}, one at a time, and compute the determinant, $|B_{hv}|$. Record and store the signatures, h and v, of the K largest determinants. (K should be a parameter specified by the user, and probably should depend on both m and n.)
3. Systematically go through the list of K signatures determined in part 2, and, for each basic matrix B_{hv} so determined, consider all possible stratifier items, k.

(i) Given B_{hv} and $B_{hv;k}$, find the characteristic roots and vectors of

$$B_{hv}^{-1}B_{hv;k}.$$

The characteristic roots will be estimates of the latent probabilities p_k^α of the stratifier item.

(ii) If any of the estimated p_k^α are not between 0 and 1, stop, and consider the next possible stratifier item. If all possible stratifiers have been considered, go to the next choice of signatures h, v, and continue at step 3(i).

(iii) If all p_k^α are between 0 and 1, compute the remaining latent probabilities. Since

$$B_{hv}^{-1}B_{hv;k} = L_h^{-1}D_kL_n,$$

the estimates of the probabilities p_i^α, where i is in h, are the row characteristic vectors of $B_{hv}^{-1}B_{hv;k}$. The v^α are the first column of

$$L_h^{-1}B_{hv}$$

and any other item probabilities are found by solving

$$L_r^1 = L_h^{-1}V^{-1}B_{hr}.$$

(iv) Print the estimates obtained in (iii) and proceed to the next choice of k, or h and v, as the case may be, in part 3(i).

4. Examine the various estimates that are presented. Whenever all estimated probabilities lie between 0 and 1, then either compare fit of different estimates by chi-square, or use them as initial estimate for BAN estimation, or average them to obtain a unique estimate of the latent structure.

3.4.3 *The Usefulness of the Asymptotic Theory.* In Appendix B, Anderson has obtained expressions for the asymptotic variances of the roots of the determinantal equation, and also of the sample determinant itself.

Since the large sample normal theory is only approximately correct for a finite N, it is important, as we have noted, to find out how large N must be to make the approximation adequate. Anderson and Carleton were able to study the effect of varying sample size on the distribution of estimates of the sample unstratified determinant by choosing subsamples of varying size from the total sample of 4,000. They concluded that the use of the normal distribution was appropriate for the sample determinant whenever the sample was larger than 800, but that it should not be used for N less than 600.

This finding was obtained by comparing the observed distribution of different estimates of the determinants with that distribution predicted by the large sample theory. When large deviations are observed, the conclusion is that the theory does not apply for that particular sample size.

On the other hand, they found that the asymptotic normal distribution was not adequate to calculate 90% and 95% confidence intervals for the item probabilities (the roots of the cubic, determinantal equations) when $N = 1,000$, although it was practical to use the theory to predict whether an estimate would lie within 0.1 of the true value.

We note once more that even when the sample size is as large as 1,000, the large-sample theory predicts variances so large that we should expect many estimates to lie outside the acceptable zero-one limits. It would be informative to carry out another large-scale study of randomly generated data, to clarify some of the still unanswered questions about parameter estimation. With a large computer, the amount of work needed to generate samples and compute some of the possible determinantal estimates is not exorbitant. Evaluating the BAN methods of estimation would be somewhat more costly, however, for the computer programs needed are much more complicated.

4. Defining a "Best Estimate": Minimum χ^2 and Maximum Likelihood

If we have some data, the nth-order relative frequencies being n_s/N, it is possible to ask what estimates of the latent parameters will minimize the χ^2 function. That is, we take

$$\chi^2 = \sum_s (n_s - Np_s)^2/Np_s,$$

where the manifest probabilities p_s are functions of the p_i^α and v^α, and try to choose values of these latent probabilities which will minimize the function χ^2.

The standard way of carrying out such a minimization is to differentiate the function with respect to each of the unknowns in turn, set the resulting partial derivatives equal to zero, and solve for the p_i^α and v^α. Since the sum of the v^α is known to be 1, it is necessary to replace v^m by

$$1 - v^1 - \cdots - v^{m-1},$$

and consider only the first $m - 1$ probabilities as parameters of the system. There will be $nm + m - 1$ equations, therefore:

$$\frac{\partial \chi^2}{\partial p_i^\alpha} = 0, i = 1, \ldots, n, \alpha = 1, \ldots, m,$$

$$\frac{\partial \chi^2}{\partial v^\alpha} = 0, \alpha = 1, \ldots, m - 1.$$

(2)

The partial differential Equations (2) are derived in the following way.[3] First, we rewrite χ^2 as:

$$\chi^2 = \sum_s (n_s)^2/Np_s - N. \tag{3}$$

Equation (3) is easy to obtain: we simply expand the square in the numerator of χ^2 and sum each term separately, remembering that the p_s sum to 1 and the n_s sum to N.

The n_s are data: only the p_s depend on the unknowns. If θ stands for any one unknown parameter, then the partial derivative with respect to θ is:

$$\frac{\partial \chi^2}{\partial \theta} = -\sum_s (n_s)^2/N(p_s)^2 \frac{\partial p_s}{\partial \theta}. \tag{4}$$

The accounting equations tell us that:

$$p_s = \sum_{\alpha=1}^{m} v^\alpha p_s^\alpha = \sum_{\alpha=1}^{m-1} v^\alpha (p_s^\alpha - p_s^m) + p_s^m, \tag{5}$$

and so the derivative of p_s with respect to v^α is simply $p_s^\alpha - p_s^m$. Thus:

$$\frac{\partial \chi^2}{\partial v^\alpha} = \sum_s ((n_s)^2/N(p_s)^2)(p_s^\alpha - p_s^m), \tag{6}$$

which, when set equal to zero, implies that:

$$\sum_s (n_s/p_s)^2 p_s^\alpha = \sum_s (n_s/p_s)^2 p_s^m. \tag{7}$$

The derivative of p_s with respect to an item probability, p_i^α, is harder to express, since p_s^α is a product in which p_i^α appears if item i is positive in the response pattern s, and $1 - p_i^\alpha$ appears if item i is negative in s. The result is:

$$\frac{\partial p_s}{\partial p_i^\alpha} = \begin{cases} v^\alpha p_s^\alpha/p_i^\alpha & \text{if } i \text{ is in } s, \\ -v^\alpha p_s^\alpha/(1 - p_s^\alpha) & \text{if } \bar{\imath} \text{ is in } s, \end{cases} \tag{8}$$

since all of the factors in the product p_s^α except that one involving item i are considered to be constants. Upon substituting in Equation (4) and setting equal to zero, the equation becomes:

$$\sum_{S_i} (n_s/p_s)^2 v^\alpha p_s^\alpha/p_i^\alpha = \sum_{S_{\bar{\imath}}} (n_s/p_s)^2 v^\alpha p_s^\alpha/(1 - p_i^\alpha). \tag{9}$$

S_i stands for the set of all response patterns which contain i, that is, a positive response to item i; $S_{\bar{\imath}}$ is the complementary set of all s which contain $\bar{\imath}$.

The p_s, the p_s^α, and the p_i^α are all functions of the unknowns. It should be clear by now that the Equations (7) and (9) whose solution is the desired set of estimates of the latent parameters are too complex to be solved directly. (They are even more complicated than the accounting equations of the model.) We are

---

[3] Anyone who has not been exposed to partial derivatives and problems of maximization and minimization using the calculus should refer to a calculus text, such as Apostol (1961), Chs. 2 and 8. The remainder of this section may be skipped at the first reading.

100

not going to discuss any numerical methods by which the equations might be solved for we have not studied the problem in any depth. The book by Saaty and Bram (1964) would probably be of use in that task, and of course, a large computer would be a necessity, since the number of equations, $nm + m - 1$, gets large very quickly.

We turn now from the concept of minimum chi-square estimation to maximum likelihood estimation. In brief, this means that we consider the function

$$\log L = \sum_s n_s \log p_s \qquad (10)$$

mentioned above, and the problem of finding estimates which will maximize it. "L" is called the *likelihood function*, because it is proportional to the probability of the sample frequencies actually being observed, given some value of the latent parameters.[4] Since the data, n_s, *have* been observed, the larger L is, the more likely it is that the particular estimate of the parameters is close to the true values.

We are going to derive the equations whose solutions give the maximum likelihood estimates of the parameters, and the method used in the BAN computer program. The method of maximum likelihood is well known, and this is one reason for emphasizing it in preference to the minimum chi-square procedure. Another reason, however, is that it involves somewhat simpler equations which is important if we are to apply the theory.

The derivative of $\log L$ with respect to any parameter θ is

$$\frac{\partial \log L}{\partial \theta} = \sum_s (n_s/p_s)\frac{\partial p_s}{\partial \theta}. \qquad (11)$$

Since we have already written down the partial derivatives of p_s with respect to v^α and p_i^α, Equations (5) and (8), we can substitute directly:

$$0 = \frac{\partial \log L}{\partial v^\alpha} = \sum_S (n_s/p_s)(p_s^\alpha - p_s^m), \qquad \alpha = 1, \ldots, m - 1, \qquad (12)$$

$$0 = \frac{\partial \log L}{p_i^\alpha} = \sum_{S_i} (n_s/p_s)v^\alpha p_s^\alpha/p_i^\alpha - \sum_{S_{\bar{\imath}}} (n_s/p_s)v^\alpha p_s^\alpha/(1 - p_i^\alpha),$$
$$\alpha = 1, \ldots, m, i = 1, \ldots, n. \qquad (13)$$

Because the p_s^α are products, and the ratios p_s^α/p_i^α and $p_s^\alpha/(1 - p_i^\alpha)$ are simply products of $n - 1$ factors, with the ith factor removed, we shall introduce the notation p_{s-i}^α to stand for the probability within class α of the response pattern defined by s with item i ignored. Then, Equation (13) becomes:

$$0 = \sum_{S_i} (n_s/p_s)p_{s-i}^\alpha - \sum_{S_{\bar{\imath}}} (n_s/p_s)p_{s-i}^\alpha.$$

Notice the difference between Equations (12) and (13) and Equations (5) and (9): in the chi-square equations, $(n_s/p_s)^2$ appears, while in the likelihood equations, it is (n_s/p_s). This difference does make some difference in the com-

---

[4]See Cramér (1946), Ch. 33 or a text in mathematical statistics such as Mood and Graybill (1963), Ch. 8 for a discussion of the likelihood function and of maximum likelihood estimation.

putations needed to obtain a solution in the two cases. It is still necessary to use an iterative method of solution, however.

ASIDE: It is possible to manipulate Equations (12) and (13) to get a few interesting results. For example, multiplying through Equation (12) by v^α would give:

$$\sum_S (n_s/p_s)p_s^\alpha v^\alpha = \sum_S (n_s/p_s)p_s^m v^\alpha;$$

then summing over all α,

$$\sum_S (n_s/p_s)p_s = \sum_S (n_s/p_s)p_s^m,$$

$$\sum_S n_s = N = \sum_S (n_s/p_s)p_s^m.$$

Thus, for any α, we have

$$\sum_S (n_s/p_s)p_s^\alpha = N.$$

Multiplying Equation (13) through by $(1 - p_i^\alpha)/v^\alpha$, we get:

$$\sum_{S_i} (n_s/p_s)p_s^\alpha(1/p_i^\alpha - 1) = \sum_{S_{\bar{i}}} (n_s/p_s)p_s^\alpha,$$

$$\sum_{S_i} (n_s/p_s)p_{s-i}^\alpha = \sum_{S_i} (n_s/p_s)p_s^\alpha + \sum_{S_{\bar{i}}} (n_s/p_s)p_s^\alpha.$$

Using the previous result, we find that

$$\sum_{S_i} (n_s/p_s)p_{s-i}^\alpha = \sum_S (n_s/p_s)p_s^\alpha = N. \quad \blacksquare$$

The method of solution described in this section is based on the Taylor series expansion of a function of several variables. It is called the *method of scoring* by Rao (1952), and is the multivariate analog of Newton's method of solving nonlinear equations by successive linear approximations. We shall begin by talking about the one-variable case, in case the reader is unfamiliar with the method.

If $f(x)$ is a function of a single variable, x, and the derivatives of all order exist at some point x_0, then the Taylor series expansion of $f(x)$ at x_0 is:

$$f(x) = f(x_0) + (x - x_0)f'(x_0) + (x - x_0)^2 f''(x_0)/2 + \cdots$$

$$= \sum_{n=0}^{\infty} f^{(n)}(x_0)(x - x_0)^n/n!$$

where $f^{(n)}(x_0)$ is the value of the nth derivative of f at $x = x_0$.

If $f(x)$ is supposed to be zero, and x_0 is some given value, an approximate value of x can be obtained by looking at the first two terms in this series, namely:[5]

$$0 \doteq f(x_0) + (x - x_0)f'(x_0),$$

$$x \doteq x_0 - f(x_0)/f'(x_0). \tag{14}$$

[5]The symbol $\doteq$ stands for "approximately equals."

This equation forms the basis for successive approximations of the solution of the equation $f(x) = 0$, for we can keep on generating new values of x:

$$x_t = x_{t-1} - f(x_{t-1})/f'(x_{t-1}). \qquad (15)$$

If the series $x_0, x_1, \ldots, x_t, x_{t+1}, \ldots$ converges to some value, we have a solution to the equation $f(x) = 0$.

In the situation we are dealing with, there are many unknowns: a vector θ of latent parameters. (Let θ be a column vector of latent probabilities in some specific, but arbitrary order. We shall assume that the order is $p_1^1, p_2^1, p_3^1, \ldots, p_n^1, p_1^2, \ldots, p_n^m, v^1, \ldots, v^{m-1}$.) The function which is set equal to zero is the vector of derivatives of $\log L$, given in Equations (12) and (13). Call this vector $A(\theta)$, indicating that it is indeed a function of the parameters, θ. We want to find the particular value of θ, $\hat{\theta}$, which will make A exactly equal zero. The "first derivative" of the vector A, in this multivariate problem, is the square matrix whose i, jth entry is the partial derivative of the ith element of A with respect to the jth element of θ: in other words, it is the second partial derivative of $\log L$ with respect to the ith and jth elements of θ.

If we call this matrix $B(\theta)$, and let θ^0 be some given *a priori* estimate of θ, the analog of Equation (14) becomes:

$$\theta \doteq A(\theta^0) + B(\theta^0)(\theta - \theta^0),$$

leading to

$$\theta \doteq \theta^0 - B_0^{-1}A_0.$$

We shorten the notation a bit by writing $B_0 = B(\theta_0)$ and $A_0 = A(\theta_0)$. The iterative procedure, corresponding to Equation (15) is:

$$\theta^{t+1} = \theta^t - B_t^{-1}A_t, \qquad (16)$$

where B and A are evaluated at the given values, θ^t, of the parameters.

If the sequence of vectors θ^t converges to a limit, that limit is the maximum likelihood estimate of the parameters.[6]

In the research reported below, the matrix B of second derivatives was replaced by an approximation that is somewhat simpler to compute, and which is a good approximation to B for large N. If θ_i and θ_j are two latent parameters, then the i, j element of B is:

$$\frac{\partial^2 \log L}{\partial \theta_i \, \partial \theta_j} = \sum_s n_s \frac{\partial^2 \log p_s}{\partial \theta_i \, \partial \theta_j}$$

$$= \sum_s (n_s/p_s) \frac{\partial^2 p_s}{\partial \theta_i \, \partial \theta_j} - \sum_s n_s/(p_s)^2 \frac{\partial p_s}{\partial \theta_i} \cdot \frac{\partial p_s}{\partial \theta_j}.$$

We shall approximate this by dropping out the first sum. This means that we shall not have to bother calculating the second derivatives of p_s: the second

---

[6]The "regularity" conditions which insure that a solution of the likelihood equations actually does maximize $\log L$ were set down by McHugh (1956) and are satisfied except in trivial cases, such as when probability p_s is exactly zero for some s.

sum depends on the products of the first derivatives, which we have already derived. The validity of the approximation depends on the fact that as the sample size gets large, the sample frequencies n_s can be expected to approach Np_s: the first sum will approach:

$$N \sum_s \frac{\partial^2 p_s}{\partial \theta_i \, \partial \theta_j} = N \frac{\partial^2}{\partial \theta_i \, \partial \theta_j} \left(\sum_s p_s \right) = 0,$$

since the sum of the p_s is 1, a constant.

Therefore, we define a matrix H, whose i, j element is

$$h_{ij} = \sum_s \left(n_s/(p_s)^2 \right) \frac{\partial p_s}{\partial \theta_i} \frac{\partial p_s}{\partial \theta_j}.$$

The iterative equations thus become:

$$\theta^{t+1} = \theta^t + H_t^{-1} A_t, \tag{17}$$

where A_t and H_t are short for $A(\theta^t)$ and $H(\theta^t)$.

The limiting value of H, that is $H(\hat{\theta})$, is usually called the *information matrix* and its inverse is the estimate of the variance-covariance matrix of the estimates of the parameters.

ASIDE: There are three kinds of entries in the matrix $H(\theta)$:

(i) θ_i and θ_j are both item probabilities (p_i^α and p_j^β);
(ii) θ_i and θ_j are both class frequencies (v^α and v^β);
(iii) one of the two is an item probability and the other is a class frequency (p_i^α and v^β).

We write out these entries in detail, using the symbols S_{ij}, $S_{i\bar{j}}$, $S_{\bar{i}j}$, and $S_{\bar{i}\bar{j}}$ to stand for the sets of response patterns for which: (a) items i and j are positive; (b) item i is positive and j is negative; (c) item i is negative and item j is positive; and (d) both i and j are negative.

(i) $H(p_i^\alpha, p_j^\beta)$:

$$\sum_{S_{ij}} n_s v^\alpha v^\beta p_s^\alpha p_s^\beta / p_i^\alpha p_j^\beta (p_s)^2 - \sum_{S_{i\bar{j}}} n_s v^\alpha v^\beta p_s^\beta / p_i^\alpha (1 - p_j^\beta)(p_s)^2$$

$$- \sum_{S_{\bar{i}j}} n_s v^\alpha v^\beta p_s^\alpha p_s^\beta / (1 - p_i^\alpha) p_j^\beta (p_s)^2$$

$$+ \sum_{S_{\bar{i}\bar{j}}} n_s v^\alpha v^\beta p_s^\alpha p_s^\beta / (1 - p_i^\alpha)(1 - p_j^\beta)(p_s)^2.$$

(ii) $H(v^\alpha, v^\beta)$:

$$\sum_S n_s (p_s^\alpha - p_s^m)(p_s^\beta - p_s^m)/(p_s)^2.$$

(iii) $H(p_i^\alpha, v^\beta)$:

$$\sum_{S_i} n_s v^\alpha p_s^\alpha (p_s^\beta - p_s^m)/p_i^\alpha (p_s)^2 - \sum_{S_{\bar{i}}} n_s v^\alpha p_s^\alpha (p_s^\beta - p_s^m)/(1 - p_i^\alpha)(p_s)^2. \quad \blacksquare$$

The BAN computer program which was used in the examples of Section 3 followed the iterative equations (17), with the vector A computed according to the formulas (12) and (13), and the matrix H computed according to the formulas in the preceding Aside. Our experience with this program suggests that this method is valuable in a fairly limited range of applications, namely for problems with no more than five classes and about ten items. Beyond this point the expense involved in examining the fit of all 2^n response pattern frequencies to the model becomes prohibitive. Furthermore, the sample sizes would have to be very large in order to insure that there be positive frequencies for all 2^n patterns. (When the sample size is small relative to the number of response patterns, the large sample theory is obviously not applicable.) Because this particular program was written for experimental purposes, it permits many items and classes to be specified. As a result, it is rather inefficient for "ordinary" problems, and we cannot recommend its use. We hope that a new, more efficient version, will be written soon.

5. An Approximate Method of Estimation

In this section, we briefly summarize some research done by W. A. Gibson (1951, 1956) on the estimation of latent class parameters using only first- and second-order data.

5.1 *The General Framework*

In Chapter 3, we introduced non-symmetric matrices of first- and second-order data, defined by specifying two signatures h and v. The matrix equations were

$$P_{hv} = L_h V L_v'.$$

Assuming that h and v both included the dummy item 0, then P_{hv} was a bordered matrix, such as

$$\begin{pmatrix} 1 & p_1 & p_2 & p_3 \\ p_4 & p_{14} & p_{24} & p_{34} \\ p_5 & p_{15} & p_{25} & p_{35} \end{pmatrix}.$$

If h and v each include all n items, then $P_{hv} = P$ has order $n + 1$ and is symmetric. Dropping the subscripts, we write:

$$P = LVL'. \tag{18}$$

The off-diagonal entries of P are manifest probabilities, but except for $p_{00} = 1$, the diagonal entries p_{ii} are not observable. Nevertheless, if the number of classes, m, is known, and there are enough items, the p_{ii} could be calculated from the off-diagonal elements by constructing an $(m + 1) \times (m + 1)$ determinant that included only one diagonal entry, p_{ii}. This determinant must equal zero; the p_i and p_{ji} are given; hence there is an equation in one unknown, p_{ii}.

105

For the moment, suppose that the p_{ii} are known, and we want to determine L and V. Since V is a diagonal matrix, we can write

$$LVL' = LV^{1/2}V^{1/2}L' = FF',$$

where $F = LV^{1/2}$. (By $V^{1/2}$ we mean the diagonal matrix whose non-zero entries are the positive square roots of the diagonal entries of V.)

In this form, the equation looks just like the basic equation of factor analysis: given a symmetric matrix P, we want to find an $(n + 1) \times m$ matrix F such that $P = FF'$, in other words, to factor P. It is easy to find "a" matrix F: many computer programs exist to do this. The difficult task is to find the *right F*, that is, the one which is exactly equal to the product of the latent matrices, $LV^{1/2}$. Since the first row of L is known to be all ones, by definition, the first row of F must be $(\sqrt{v^1}, \sqrt{v^2}, \ldots, \sqrt{v^m})$, and so both V and L could be found if F were known.

What is known, however, is that if G is any matrix of m columns such that

$$P = GG',$$

then there exists a square matrix T with the property

$$TT' = I,$$

such that $F = GT$. (A matrix satisfying $TT' = I$ is called an *orthogonal* matrix.) This result follows from a basic theorem included in Appendix A. Since each row of F and G can be considered to be the m coordinates of a point in m-dimensional space, the statement $F = GT$ has the geometric form, "F can be obtained by an orthogonal rotation of G."

There are, of course, no restrictions imposed on possible rotations in ordinary factor analysis. Here, however, we know that every entry of F must be positive, since:

and
$$f_{0j} = \sqrt{v^j},$$
$$f_{ij} = p_i^j \sqrt{v^j}.$$

In addition, since the p_i^j are less than one, we know that:

$$f_{0j} > f_{ij}$$

for every item i. In the next section, we shall show how this information can be used to analyze a two-class model.

5.2 Factoring Methods for Two Classes

The two-class model is particularly easy to analyze using these methods. We can represent the two-dimensional rotation graphically, of course, and also, it is much easier to obtain the initial factor matrix, G.

To illustrate, we consider the following example. The data are taken from Chapter 11 of *Measurement and Prediction* (Lazarsfeld (1950b), pp. 417–429). The items all deal with attitudes of draftees toward the Army, and the positive response was considered to be favorable to the Army ($N = 1000$).

The matrix P, of first- and second-order data is given in Table 22.

TABLE 22

Observed Relative Frequencies
First and Second Order

Item	0	1	2	3	4
0	1.0	0.641	0.374	0.300	0.254
Feel Army is run well	0.641	—	0.295	0.246	0.217
Favorable attitude to Army	0.374	0.295	—	0.163	0.141
Have gotten a square deal	0.300	0.246	0.163	—	0.130
Army looks out for my welfare	0.254	0.217	0.141	0.130	—

We shall determine the matrix G in the following way. First, let

$$g_{i1} = p_i$$

and let

$$g_{02} = 0. \quad \text{(By definition } p_0 = 1.)$$

This arbitrary specification insures that the resulting estimates of the parameters will fit the observed marginal proportions exactly.

Since

$$p_{ij} = g_{i1}g_{j1} + g_{i2}g_{j2},$$

we find that

$$g_{i2}g_{j2} = p_{ij} - p_ip_j = [ij].$$

The task of determining the second column of G thus is one of finding the best fit to the cross products. The best fit (in the sense of minimum squared deviation) can be shown to be given by the well known formula (Thurstone, 1947, pp. 274–276)

$$g_{i2} = \sqrt{\left(\left(\sum_{j \neq i}[ij]\right)^2 - \sum_{j \neq i}[ij]^2\right) \Big/ \sum_{\substack{j \neq i \\ k \neq i}}\sum[jk]} \, .$$

The cross product matrix is shown in Table 23, and the factor matrix G in Table 24. The degree of fit of the factors to the data is seen in Table 25.

TABLE 23

Matrix of Cross Products

Item	1	2	3	4
1	—	0.0553	0.0537	0.0542
2	0.0553	—	0.0508	0.0460
3	0.0537	0.0508	—	0.0538
4	0.0542	0.0460	0.0538	—

TABLE 24

Factor Matrix G

Item 0	1	0
1	0.641	0.243
2	0.374	0.218
3	0.300	0.232
4	0.254	0.222

TABLE 25

Matrix of Residuals

Item	1	2	3	4
1	—	0.0023	−0.0027	0.0003
2	0.0023	—	0.0002	−0.0024
3	−0.0027	0.0002	—	0.0023
4	0.0003	−0.0024	0.0023	—

Now, the problem is to find a matrix T so that the resulting matrix $F = GT$ has the form $LV^{1/2}$.

The matrix of transformation T has the following form, in terms of the angle of rotation θ:

$$T = \begin{pmatrix} \cos \theta & \sin \theta \\ -\sin \theta & \cos \theta \end{pmatrix}.$$

(It is not hard to demonstrate this geometrically. However, one can easily verify algebraically that if $TT' = I$, then $t_{11} = t_{22}$; $t_{12} = -t_{21}$; and $t_{11}^2 + t_{12}^2 = 1$.)

Now, since $F = GT$, we find that

$$f_{01} = \cos \theta, f_{02} = \sin \theta,$$
$$f_{i1} = g_{i1} \cos \theta - g_{i2} \sin \theta,$$
$$f_{i2} = g_{i1} \sin \theta + g_{i2} \cos \theta.$$

Now, θ must be such that both $\cos \theta$ and $\sin \theta$ are positive. Since both g_{i1} and g_{i2} were positive, f_{i2} will always be positive. The restriction, therefore, of F to positive values means that

$$f_{i1} = g_{i1} \cos \theta - g_{i2} \sin \theta > 0.$$

In other words,

$$g_{i1} \cos \theta > g_{i2} \sin \theta, \quad \text{or,}$$
$$g_{i1}/g_{i2} > \tan \theta$$

for every i.

Therefore, the ratios g_{i1}/g_{i2} define an upper bound of θ (since $\tan \theta$ is an increasing function of θ):

$$\tan \theta < \min_{i} (g_{i1}/g_{i2}).$$

In our example, the minimum ratio is that of item 4, so that we find:

$$\tan \theta < 0.254/0.222 = 1.144,$$
$$\theta < 48° \, 52'.$$

This particular rotation would give

$$T = \begin{pmatrix} 0.658 & 0.753 \\ -0.753 & 0.658 \end{pmatrix}$$

and

$$F = \begin{pmatrix} 0.658 & 0.753 \\ 0.239 & 0.641 \\ 0.082 & 0.424 \\ 0.023 & 0.378 \\ 0.000 & 0.337 \end{pmatrix}.$$

The other restriction, that $f_{i2} < f_{02}$, becomes

$$g_{i1} \sin \theta + g_{i2} \cos \theta < \sin \theta,$$
$$g_{i2} \cos \theta < (1 - g_{i1}) \sin \theta,$$
$$g_{i2}/(1 - g_{i1}) < \tan \theta.$$

Thus, the lower bound on the rotation, θ, is given by:

$$\tan \theta > \max_{i} g_{i2}/(1 - g_{i1}).$$

In this example, the largest ratio is that of item 1, so that:

$$\tan \theta > g_{12}/(1 - g_{11}) = 0.243/0.359,$$
$$\tan \theta > 0.6769,$$
$$\theta > 34° \, 10'.$$

The matrix T for this rotation is:

$$T = \begin{pmatrix} 0.827 & 0.562 \\ -0.562 & 0.827 \end{pmatrix}$$

109

and

$$F = \begin{pmatrix} 0.828 & 0.561 \\ 0.395 & 0.561 \\ 0.188 & 0.390 \\ 0.119 & 0.360 \\ 0.086 & 0.326 \end{pmatrix}$$

The estimates of the latent parameters are easily obtained:

$$v^i = (f_{0j})^2,$$
$$p^j_i = f_{ij}/f_{0j}.$$

This analysis, then, tells us that an acceptable rotation must be between the bounds:

$$(48° \ 52', \ 34° \ 10').$$

The amount of freedom left can be observed in Table 26, where we have given the two extreme latent structures.

TABLE 26

Extreme Latent Structure Solutions

			Item			
Rotation	Class	Size	1	2	3	4
$\theta = 48° \ 52'$:	1	0.43	0.36	0.12	0.03	0.00
	2	0.57	0.85	0.56	0.50	0.45
$\theta = 34° \ 10'$:	1	0.69	0.48	0.23	0.14	0.10
	2	0.31	1.00	0.70	0.64	0.58

If we want to choose some unique set of latent parameters, a reasonable criterion would be to choose that one that is midway between these extremes. This could be done by taking the average value of θ, or by taking the mean class frequency. Just for purposes of comparison, we present the solution obtained by averaging the class frequencies:

		Item			
Class	Size	1	2	3	4
1	0.56	0.42	0.18	0.10	0.06
2	0.44	0.92	0.62	0.56	0.50

and that obtained by Lazarsfeld using third-order data (Lazarsfeld, 1950b, Table 6, rounded to two places):

		Item			
Class	Size	1	2	3	4
1	0.58	0.43	0.19	0.10	0.06
2	0.42	0.92	0.63	0.57	0.51

5.3 *The General Problem*

When there are more than two factors the usual problems arise. It becomes difficult to obtain an initial factorization of the matrix P, since the diagonal entries are unspecified. We always choose to fit the marginal proportions, and so will always define the first factor by:

$$g_{i1} = p_i, \qquad i = 1, 2, \ldots, n,$$
$$g_{01} = 1,$$
$$g_{0j} = 0, \qquad \text{for } j = 2, 3, \ldots, m.$$

The remaining factors are then to be found by examining the cross product matrix. The usual methods of factor analysis must be used (see Harman, 1960):

(1) estimate the diagonals in some way;
(2) factor the matrix by principal components
    (characteristic roots and vectors);
(3) re-estimate diagonals, and re-factor, until the products

$$\sum_{j=2}^{m} g_{ij}^2$$

are very close to the estimated values of [*ii*].

Once we have found a matrix G, the permissible rotations must be defined. There are $m - 1$ degrees of freedom to be calculated for any rotation, and it is harder to determine the bounds on the rotations, especially the bounds that are determined by the restriction $f_{ij} < f_{0j}$.

There is a way of handling this restriction, however, which was suggested by Gibson (1962b). Suppose that we consider n "negative items," that is, the items obtained by considering negative responses to the n items, rather than positive response. If $\bar{i}$ stands for the "negative item i," then we know that:

$$p_{\bar{i}} = 1 - p_i,$$

and

$$[\bar{i}j] = -[ij].$$

Furthermore, the latent structure must apply to these items, and

$$p_{\bar{i}}^{\alpha} = 1 - p_i^{\alpha}.$$

111

If we add these items to the item list, so that there is a total of $2n + 1$ items (including 0), we find that:

$$g_{\bar{i}1} = 1 - g_{i1}$$

since we have taken the first column to be the marginals, and

$$g_{\bar{i}j} = -g_{ij}, \quad j = 2, \ldots, m.$$

This last equality is derivable from the relations $[\bar{i}j] = -[ij]$ and $[\bar{i}\bar{j}] = [ij]$.

It is still necessary that an admissible rotation produce an F matrix that is completely positive. But, in satisfying this for the augmented matrix, the condition that $f_{ij} < f_{i0}$ will be satisfied automatically.

Suppose that

$$f_{ij} > 0,$$

and

$$f_{\bar{i}j} > 0, \quad \text{for all } i \text{ and } j.$$

Since

$$f_{ij} = \sum_k g_{ik} t_{kj},$$

$$f_{\bar{i}j} = \sum_k g_{\bar{i}k} t_{kj},$$

we can substitute:

$$g_{\bar{i}k} = -g_{ik} \quad \text{if } k > 1$$

and

$$g_{\bar{i}1} = 1 - g_{i1}.$$

We have the result:

$$f_{\bar{i}j} = t_{1j} - \sum_k g_{ik} t_{kj}$$

$$= t_{1j} - f_{ij}.$$

Thus, $f_{ij} + f_{\bar{i}j} = t_{1j} = f_{0j}$.

If both f_{ij} and $f_{\bar{i}j}$ are positive, they must both be less than f_{0j}, and, conversely, if they are both less than f_{ij}, they must both be positive.

If we choose only to use first- and second-order data, then there will be some arbitrariness in determining a proper rotation, even though the knowledge that all parameters must lie between 0 and 1 will be of some use. Unlike the usual factor analysis situation, however, we always have available the third- and higher-order data which in theory can be used to fix the proper rotation. Bert Green has given the algebra of such a procedure which uses all of the third-order data (Green, 1951). Since this approach requires the estimation of quantities such as $[ii]$ and p_{112}, before the actual factoring begins, we do not think that it is a workable estimation procedure in practice. We have not attempted to program Green's solution for the computer.

As far as we know, there do not exist any computer programs which will carry out the rotations of factors required by Gibson's method, i.e., rotations which lead to positive factor matrices F and F'. Gibson, nevertheless, was able to carry out some rather complicated analyses using this procedure, and we include in the next section an example taken from his report.

5.4 *The Six Classes of Urban Evening Radio Listeners*[7]

Our empirical example is taken from a survey of radio program preferences conducted for the National Association of Broadcasters by the National Opinion Research Center of Chicago. The survey covered a national sample of owners of radios in working order. The present set of data is for an urban population of 2,198 people. Each respondent was asked, "Which types of programs there [i.e., on a set of cards handed to him] do you like to listen to in the evening?" In every case, the expression of liking was taken as the positive response. The thirteen program types that were used in the present analysis appear in Table 27.

TABLE 27

NAB-NORC Program Types

1. News broadcasts
2. Quiz shows and other programs where the studio audience takes part
3. Comedy programs
4. Dance and popular music
5. Complete drama plays (other than mystery)
6. Talks or discussions about public issues
7. Mystery programs
8. Sports programs
9. Semi-classical music
10. Classical music (symphonies, opera, etc.)
11. Hillbilly and western music
12. Religious and devotional programs
13. Serial stories

Here no single psychological continuum was expected or even hoped for. Instead, we wanted to test the applicability of latent structure analysis to multi-dimensional joint occurrence data by trying it out in a purely inductive fashion on such a set of data to see if meaningful latent classes would result. We shall presently see that the results of this example speak well for the applicability of latent structure analysis to multi-dimensional domains.

Table 28 shows the joint proportions matrix P for this set of thirteen items. In the factoring process, it was found that six latent classes were necessary to account for the manifest data of Table 28. The resulting initial factor matrix F, obtained by the centroid method[8] and with stabilization of the communalities, appears in Table 29. The residual table appears in Table 30. This is quite a good set of final residuals, and the one residual of 0.010 (between quiz and comedy programs) could be attributed to the special humorous element shared by those two types of programs.

[7]Excerpt from W. A. Gibson, "Applications of the Mathematics of Multiple-Factor Analysis to Problems of Latent Structure Analysis," unpublished Ph.D. dissertation, University of Chicago, 1951. Reprinted with the permission of the author.
[8]See Harman, 1960, for a description of this method of factor analysis.

TABLE 28

Joint Proportions Matrix P

Item	0	1	2	3	4	5	6	7	8	9	10	11	12	13
0	1.000	0.770	0.590	0.621	0.523	0.495	0.470	0.445	0.371	0.372	0.340	0.233	0.207	0.088
1	0.770		0.480	0.504	0.422	0.399	0.410	0.356	0.326	0.312	0.283	0.189	0.181	0.068
2	0.590	0.480		0.416	0.334	0.327	0.303	0.290	0.250	0.241	0.205	0.155	0.139	0.063
3	0.621	0.504	0.416		0.367	0.348	0.314	0.308	0.268	0.253	0.219	0.163	0.126	0.057
4	0.523	0.422	0.334	0.367		0.286	0.253	0.270	0.225	0.220	0.177	0.139	0.096	0.060
5	0.495	0.399	0.327	0.348	0.286		0.264	0.276	0.199	0.229	0.194	0.121	0.110	0.056
6	0.470	0.410	0.303	0.314	0.253	0.264		0.213	0.223	0.231	0.216	0.106	0.116	0.045
7	0.445	0.356	0.290	0.308	0.270	0.276	0.213		0.187	0.161	0.142	0.119	0.084	0.058
8	0.371	0.326	0.250	0.268	0.225	0.199	0.223	0.187		0.153	0.131	0.100	0.084	0.041
9	0.372	0.312	0.241	0.253	0.220	0.229	0.231	0.161	0.153		0.213	0.080	0.087	0.033
10	0.340	0.283	0.205	0.219	0.177	0.194	0.216	0.142	0.131	0.213		0.072	0.082	0.027
11	0.233	0.189	0.155	0.163	0.139	0.121	0.106	0.119	0.100	0.080	0.072		0.080	0.036
12	0.207	0.181	0.139	0.126	0.096	0.110	0.116	0.084	0.084	0.087	0.082	0.080		0.030
13	0.088	0.068	0.063	0.057	0.060	0.056	0.045	0.058	0.041	0.033	0.027	0.036	0.030	

TABLE 29

F Matrix

	A_1	B_1	C_1	D_1	E_1	F_1
0	1.000	0.000	0.000	0.000	0.000	0.000
1	0.770	0.164	−0.051	−0.091	0.053	−0.019
2	0.590	0.179	0.072	−0.056	0.014	−0.003
3	0.621	0.181	0.105	−0.024	0.073	−0.066
4	0.523	0.144	0.118	0.056	0.039	−0.079
5	0.495	0.195	0.051	0.108	0.030	0.106
6	0.470	0.195	−0.134	−0.051	0.081	−0.009
7	0.445	0.135	0.168	0.085	0.019	0.103
8	0.371	0.169	0.024	−0.098	0.077	−0.085
9	0.372	0.198	−0.178	0.124	0.030	−0.051
10	0.340	0.149	−0.221	0.105	−0.013	0.002
11	0.233	0.083	0.064	−0.072	−0.140	0.017
12	0.207	0.075	−0.055	−0.103	−0.133	0.079
13	0.088	0.057	0.048	0.021	−0.076	0.029

Table 31 shows the final factor matrix which results from choosing a rotation which seems to center fairly well between the required limits, as can be seen if the plots of the factors, two at a time, are examined. The appearance of those plots has served to give us considerable confidence in the adequacy of our approximate solution and in the general applicability of latent structure analysis to multi-dimensional data. The centering is good and the rotational freedom is about the same on all plots. The general vicinity of most of the rotational limits is multiply determined by points which give a considerable degree of stability to those limits. Finally, the arrangement of the points on those plots is such as to differentiate sharply, both statistically and psychologically, between the resulting latent classes. That there could exist, by chance alone, a position of the reference frame which exemplifies so well all of our five centering principles simultaneously is beyond the realm of likelihood. We shall want to make further use of these plots in the process of interpreting the six latent classes.

Table 32 contains the *L* and *V* matrices. Because of the remaining rotational indeterminacy, we may not rely on the exact values of single latent marginals. Rather, we must base our interpretations only on gross differences between those latent marginals. The gross size pattern of *L* has exhibited a remarkable stability during the rotational process, being practically the same for the ten or more positions of the reference frame just previous to the present one. For this reason

115

TABLE 30

Six-factor Residual Table

Item	0	1	2	3	4	5	6	7	8	9	10	11	12	13
0	0.000	0.000	0.000	0.000	0.000	0.000	0.000	0.000	0.000	0.000	0.000	0.000	0.000	0.000
1	0.000		−0.003	−0.001	0.004	−0.003	0.001	0.005	0.000	−0.002	−0.002	0.002	0.003	−0.004
2	0.000	−0.003		0.010	−0.006	0.000	−0.003	−0.007	−0.004	0.002	−0.002	−0.001	0.005	−0.001
3	0.000	−0.001	0.010		−0.001	0.006	−0.003	−0.005	−0.001	0.000	0.005	0.005	0.000	−0.007
4	0.000	0.004	−0.006	−0.001		−0.002	−0.002	0.005	0.003	0.004	−0.002	0.002	−0.005	0.003
5	0.000	−0.003	0.000	0.006	−0.002		0.001	0.006	−0.002	0.003	−0.005	−0.002	0.004	0.002
6	0.000	0.001	−0.003	−0.003	−0.002	0.001		0.001	0.008	0.003	0.004	−0.004	−0.002	0.004
7	0.000	0.005	−0.007	−0.005	0.005	0.006	0.001		0.007	−0.002	0.005	−0.002	−0.007	0.002
8	0.000	0.000	−0.004	−0.001	0.003	−0.002	0.008	0.007		−0.002	−0.002	0.001	−0.004	0.004
9	0.000	−0.002	0.002	0.000	0.004	0.003	0.003	−0.002	−0.002		0.002	−0.005	0.005	0.000
10	0.000	−0.002	−0.002	0.005	−0.002	−0.005	0.004	0.005	0.001	0.002		0.002	0.001	0.001
11	0.000	0.002	−0.001	0.005	0.002	−0.002	−0.004	−0.002	0.001	−0.005	0.002		0.006	0.001
12	0.000	0.003	0.005	0.000	−0.005	0.004	−0.002	−0.007	−0.004	0.005	0.001	0.006		−0.003
13	0.000	−0.004	−0.001	−0.007	0.003	0.002	0.004	0.002	0.004	0.000	0.001	−0.003	−0.001	

TABLE 31

Rotated Factor Matrix

	A_{32}	B_{32}	C_{32}	D_{32}	E_{32}	F_{32}
0	0.520	0.438	0.336	0.460	0.310	0.339
1	0.237	0.402	0.308	0.388	0.249	0.324
2	0.173	0.353	0.233	0.258	0.273	0.152
3	0.194	0.392	0.293	0.268	0.264	0.127
4	0.193	0.303	0.256	0.231	0.257	0.049
5	0.141	0.366	0.066	0.290	0.238	0.089
6	0.038	0.272	0.182	0.338	0.116	0.230
7	0.174	0.364	0.079	0.132	0.260	0.075
8	0.030	0.241	0.245	0.156	0.140	0.152
9	0.042	0.150	0.122	0.422	0.127	0.030
10	0.049	0.114	0.064	0.409	0.078	0.090
11	0.070	0.060	0.096	0.065	0.242	0.096
12	0.020	0.028	0.034	0.106	0.170	0.206
13	0.019	0.035	0.018	0.018	0.125	0.025

we may feel quite confident in the essential correctness of that gross pattern, even though single entries are subject to some variation. Because of the still greater variability of the latent class frequencies, however, we shall be able to say little about the relative sizes of these six latent classes.

The most outstanding single characteristic of class *A* is that none of its latent marginals are greater than 0.50. This class must, therefore, consist principally of people who do not care much for listening to the radio in the evening. The fact that item 1 (news broadcasts) has the highest latent marginal in this class is easily understood, for even many people who do not like radio will listen to news programs in order to get the most up-to-the-minute news. Interestingly enough, although item 1 is, in general, a poor discriminator because news programs are so universally popular, that item can do an effective job of assigning to their most probable class (class *A*) those respondents who *do not* indicate a liking for news programs.

Classes *B* and *C* should be considered together because of the similarity of the two sets of latent probabilities. Except for two items, these two classes are very similar in the ordering of their latent marginals. Classes *B* and *C* are both higher than all others but one (class *E*, which we shall discuss presently) on quiz, comedy, and popular music programs, and higher than all others on sports programs. These are the popular, agreeable kinds of programs that normal,

117

TABLE 32

Estimates of Latent Probabilities

Item	Class					
	A	*B*	*C*	*D*	*E*	*F*
0	1.000	1.000	1.000	1.000	1.000	1.000
News	0.455	0.918	0.918	0.843	0.803	0.955
Quiz	0.333	0.806	0.693	0.562	0.881	0.535
Comedy	0.373	0.896	0.871	0.582	0.850	0.374
Pop Music	0.372	0.692	0.760	0.502	0.828	0.145
Drama	0.272	0.835	0.195	0.631	0.769	0.262
Discussion	0.072	0.620	0.540	0.734	0.375	0.679
Mystery	0.335	0.830	0.236	0.286	0.837	0.221
Sports	0.057	0.550	0.730	0.339	0.451	0.448
Semi-Classical	0.080	0.342	0.362	0.917	0.408	0.087
Classical	0.095	0.260	0.189	0.889	0.251	0.265
Country	0.134	0.136	0.286	0.142	0.779	0.283
Religious	0.039	0.065	0.102	0.231	0.548	0.609
Serials	0.037	0.081	0.055	0.040	0.404	0.074
Class Sizes	0.270	0.192	0.113	0.212	0.096	0.115

average people like to listen to. It seems reasonable, therefore, to call classes *B* and *C* the "middle-brows" or the "average American listeners." We shall see presently that they are appropriately different both from the "high-brows" and from the "low-brows." Now, if these are average people, then there should be a lot of them. We can see from *V* that the combined size of these two groups *is* substantial, *if* our approximate solution is anywhere near correct in that respect. The arrangement of points on the *AB* and *AC* plots shows that, although on a much lower level of intensity, class *A* likes most the same kinds of programs liked most by *B* and *C*, and especially by *B*. This suggests that perhaps class *A* is still another group of "middle-brows" whose principal difference from members of classes *B* and *C* is only in the degree with which they enjoy the radio.

The striking difference between classes *B* and *C* on mystery and drama programs tempts one to go beyond what the data gives and to try to understand what it is that could produce such a sharp cleavage between two groups that are otherwise so very similar. One hypothesis is that of sex differences. Another idea is that those two kinds of programs provide a temporary escape from reality which is utilized by class *B*, but rejected by *C*. Still other interpretations are,

118

of course, possible. Unfortunately, the present set of data, by itself, seems inadequate to really clear up this mystery. Although it has been beyond the scope of the present research, these various hypotheses could be tested out in a number of ways. For example, the hypothesis of sex differences could be subjected to a test of the significance of the differences between the male and female populations in their proportions of liking of these two kinds of radio programs. Perhaps a better way to proceed would be first to classify the members of this population according to their most probable latent classes on the basis of their response patterns. Then we could test the significance of the difference between classes B and C in their proportions of male and female members. The other hypotheses could be tested in an analogous way, using the auxiliary data that was collected along with the data of the present study. Still another way to inquire further into this mystery would be to set up a fresh latent structure study so designed as to crucially test all of these hypotheses at the same time. Such a collection of items would include, in addition to mystery and drama programs, an item concerned with the sex designation of the respondents, one or more indices of withdrawing tendencies or introversion, etc. This is but one example of the way in which latent structure analysis could be used to test multiple hypotheses about the underlying nature of a certain psychological or sociological domain.

If items 5 and 7 had not been included in this study, then classes B and C would have merged into a single class, leaving only a slight residual dimension. This suggests that a very effective way of limiting the number of latent classes necessary to account for a particular set of manifest data is to carry out a complete latent structure solution for the entire set of data and only then to reduce the dimensionality of the vector configuration by weeding out certain items. The possibility of just such a reduction as this was not at all apparent during the factoring process.

Class D is not difficult to identify, for a very high proportion of its members, in contrast to those of other classes, like to listen to semi-classical and classical music. They are also fairly high on talks on public issues. These are undoubtedly the sophisticates or "high-brows." It is interesting that this is the only group that differs sharply in its liking for mystery and complete drama programs. Note that the "middle-brow" groups are appropriately low on semi-classical and classical music.

In contrast with class A, class E is characterized primarily by consistently *high* latent marginals, none of which are lower than 0.25. Substantial proportions of this class even like to listen to serials and to hillbilly music, which are quite unpopular with all other classes. It is interesting to note further that the three programs liked least by this group (serials excluded) are the same ones that are liked most (except for news) by the sophisticates. All of these characteristics, a tendency toward indiscriminate radio listening, the enjoyment of serials and hillbilly music, and the *relative* disliking of "high-brow" programs, suggest that this might well be the "low-brow" group. This interpretation is supported by the fact that classes D and E are about as different as it is possible to be with respect to their patterns of reaction to these items, and this is, of course, what would be expected of the two groups at the extreme ends of the social scale.

119

Again, we notice that the "middle-brows" shy away, as does everyone else, from such "low-brow" programs as serials and hillbilly music.

Finally, we come to class F, which is distinguished by the highest latent marginal for religious programs, the lowest for popular music, quite low ones for comedy, complete drama, and mystery, and no *extremely* strong likes other than for news. This combination of a religious component, a lack of interest in what might be regarded as a younger type of program, and a somewhat subdued enjoyment of radio in general, except for news programs, points toward one large group of radio listeners, that of older people, whose unique pattern of preferences is perhaps not adequately accounted for by any other latent class.

The foregoing interpretations have been made with varying degrees of confidence. Even though some of them could hardly be refuted, it might be better to regard them all as being more in the nature of hypotheses which should be subjected to further verification. There are many more possible comparisons between these six classes which can serve as further checks on those hypotheses. These comparisons are perhaps most effectively carried out by examining the appropriate plots of the rotated factors. Each such plot indicates clearly which items discriminate well between the two associated latent classes and which items are of little value in differentiating members of the two groups. These two kinds of items correspond to points which lie, respectively, far away from or close to the diagonal. By studying the psychological nature of these two groups of items for each pair of latent classes, we could acquire a still better understanding, both of the way in which those two classes differ, and of the way in which they are alike. Still further clues as to the fundamental nature of any of the latent classes might be provided by auxiliary data or by a new latent structure study, as we have already illustrated.

The data of the present study was not collected with this kind of analysis in mind. It just happened to be already available for our use. In view of this fact, the meaningfulness of our results constitutes a doubly convincing demonstration of the fruitfulness of the inductive application of latent structure analysis to multi-dimensional domains. If latent structure analysis can establish so much order in a complex set of data not specifically meant for that purpose, how much more might it accomplish in a study so designated as to test crucially as many hypotheses as possible about the fundamental nature of a multi-dimensional domain.

6. Estimation by Partitioning Methods

There is one method of estimating the parameters of a latent class model which was implicit in our first description of the model in Chapter 1. There we stated the basic problem of empirical research, of inferring some classification of the respondents in a sample. Given a particular sample of size N, and assuming that the m-class model was appropriate, we might attempt to partition the sample into m groups, to sort the respondents into m groups, hoping that our sorting procedure might approximate the theoretical division into m classes.

Once a partition of the sample had been effected, the latent parameters would be estimated by simply looking at the marginal response frequencies within each of the subsamples. That is, a latent probability such as p_1^1 would be estimated by the proportion of subgroup 1 who responded positively to item 1.

We could try to devise an effective sorting method, but the difficulties seem enormous. On the other hand, we could make all possible partitions of the N respondents into m subgroups, and try to decide which of these partitions best satisfied the assumptions of the latent class model. One good feature of this last approach is that it is fairly simple to program a computer to carry out the required sorting and calculating. The obvious drawback is that the total number of possible partitions becomes enormous very quickly.

This method of estimation has been studied at some length by Madansky (1959). One important point which we note is his choice of a criterion for evaluating the "goodness" of a partition. Rather than using the chi-square or likelihood criteria which we discussed earlier in this chapter, Madansky chose a function of the data and the estimates which tested more directly the implications of the axiom of local independence. This function is constructed as follows.

Let n_i^α be the number of respondents in partition α who gave the positive response to item i; let n^α be the number of respondents in partition α; and let n_s^α be the number of respondents in partition α who gave the response s, where s stands for a complete response pattern sequence. If local independence held exactly, within partition α, then n_s^α/n^α would equal the product of n_i^α/n^α, for all items i which are positive in response pattern s, times the product of $(1 - n_j^\alpha/n^\alpha)$, for all items j which were negative in s. It is this difference,

$$d_s^\alpha = n_s^\alpha/n^\alpha - \prod_{i \in s} n_i^\alpha/n^\alpha \prod_{j \in s} (1 - n_j^\alpha/n^\alpha),$$

which is the basis for Madansky's measure of agreement between the particular partition in question and the requirements of the latent class model. That measure is:

$$\Delta^* = \sum_s \sum_{\alpha=1}^m (n^\alpha d_s^\alpha)^2 / p_s,$$

where $p_s = n_s/N$ is simply the proportion giving response s in the entire population.

Examining all possible partitions of a sample does not seem to be a practical solution to the problem of estimation, although it might be useful in the two-class case with a small sample size (less than 100, say). We don't really know how fast such a procedure could be carried out on the newest computers, but Madansky reported that the analysis of a two-class, three-item problem, with $N = 40$, took four hours on the IBM 704. Our opinion is that practical solutions to the estimation problem will have to combine several of the techniques described in this chapter. That is, the basic algebraic solution will have to be used in conjunction with an overall goodness of fit criterion, and an iterative procedure which will, if not find the best fitting estimates, at least provide better estimates than the initial solution. A great deal of imaginative thinking and sophisticated programming is still needed before latent class analysis can be routinely applied to a set of data.

5

The Problem of Ordered Classes

1. Ordering Latent Classes

It is never difficult to interpret a two-class latent structure, primarily because we can always call one class "high" and the other "low"; those individuals in the one class possess an attribute which the individuals in the other class do not. As soon as the *general* latent class model is introduced, however, such language cannot always be used. The m classes define a typology, a segmentation of the population, but nothing in the assumptions of the model permit us to say that one class ranks higher than another, or that those in one class possess more of something than those in another class.

Of course, we can always try to infer the existence of an ordering of the classes. If a set of items all relating to political liberalism had been analyzed, and three latent classes developed, we would probably label the classes "High," "Medium," "Low," *if* it had turned out that $p_j^1 > p_j^2 > p_j^3$ for all the items in the set. The statement "the more liberal an individual, the higher his probability of responding positively to any item in the set" would be consistent with the assumption that the three classes define different levels of an underlying variable, "liberalism."

What, on the other hand, would we do if the within-class probabilities did not turn out to be ordered consistently? One interpretation might be that the underlying variable, e.g., liberalism, is not unidimensional, i.e., the classes simply cannot be ordered with respect to a simple dimension. Another interpretation might be that the classes are indeed ordered, but that the proposition "the more liberal, the higher the probability of positive response to any item" is not true. Other interpretations are also possible.

Recall, for instance, the four-class example of Chapter 4, where there appeared to be two dimensions to the latent structure. This conclusion was based on: a) knowledge about the content of the items; and b) the patterns of the latent probabilities that actually existed. As long as the latent class model is general, with no restrictions on the pattern of latent probabilities, all inferences about ordering of classes, or of the existence of scales and unidimensional concepts are made outside of the latent structure model, not within it.

The natural thing to do when one believes that latent classes should have a natural order is to incorporate the assumption into the model itself. In this chapter, we shall examine some attempts to do this. The first model studied is the latent distance model, which appeared first in *Measurement and Prediction* (Lazarsfeld, 1950a, 1950b) and which can be considered to be a direct generalization of Guttman's perfect scale analysis, referred to in Chapter 1. The second class of models is closely related to the "traceline" models of Chapter 6, where the jump is made from discrete and ordered classes to a continuous-valued latent variable.

2. The Latent Distance Model

Suppose that there exists a set of n dichotomous items and a population of individuals satisfying these restrictions:

(i) the axiom of local independence holds;
(ii) the probability that an individual responds positively to item i is either a_i or b_i, where $0 \leq a_i \leq b_i \leq 1$.

Let x_i be the proportion of the population who have probability a_i of responding positively to item i. Only if all the x_i equalled the same value would we have the ordinary two-class model. We shall assume that these proportions, x_i, are all different. Later on it will be clear what happens if several of them take on the same value. Since the numbering of items is arbitrary, we suppose that

$$x_1 < x_2 < \cdots < x_n;$$

this is not a restriction on the model. It is with reference to this ordering of the items that we use the terms "preceding" and "succeeding items."

Assumptions (i) and (ii) indicate that there may be 2^n different *latent types* of respondents. For instance, when there are three items there will be individuals whose probabilities of positive response are a_1, a_2, and a_3; others whose probabilities are b_1, a_2, and a_3; there being eight types in all, as shown in Table 1.

TABLE 1

Eight Latent Types Possible
when Assumption (ii) *Holds for*
Three Items

	(a_1, a_2, a_3)	
(b_1, a_2, a_3)	(a_1, b_2, a_3)	(a_1, a_2, b_3)
(b_1, b_2, a_3)	(b_1, a_2, b_3)	(a_1, b_2, b_3)
	(b_1, b_2, b_3)	

The third assumption which is made will reduce the number of possible latent types from 2^n to $n + 1$, and will make clear the sense in which these latent classes are ordered.

(iii) If an individual has the lower probability a_i of giving a positive response to item i, then he must have the lower probability of positive response for all succeeding items. This rules out the latent types in which a "b" follows an "a".

Assumptions (i), (ii), and (iii) define the *latent distance model*.

In the three-item case, assumption (iii) restricts us to only four of the eight latent types shown in Table 1, namely

$$(a_1, a_2, a_3) \quad (b_1, a_2, a_3) \quad (b_1, b_2, a_3) \quad (b_1, b_2, b_3).$$

There is one latent type which has all low (a) probabilities; one which has exactly one high probability; and so on. There would be $n + 1$ types in general. If all items have the property that a positive response is associated with a high position, it is clear the latent types are ordered: if, for each item the positive response indicates political liberalism, while the negative response indicates conservatism, the latent type (a_1, a_2, a_3) is the most conservative, while the type (b_1, b_2, b_3) is most liberal.

The latent distance model is a particular case of the latent class models. There are $n + 1$ latent classes, or latent types, in the population. This typology should not be confused with the manifest division of the respondents to the questionnaire, according to their response patterns. As usual, there is a probabilistic relationship between the latent and manifest types, but the assumption that there are only $n + 1$ latent types does not mean that some of the response patterns cannot occur. Only in the special case where some of the probabilities a_i equal zero, and some of the probabilities b_i equal one, will certain response patterns be forbidden. When *all* of the a_i are zero, and *all* of the b_i are one, we have the well-known Guttman scale model. We shall mention this later in the chapter, after we have obtained the accounting equations and the solution of the general model.

2.1 Accounting Equations

The latent distance model can be considered as a special case of the latent class model, where the number of classes is $n + 1$, one more than the number of items. (We have not assumed that the $n + 1$ latent types all do exist in the population. Some may be empty.) Each type or class is characterized by a vector of n latent probabilities — made up of a's and b's — in which a b never succeeds an a.

We shall define v^α to be the relative frequency of the type whose probability vector involves exactly α high (b) probabilities. The latent parameters of the model can be arranged as shown in Table 2 (for the case of six items).

TABLE 2

Latent Parameters of the Latent Distance Model

Item	Class						
	0	1	2	3	4	5	6
1	a_1	b_1	b_1	b_1	b_1	b_1	b_1
2	a_2	a_2	b_2	b_2	b_2	b_2	b_2
3	a_3	a_3	a_3	b_3	b_3	b_3	b_3
4	a_4	a_4	a_4	a_4	b_4	b_4	b_4
5	a_5	a_5	a_5	a_5	a_5	b_5	b_5
6	a_6	a_6	a_6	a_6	a_6	a_6	b_6
Class Frequency	v^0	v^1	v^2	v^3	v^4	v^5	v^6

(sum = 1)

Now the accounting equations can be set down. The manifest probability of a positive response to item 1 is:

$$p_1 = a_1 v^0 + b_1(v^1 + v^2 + \cdots + v^n),$$

for $i = 2$,

$$p_2 = a_2(v^0 + v^1) + b_2(v^2 + \cdots + v^n).$$

The pattern for any item i is:

$$p_i = a_i(v^0 + v^1 + \cdots + v^{i-1}) + b_i(v^i + v^{i+1} + \cdots + v^n). \qquad (1)$$

Notice, however, the relation between the relative frequency of the latent types, (v^α), and the parameters x_i defined in the previous section. The proportion of the population that has probability a_i for item i is x_i. It is easy to see, by referring to Table 2, that x_i equals the sum of all the v^α for which α is less than i.

$$x_i = v^0 + v^1 + \cdots + v^{i-1}, \qquad 1 \le i \le n. \qquad (2)$$

It will be convenient to have defined

$$x_0 = 0 \quad \text{and} \quad x_{n+1} = 1.$$

Equation (2) states that the probability that a respondent has the lower latent probability on item i equals the probability that his latent type precedes type i. When we use these *cumulative* parameters, x_i, Equation (1) is much simpler.

$$p_i = a_i x_i + b_i(1 - x_i). \qquad (3)$$

To compute the joint probabilities p_{ij}, we have to multiply the latent probabilities of the two items together, for each class, and add up these products

125

weighted by the class frequencies. Referring to Table 2 will be helpful in seeing what the results are: there will be an $a_i a_j$ term, a $b_i b_j$ term, and either a $b_i a_j$ or $a_i b_j$ term, depending on whether $i < j$ or $j < i$. For instance,

$$p_{13} = a_1 a_2 v^0 + b_1 a_3(v^1 + v^2) + b_1 b_3(v^3 + v^4 + \cdots + v^n).$$

If $i < j$, then we find that:

$$p_{ij} = a_i a_j(v^0 + \cdots + v^{i-1}) + b_i a_j(v^i + \cdots + v^{j-1}) + b_i b_j(v^j + \cdots + v^n).$$

Using the cumulative parameters x_i simplifies this expression:

$$p_{ij} = a_i a_j x_i + b_i a_j(x_j - x_i) + b_i b_j(1 - x_j), \qquad \text{if } i < j. \qquad (4)$$

The latent form of higher-order manifest probabilities also depends on knowledge of the order of the items involved. Thus, if three items i, j, and k, are ordered $i < j < k$, the third-order probability p_{ijk} will be:

$$p_{ijk} = a_i a_j a_k(v^0 + \cdots + v^{i-1}) + b_i a_j a_k(v^i + \cdots + v^{j-1})$$
$$+ b_i b_j a_k(v^j + \cdots + v^{k-1}) + b_i b_j b_k(v^k + \cdots + v^n).$$

Substituting in x_i, x_j, and x_k where appropriate leads to:

$$p_{ijk} = a_i a_j a_k x_i + b_i a_j a_k(x_j - x_i) + b_i b_j a_k(x_k - x_j) + b_i b_j b_k(1 - x_k),$$
$$i < j < k. \qquad (5)$$

It should by now be evident how all higher-order probabilities are accounted for in terms of the latent probabilities, ending with the nth-order positive probability $p_{12 \cdots n}$.

$$p_{12 \cdots n} = a_1 a_2 \cdots a_n x_1 + b_1 a_2 \cdots a_n(x_2 - x_1)$$
$$+ \cdots + b_1 b_2 \cdots b_n(1 - x_n). \qquad (6)$$

A useful alternative form of these accounting equations, Equations (3)–(6) can be obtained by defining δ_i as the difference between the two latent probabilities, b_i and a_i:

$$\delta_i = b_i - a_i.$$

Also define $x_{\bar{j}} = 1 - x_j$.

The resulting equations are:

$$p_i = b_i - x_i \delta_i, \qquad (3A)$$

or

$$p_i = a_i + x_{\bar{i}} \delta_i. \qquad (3B)$$

$$p_{ij} = b_i b_j - x_i \delta_i a_j - b_i x_j \delta_j, \qquad i < j, \qquad (4A)$$

or

$$p_{ij} = a_i a_j + x_{\bar{i}} \delta_i a_j + b_i x_{\bar{j}} \delta_j, \qquad i < j. \qquad (4B)$$

$$p_{ijk} = b_i b_j b_k - x_i \delta_i a_j a_k - x_j \delta_j b_i a_k - x_k \delta_k b_i b_j, \qquad i < j < k, \qquad (5A)$$

or

$$p_{ijk} = a_i a_j a_k + x_{\bar{i}} \delta_i a_j a_k + x_{\bar{j}} \delta_j b_i a_k + x_{\bar{k}} \delta_k b_i b_j, \quad i < j < k. \quad (5B)$$

$$p_{123\cdots n} = b_1 b_2 \cdots b_n - x_1 \delta_1 a_2 a_3 \cdots a_n - \cdots x_n \delta_n b_1 b_2 \cdots b_{n-1}$$

$$= \prod_{i=1}^{n} b_i - \sum_{j=1}^{n} x_j \delta_j \prod_{i=1}^{j-1} b_i \prod_{i=j+1}^{n} a_i, \quad (6A)$$

where, by convention, $\prod_{i=k}^{m} a_i$ is equal to 1 if m is less than k.

2.2 Symmetric Parameters

Now, we shall calculate the cross products [ij] and symmetric parameters [ijk]. These are simpler functions of the latent probabilities than are the manifest joint probabilities of the same order.

[ij] = $p_{ij} - p_i p_j$, by definition. If we assume that $i < j$, Equations (3) and (4) can be used to calculate [ij].

$$p_i p_j = \big(a_i x_i + b_i(1 - x_i)\big)\big(a_j x_j + b_j(1 - x_j)\big)$$
$$= a_i a_j(x_i x_j) + b_i a_j x_j(1 - x_i) + a_i b_j x_i(1 - x_j) + b_j b_i(1 - x_i)(1 - x_j).$$

Subtracting $p_i p_j$ from p_{ij} gives:

$$[ij] = a_i a_j x_i(1 - x_j) - b_i a_j x_i(1 - x_j) - a_i b_j x_i(1 - x_j) + b_i b_j x_i(1 - x_j).$$

All of the factors involving x_i and x_j reduce to the same factor:

$$x_i(1 - x_j).$$

Factoring out $x_i(1 - x_j)$, it is easy to verify that the remainder:

$$a_i a_j - b_i a_j - a_i b_j + b_i b_j$$

also factors, giving:

$$[ij] = (b_i - a_i)(b_j - a_j)x_i(1 - x_j), \quad i < j.$$

All cross products will be positive, since we supposed that $b_i > a_i$ for every item. Using the expressions $b_i - a_i = \delta_i$ and $1 - x_j = x_{\bar{j}}$, the formula for [ij] becomes:

$$[ij] = \delta_i \delta_j x_i x_{\bar{j}}, \quad i < j. \quad (7)$$

If we had three items, and their order were $i < j < k$, then Equation (7) implies that:

$$[ij][jk]/[ik] = x_j x_{\bar{j}}(\delta_j)^2, \quad i < j < k. \quad (8)$$

Notice that this expression is valid only if j is the middle item. (It does not matter which of the items i and k is higher and which is lower.) If k had been the middle item and j the upper item, then the value of that ratio would be:

$$[ij][jk]/[ik] = (x_{\bar{j}})^2(\delta_j)^2 x_k/x_{\bar{k}}, \quad i < k < j. \quad (9)$$

$k < j$ means that an x_k appears in the numerator, and $i < k$ means that $x_{\bar{k}}$ appears in the denominator.

Most of what we have to say about the latent distance model presupposes knowledge of the proper ordering of the items. If four items are taken, and their order is $i < j < k < m$, then the determinant

$$\begin{vmatrix} [ik] & [im] \\ [jk] & [jm] \end{vmatrix}$$

will be equal to zero. This fact is immediate, since:

$$[ik][jm] - [im][jk] = (\delta_i \delta_j \delta_k \delta_m)(x_i x_{\bar{k}} x_j x_{\bar{m}} - x_i x_{\bar{m}} x_j x_{\bar{k}}) = 0 \qquad (10)$$

if $i < j < k < m$.

The determinant would remain zero if the order of i and j were interchanged; or if the order of k and m were reversed; or if the entire ordering were reversed. If the order of i and k were interchanged, however, the value would no longer be zero. (The reader should verify that this is so by substituting the proper values from Equation (7).)

This interesting observation contrasts with the situation in the two-class model. There we saw that $[ij] = \delta_i \delta_j v^1 v^2$ for any pairs of items i and j (where $\delta_i = p_i^1 - p_i^2$), and hence, *any* set of four items, arranged in *any* order, would satisfy the equality $[ij][km] = [ik][jm]$.

An easy way of summarizing this discussion is in terms of the matrix of cross products between pairs of items. Let the items be numbered from 1 to n, correctly ordered so that the pattern of Table 2 holds. The cross product matrix for the case of five items is given in Table 3. The diagonal terms are missing, since $[ii]$ is not a manifest quantity.

TABLE 3

Cross Product Matrix for Five Items

	1	2	3	4	5
1	—	[12]	[13]	[14]	[15]
2	[12]	—	[23]	[24]	[25]
3	[13]	[23]	—	[34]	[35]
4	[14]	[24]	[34]	—	[45]
5	[15]	[25]	[35]	[45]	—

Equation 10 tells us that any 2×2 determinant taken from the cross product matrix will equal zero *if* it does not cross the main diagonal at all: if all four entries in the determinant come from the same side of the main diagonal, the determinant will be equal to zero. Thus:

$$\begin{vmatrix} [13] & [15] \\ [23] & [25] \end{vmatrix} = 0.$$

On the other hand, if part of the 2×2 submatrix is from above the diagonal, while the rest is from below the diagonal, the determinant will not be zero. For example,

$$\begin{vmatrix} [12] & [14] \\ [23] & [34] \end{vmatrix} = (\delta_1\delta_2\delta_3\delta_4)x_1x_{\bar{4}}(x_{\bar{2}}x_3 - x_2x_{\bar{3}})$$

$$= (\delta_1\delta_2\delta_3\delta_4)x_1x_{\bar{4}}(x_3 - x_2)$$

would not be zero except in special cases as when $x_2 = x_3$ (i.e., when $v^2 = 0$).

If all the x_i are distinct, therefore, and if a_i is strictly less than b_i for each item, the correct ordering of the items could *almost* be inferred from the manifest cross product matrix. The qualification "almost" involves two factors:

(i) the entire ordering could be reversed;
(ii) the order of the first two items, 1 and 2, could be reversed; and the order of the last two items, $n - 1$ and n, could be reversed.

The first factor is unimportant: the wrong choice would simply lead to a scale with the high value at the "wrong" end. The second factor is more distressing, for, without making certain restrictions on the model, it cannot be overlooked.

Let us make clear why the interchange of items 1 and 2 would not be noticed (and, similarly, of items $n - 1$ and n), if we were looking at the cross products: *There is no 2×2 determinant containing* [12] *that would vanish.* At least one of the other three entries must come from the other side of the main diagonal. If the ordering $(1, 2, 3, 4, 5)$, shown in Table 3, is *correct*, then the orderings $(1, 2, 3, 5, 4)$, $(2, 1, 3, 4, 5)$, and $(2, 1, 3, 5, 4)$ also have the determinantal property mentioned here. Of course, if n is large, this uncertainty will not bother us very much. We shall have more to say on this subject later in the chapter.

The Third-Order Symmetric Parameter. Now, let us turn to the calculation of the third-order symmetric parameter in terms of the latent parameters. Recall the definition (Chapter 3),

$$[ijk] = p_{ijk} - p_i[jk] - p_j[ik] - p_k[ij] - p_ip_jp_k.$$

We must specify an ordering of the three items, say $i < j < k$, in order to apply the proper formulae. We have shown that:

$$p_i = b_i - \delta_ix_i;$$

$$[ij] = \delta_i\delta_jx_ix_{\bar{j}}, \qquad \text{if } i < j; \tag{11}$$

and

$$p_{ijk} = b_ib_jb_k - (x_i\delta_ia_ja_k + x_j\delta_jb_ia_k + x_k\delta_kb_ib_j), \qquad \text{if } i < j < k.$$

Next, we write out the products of the marginals and the cross products:

$$p_i[jk] = b_i\delta_j\delta_k x_j x_{\bar{k}} - \delta_i\delta_j\delta_k x_i x_j x_{\bar{k}},$$
$$p_j[ik] = b_j\delta_i\delta_k x_i x_{\bar{k}} - \delta_i\delta_j\delta_k x_i x_j x_{\bar{k}}, \qquad (12)$$
$$p_k[ij] = b_k\delta_i\delta_j x_i x_{\bar{j}} - \delta_i\delta_j\delta_k x_i x_j x_{\bar{k}},$$

and the product of three marginals

$$p_i p_j p_k = b_i b_j b_k - b_i b_j \delta_k x_k - b_i b_k \delta_j x_j - b_j b_k \delta_i x_i$$
$$+ b_i \delta_j \delta_k x_j x_k + b_j \delta_i \delta_k x_i x_k + b_k \delta_i \delta_j x_i x_j - \delta_i \delta_j \delta_k x_i x_j x_k. \quad (13)$$

Now, compare Equations (11), (12), and (13), and combine terms to get

$$[ijk] = x_i\delta_i(b_j b_k - a_j a_k) + x_j\delta_j(b_i b_k - b_i a_k) + x_k\delta_k(b_i b_j - b_i b_j)$$
$$- b_i\delta_j\delta_k x_j(x_k + x_{\bar{k}}) - b_j\delta_i\delta_k x_i(x_k + x_{\bar{k}}) - b_k\delta_i\delta_j x_i(x_j + x_{\bar{j}})$$
$$+ \delta_i\delta_j\delta_k x_i(x_j x_k + 2x_j x_{\bar{k}} + x_{\bar{j}} x_k).$$

Simplifying,

$$[ijk] = x_i\delta_i(b_j b_k - a_j a_k) + x_j b_i\delta_j\delta_k - b_i\delta_j\delta_k x_j - b_j\delta_i\delta_k x_i$$
$$- b_k\delta_i\delta_j x_i + \delta_i\delta_j\delta_k x_i(x_k + 2x_j x_{\bar{k}})$$
$$= x_i\delta_i(b_j b_k - a_j a_k - b_j\delta_k - b_k\delta_j) + \delta_i\delta_j\delta_k x_i(x_k + 2x_j x_{\bar{k}})$$
$$= -x_i\delta_i\delta_j\delta_k + \delta_i\delta_j\delta_k x_i(x_k + 2x_j x_{\bar{k}}).$$

The final expression for the third-order symmetric parameter is very concise when written in terms of the δ's and x's, as shown in Equation (14).

$$[ijk] = \delta_i\delta_j\delta_k x_i(1 - x_k)(2x_j - 1), \qquad i < j < k. \qquad (14)$$

Since all the b's were assumed to be greater than the a's, all δ's are positive. The sign of $[ijk]$ thus depends on the value of x_j, where j is the middle item. If $x_j > 1/2$, $[ijk]$ is positive, and if $x_j < 1/2$, $[ijk]$ is negative.

2.3 Identification of the Latent Parameters

Equations (14) and (7) enable us to solve for many of the latent parameters. If we have three items, and j is the middle item, then:

$$[ijk]^2/[ij][jk][ik] = (\delta_i\delta_j\delta_k)^2(x_i x_{\bar{k}})^2(2x_j - 1)^2/(\delta_i\delta_j\delta_k)^2(x_i x_{\bar{k}})^2 x_{\bar{j}} x_j$$
$$= (2x_j - 1)^2/x_j x_{\bar{j}}$$
$$= (x_j - x_{\bar{j}})^2/x_j x_{\bar{j}}$$
$$= (x_j + x_{\bar{j}})^2/x_j x_{\bar{j}} - 4x_j x_{\bar{j}}/x_j x_{\bar{j}},$$
$$Q_j = 1/x_j x_{\bar{j}} - 4.$$

Q_j is defined to be the expression

$$[ijk]^2/[ij][jk][ik]$$

and j is the middle item. Since $x_j + x_{\bar{j}} = 1$, these two unknowns are the two roots of the equation

$$t^2 - t + \frac{1}{Q_j + 4} = 0. \tag{15}$$

Compare this result with that of Section 5.3 of Chapter 2, where the same equation leads to the values of the two-class frequencies. There, of course, all the "x_j" are the same, since there are only two types of respondents, and there is no need to specify which is the middle item of the three.

When x_j is known (the sign of $[ijk]$ will tell us whether the larger or smaller of the roots of Equation (15) is x_j) then δ_j is found by using Equation (8):

$$(\delta_j)^2 = [ij][jk]/[ik]x_j x_{\bar{j}}. \tag{16}$$

EXERCISE. Show that $(\delta_j)^2 = 4[ij][jk]/[ik] + [ijk]^2/[ik]^2$.

Next, b_j can be found, since $p_j = b_j - \delta_j x_j$, and, of course, $a_i = b_i - \delta_i$. Since the derivation above will work as long as two items can be found which bracket item j, j could be any item from 2 to $n - 1$; the latent parameters of items 1 and n, the two extreme items, could not be calculated in that way. Let us now suppose that x_j, a_j, and b_j are known, for $j = 2, \ldots, n - 1$, and see whether the parameters of the extreme items can be found.

We know that:

(i) $p_1 = b_1 - x_1 \delta_1$;
(ii) $p_n = b_n - x_n \delta_n = a_n + x_{\bar{n}} \delta_n$;
(iii) $[1n] = \delta_1 \delta_n x_1 x_{\bar{n}}$;
(iv) $[1j] = \delta_1 \delta_j x_1 x_{\bar{j}}, \quad 1 < j < n$;
(v) $[jn] = \delta_j \delta_n x_j x_{\bar{n}}, \quad 1 < j < n$.

(iv) and (v) allow us to solve for the products $\delta_1 x_1$ and $\delta_n x_{\bar{n}}$:

$$\delta_1 x_1 = [1j]/x_{\bar{j}} \delta_j;$$

and

$$\delta_n x_{\bar{n}} = [jn]/x_j \delta_j.$$

Therefore, using (i) and (ii), b_1 and a_n can be determined.

$$b_1 = p_1 + [1j]/x_{\bar{j}} \delta_j;$$

and

$$a_n = p_n - [jn]/x_j \delta_j;$$

where j is any item between 1 and n.

It is impossible to solve for x_1, x_n, a_1, or b_n. The reason for this is that any manifest probabilities involving item n will contain the factor $x_{\bar{n}} \delta_n$, since n is the last item; and if they involve item 1, the factor $x_1 \delta_1$ will always appear. The two parameters, i.e., x_1 and δ_1 cannot be separated.

Thus there is a fundamental indeterminacy of the model: we are only able to determine the products $x_1 \delta_1$ and $x_{\bar{n}} \delta_n$. There are some inequalities which will limit the range of possible values of these four parameters, however. By definition (Equation (2)),

$$0 \leq x_1 \leq x_2 \leq \cdots \leq x_{n-1} \leq x_n \leq 1.$$

When x_2 and x_{n-1} are known, the values of x_1 and x_n are restricted, and thus δ_1 and δ_n are also restricted. Also, since a_n and b_1 are known, other restrictions exist:

$$b_n = a_n + \delta_n \leq 1, \qquad \text{so } \delta_n \leq 1 - a_n;$$
$$a_1 = b_1 - \delta_1 \geq 0, \qquad \text{so } \delta_1 \leq b_1.$$

A lower bound for δ_1 can be obtained as well:

$$0 \leq x_1 \leq x_2,$$
$$\delta_1 \leq b_1,$$

and

$$\delta_1 x_1 = b_1 - p_1,$$

implies that

$$\delta_1 = (b_1 - p_1)/x_1 \geq (b_1 - p_1)/x_2.$$

Therefore,

$$(b_1 - p_1)/x_2 \leq \delta_1 \leq b_1. \tag{17}$$

The lower bound on x can be improved, since

$$\delta_1 \leq b_1 \Rightarrow$$
$$\delta_1 x_1 \leq b_1 x_1 \Rightarrow$$
$$b_1 - p_1 \leq b_1 x_1 \Rightarrow$$
$$x_1 \geq (b_1 - p_1)/b_1.$$

We know, therefore, that:

$$(b_1 - p_1)/b_1 \leq x_1 \leq x_2. \tag{18}$$

Similarly, for item n we find that:

$$(p_n - a_n)/(1 - x_{n-1}) \leq \delta_n \leq 1 - a_n, \tag{19}$$

and

$$x_{n-1} \leq x_n \leq (1 - p_n)/(1 - a_n). \tag{20}$$

If there are many items, the indeterminacy of these parameters would bother us less: we might even choose to construct a scale using only the intermediate items, whose characteristic parameters would all be known. In practical terms, this result also lends some support to the practice of including two very extreme items in a scale, one which nearly everyone is expected to agree with, and one which nearly everyone is expected to reject. We would arbitrarily set x_1 as small as possible, and x_n as large as possible, given the inequalities above. These items help to fix the scale, which is, actually, constructed using the less extreme, more informative, items.

In this section, we have assumed that the ordering of the items is known *a priori*, ignoring the problem of distinguishing the two items at either end of the scale. In Section 2.4, we shall discuss inferring the proper ordering of the items. First, however, we shall look at a hypothetical example, in order to illustrate the results of this analysis.

Example. Suppose that there are five items which satisfy the assumptions of the latent distance model, set out in Section 2.1, and whose latent parameters are as given in Table 4.

TABLE 4

Latent Parameters of 5 Items

Item	1	2	3	4	5
x	0.1	0.2	0.5	0.7	0.9
a	0.1	0.2	0.1	0.1	0.2
b	0.9	0.8	0.7	0.8	0.9
$\delta = b - a$	0.8	0.6	0.6	0.7	0.7

We have foregone our original description of the latent structure in terms of the "class sizes" $v^0, v^1, \ldots, v^6$, but these can always be calculated from the x_j, if desired. In the example, $v^0 = x_1 = 0.1$, $v^1 = x_2 - x_1 = 0.1$, etc.

Manifest probabilities can be calculated according to the accounting equations of Section 2.2. For instance,

$$p_1 = (0.1)(0.1) + (0.9)(0.9) = 0.82,$$
$$p_2 = (0.2)(0.2) + (0.8)(0.8) = 0.68,$$
$$p_{12} = (0.1)(0.1)(0.2) + (0.2 - 0.1)(0.9)(0.2) + (0.8)(0.9)(0.8),$$
$$= 0.002 + 0.018 + 0.576 = 0.596.$$

The cross product is, therefore, equal to

$$p_{12} - p_1 p_2 = 0.596 - 0.5576 = 0.0384.$$

We can check this calculation by comparing it with Equation (7), which implies that

$$[12] = \delta_1 \delta_2 x_1 x_{\bar{2}} = (0.8)(0.6)(0.1)(0.8) = 0.0384.$$

The manifest probabilities of first- and second-order are given in Table 5, and the matrix of cross products in Table 6. The third-order symmetric parameters have also been computed and are set out in Table 7.

TABLE 5

First and Second Order
Manifest Probabilities Generated From
Model of Table 4

Item	1	2	3	4	5
0 (marginals)	0.82	0.68	0.40	0.31	0.27
1	—	0.596	0.352	0.271	0.227
2		—	0.308	0.236	0.192
3			—	0.187	0.129
4				—	0.118

TABLE 6

Matrix of Cross Products for the Model of Table 4

Item	1	2	3	4	5
1	—	0.0384	0.0240	0.0168	0.0056
2		—	0.0360	0.0252	0.0084
3			—	0.0630	0.0210
4				—	0.0343
5					—

TABLE 7

Third-Order Symmetric Parameters for the Model of Table 4

[123] = −0.008640	[124] = −0.006048	[125] = −0.002016
[134] = 0	[135] = 0 [234] = 0	[235] = 0
[145] = 0.001568	[245] = 0.002352	[345] = 0.005880

Notice, again, how the entries in the cross product matrix satisfy the conditions described in Section 2.3. 2 × 2 determinants that are entirely on one side of the main diagonal are equal to zero. Notice, also, how the cross products are highest between adjacent items, dropping off as we move away from the main diagonal in either direction. This is not an absolute requirement of the latent distance model as we have formulated it, but is a situation that often occurs in scale analysis for the following reasons: The cross product equals

$$\delta_i \delta_j x_i x_{\bar{j}} = (\delta_i x_i)(\delta_j x_{\bar{j}}), \qquad \text{if } i < j.$$

If we take i as fixed, and let j increase, what happens to the value of $[ij]$? We know that x_j increases, so $x_{\bar{j}} = 1 - x_j$ must decrease. If the values of δ_j increased, the product $\delta_j x_{\bar{j}}$ might not decrease; but when the values of δ_j are of about the same size, as in this example, the decreasing value of $x_{\bar{j}}$ will cause the cross products $[ij]$ to decrease as well, as we move away from the diagonal.

Taking the information in Tables 6 and 7, we may calculate x_j, δ_j, a_j, and b_j for $j = 2, 3, 4$, and also b_1 and a_5. We shall apply the equations of the previous section to calculate the parameters for item 2, and leave the rest as an exercise for the reader. Using [123], [12], [13], and [23], we calculate

$$Q_2 = [123]^2/[12][23][13] = (0.00864)^2/(0.0384)(0.0240)(0.0360)$$
$$= 2.25.$$

x_2 and $1 - x_2$ are the roots of

$$t^2 - t + \frac{1}{Q_2 + 4} = 0,$$

$$t^2 - t + 1/6.25 = t^2 - t + 0.16 = (t - 0.8)(t - 0.2).$$

Since [123] was negative, x_2 must be the smaller root, 0.2.

Next, δ_2 is the square root of $[12][23]/[13]x_2 x_{\bar{2}}$, which is

$$(0.0384)(0.0360)/(0.024)(0.16) = (0.24)(1.5) = 0.36.$$

Therefore,

$$\delta_2 = b_2 - a_2 = 0.6.$$

Finally, $b_2 = p_2 + x_2 \delta_2 = 0.68 + (0.2)(0.6) = 0.8$.
    Using these figures, we find that

$$\delta_1 x_1 = [12]/x_{\bar{2}} \delta_2 = 0.0384/0.48 = 0.08,$$

and

$$\delta_5 x_{\bar{5}} = [25]/x_2 \delta_2 = 0.0084/0.12 = 0.07$$

but, as noted above, there is no way to obtain the true values of x_1, x_5, δ_1, and δ_5. We can get b_1 and a_5,

$$b_1 = p_1 + \delta_1 x_1 = 0.82 + 0.08 = 0.9,$$
$$a_5 = p_5 - \delta_5 x_{\bar{5}} = 0.27 - 0.07 = 0.2.$$

The inequalities (17)–(20) imposed on the indeterminate parameters are:

$$0.4 < \delta_1 < 0.9;$$
$$0.08/0.9 = 0.089 \leq x_1 \leq 0.2;$$
$$0.07/0.3 = 0.233 \leq \delta_5 \leq 0.8$$
$$0.7 \leq x_5 \leq 0.73/0.8 = 0.91.$$

2.4 Ordering the Items

The solution of the accounting equations discussed in the previous section depended on knowledge of the correct order of the items. We pointed out in Section 2.2 that the ordering of the items 3 through $n - 2$ could be determined unambiguously by examining the cross product matrix, while the order of the two items at either end of the item list could not be determined. The "vanishing determinant" criterion cannot distinguish whether (1, 2) or (2, 1) is the correct ordering; or whether $(n - 1, n)$ or $(n, n - 1)$ is correct.

It turns out that this indeterminancy cannot be avoided without making some restrictions on the general latent distance model, unless the latent structure has some very particular characteristics.

Suppose, then, that the method of the previous section has given us all the latent parameters associated with items 3 through $n - 2$, their order having been determined by examination of the cross products. Items 1 and 2 are in an arbitrary order. This means that when the solution involving $[123]^2/[12][13][23]$ is carried out, we do obtain an x value, that of the second item in the correct ordering, but we do not know whether this is item 1 or item 2. (The arguments that follow apply, *mutatis mutandi*, to items $n - 1$ and n.) Call this value x_*.

Since we know that both items 1 and 2 precede item 3, for instance, we know that

$$[13] = x_1 x_3 \delta_1 \delta_3 \quad \text{and} \quad [23] = x_2 x_3 \delta_2 \delta_3,$$

so that the products $x_1 \delta_1$ and $x_2 \delta_2$ can be calculated. This tells us that b_1 and b_2 can be found:

$$b_1 = p_1 + x_1 \delta_1 = p_1 + [13]/x_3 \delta_3,$$

and

$$b_2 = p_2 + [23]/x_3 \delta_3.$$

We have a number, x_*, which is equal to either x_1 or x_2. One might think that the cross product [12] of the two items would provide some additional information, but this is not the case. Let "e" stand for the "extreme" item. Then

$$[12] = x_e(1 - x_*)\delta_1 \delta_2 = x_e x_* \delta_1 \delta_2 / x_* - x_e x_* \delta_1 \delta_2$$
$$= x_1 \delta_1 x_2 \delta_2 / x_* - x_1 \delta_1 x_2 \delta_2.$$

Since we already know what the products $x_i \delta_i$ are, this equation merely serves as a check on the computation of x_*. Alternatively, we could use it to solve for

x_*, rather than using the third-order information and having to solve a quadratic equation.

The information that can be obtained about the latent parameters of items 1 and 2 is, therefore, not much more than is known about the extreme item when the correct order is known: b_1, b_2, $x_1\delta_1$, and $x_2\delta_2$, plus x_*, the larger of the two unknown x's. Of course, for the last two items, the values of: a_{n-1}, a_n, $x_n - \delta_n$, $x_{n-1}\delta_n$, and x_{**}, the smaller of x_{n-1} and x_n can be calculated.

These results suggest the kind of approximations and restrictions that might be made to the model. For instance, we might suppose that $x_1 = x_2$ and $x_{n-1} = x_n$, and compute the remaining parameters on the basis of this assumption. If n is large, so that the average distance between adjacent x_i is relatively small anyway, or if x_* is very small (and x_{**} very large), the error introduced in this way would be fairly small.

Another choice is to assume that $a_1 = a_2 = a$, say. Then we have:

$$(b_1 - a)x_1 = b_1 - p_1 \quad \text{and} \quad (b_2 - a)x_2 = b_2 - p_2.$$

If $x_1 = x_*$, then $a = b_1 - (b_1 - p_1)/x_*$,

and $\qquad x_2 = (b_2 - p_2)x_*/[(b_2 - b_1)x_* + (b_1 - p_1)].$

If x_2 turns out to be *larger* than x_*, then we have made the wrong choice, for by definition, x_* is the larger of x_1 and x_2. If this contradiction arises, we then try $x_2 = x_*$, when $a = b_2 - (b_2 - p_2)/x_*$ and

$$x_1 = (b_1 - p_1)x_*/[b_1 - b_2)x_* + (b_2 - p_2)].$$

If only one choice (x_* equal to x_1 or x_2) does not lead to a contradiction, then we could use that ordering and the derived values of the latent parameters. If both lead to contradictions, it means that the assumption of equal a's is untenable. If neither leads to a contradiction, we are back where we started, and would be left with an arbitrary decision which would have to be made on the basis of the content of the items. (At the other end of the item list, we would set $b_1 = b_2$, of course, and apply the same kind of analysis.)

Take, as an example, the latent structure discussed in Section 2.3. There $b_1 = 0.9$, $b_2 = 0.8$, and $x_* = 0.2$. The marginals are $p_1 = 0.82$ and $p_2 = 0.68$. If we set $a_1 = a_2$, and try $x_1 = x_*$, we find that:

$$a = 0.9 - 0.08/0.2 = 0.9 - 0.4 = 0.5,$$
and
$$x_2 = (0.12)(0.2)/[-0.02 + 0.08] = 0.2(0.12/0.06) = 0.4.$$

This is impossible, since by setting $x_1 = x_*$ we assumed that item 2 was the extreme item.

Next, we try setting $x_2 = x_*$. This implies that:

$$a = 0.8 - 0.12/0.2 = 0.8 - 0.6 = 0.2,$$
$$x_1 = (0.108)(0.2)/[0.02 + 0.12] = 0.2(0.08/0.14) = 0.114,$$

and this is acceptable. Thus if we made this choice, we would have discovered the correct order, $x_1 < x_2$, and the x_1 is only 0.014 away from its true value (0.1). Of course, the true difference between a_1 and a_2 is not very large in this case ($a_2 = 0.2$ and $a_1 = 0.1$); if it had been larger, this approximation might not turn out to be so reasonable.

On the other hand, if we assume that $x_1 = x_2 = x_* = 0.2$ in this example, we find that

$$a_1 = b_1 - (b_1 - p_1)/x_* = 0.9 - 0.08/0.2 = 0.5,$$

and

$$a_2 = 0.8 - 0.12/0.2 = 0.2.$$

The a_1 of 0.5 is quite a way from the true value of 0.1. We can not really expect to obtain nearly correct values of these indeterminate parameters when we are forced to make assumptions that are arbitrary, since the statistical data provide no information. It is always a good idea to include in the item list items which we are sure *a priori*, on the basis of their content, will serve as "anchors" for the scale. This will, at least, remove the problem of deciding which items should be first and nth in the ordering, although it will leave open the problem of not being able to determine a_1, x_1, b_n, and x_n.

2.5 *Using the Model to Score Respondents*

We should remember that one purpose of a latent structure analysis is to score, classify, or otherwise discriminate among the respondents to the items. We concentrate on the item parameters (usually) not because we are overly interested in *their* structure *per se*, but because we have to know the values of the item parameters in order to combine them properly in constructing a scale or typology.

We can treat the latent distance model just like any other latent class model, and compute the probability that a respondent with response pattern s actually belonged to each class. Here, of course, there are $n + 1$ classes, of size $v_0, v_1, \ldots, v_n$. If all of the latent parameters have been estimated, the recruitment probability has the same form as in the ordinary class models, Prob(Class i given response s) equals

$$P(i|s) = p_s^i v^i / p_s.$$

Because of the structure of this model, we know that:

$$p_s^i = \left(\prod_{j=1}^{n-i} a_j^{z_j} (1 - a_j)^{1-z_j}\right)\left(\prod_{k=n-i+1}^{n} b_k^{z_k} (1 - b_k)^{1-z_k}\right),$$

where z_j equals 1 if the response to item j is $+$, and 0 if the response to item j is $-$. (This simply specifies whether the probability of positive response, a_j or b_j, or the probability of negative response $1 - a_j$ or $1 - b_j$, should be included in the product.) p_s, of course, is the sum $\sum_i v^i p_s^i$.

The $n + 1$ values of $P(i|s)$ tell us which class a respondent probably came from, without utilizing the order implicit in the model. For example, when we think of the classes as ordered, we naturally say that someone in class i ranks higher than everyone in the classes $v^0, v^1, \ldots, v^{i-1}$. In other words, that he ranks higher than x_i of the population. We can, therefore, characterize this individual by the number x_i, which has many of the properties of what is usually called a scale value.

The probability of being in class i is set equal to the probability of having the scale value x_i. As such, we can properly ask for the average or expected scale value, given the response s. With

$$P(i|s) = P(x_i|s),$$

then the average value of x, given response s, is

$$\bar{x}(s) = \sum_{i=0}^{n} x_i P(x_i|s).$$

$\bar{x}$, being an average, will probably lie between two values of x_i. Thus, it cannot be referred to as the average *class* of that respondent, but must be considered in terms of the entire range from zero to one: on the average, a respondent giving response pattern s will rank higher than $\bar{x}(s)$ of the population. There being 2^n response patterns, the model thus generates a unidimensional scale that has 2^n points on it. They need not all be different[1] but the numbers $\bar{x}(s)$ can certainly be manipulated as though they were continuous-valued variables, even when there are as few as 7 or 8 items.

In what precedes, we assumed that someone in class 0 had scale value x_0, someone in class 1 had value x_1, and so on. Once we accept the idea that there is actually a continuous number of scale values between 0 and 1, we would probably assume that the person in class i not only exceeds the individuals in the lower classes, but also exceeds half of the individuals in "his" class. Then we would consider class 0 as being centered about the scale value $v^0/2$; class 1 as being centered about the point $x_1 + v^1/2$, and so on. The equation for $\bar{x}(s)$ then becomes:[2]

$$\bar{x}^*(s) = \sum_{i=1}^{n} x_i P(x_i|s) + \sum_{i=0}^{n} v^i P(x_i|s)/2.$$

If, as suggested in previous sections, the extreme items 1 and n were left out of this part of the analysis, since the latent parameters of these items cannot be identified, the arguments would remain the same. The interior $n - 2$ items would appear in a response pattern s; there would be $n - 1$ ordered classes; and there would be 2^{n-2} possible scale values.

---

[1]The Guttman perfect scale, with all $a_i = 0$ and all $b_i = 1$, leads to only $n + 1$ possible values for the ranking.

[2]Exercise. Show that $\bar{x}^*(s) = \sum_{i=0}^{n} p_s^i (x_{i+1}^2 - x_i^2)/2$. Remember the convention that $x_0 = 0$ and $x_{n+1} = 1$.

2.6 *A Special Case*

Because of the wide use of Guttman scale analysis in empirical work, we present a simpler model that more nearly approximates the "perfect scale" model. This model is identical to that discussed above, but with the restriction:

$$a_i = 1 - b_i$$

for all items. It is discussed in Hays and Borgatta (1954).

The parameter a_i would usually be interpreted as "error" or "noise" present in an otherwise perfect threshold model: the probability that someone below threshold will give a positive response is the same as the probability that someone who is above threshold will give a negative response. If the "noise" were considered to be something external to the actual item list, we might even want to let all the a_i be the same. This single parameter, a, would be a meaningful measure of the departure of the scale from the perfect scale assumptions.

The modifications of the accounting equations are easily made.

$$\delta = 1 - 2a,$$
$$2a = (1 - \delta)/2.$$

δ_i, which is now equal to $1 - 2a_i$, can be considered as the basic parameter and no change need be made in the equations for $[ij]$ and $[ijk]$.

Only the marginal is affected:

$$p_i = b_i - \delta_i x_i$$

becomes

$$p_i = (1 + \delta_i)/2 - x_i \delta_i.$$

Third-order information is not needed to determine the parameters. If item j lies between items i and k in the correct ordering, then:

$$[ij][jk]/[ik] = \delta_j^2 x_j(1 - x_j)$$
$$= (\delta_j x_j)(\delta_j - \delta_j x_j).$$

From the equation for p_j, however, we have:

$$\delta_j x_j = 1/2 + \delta_j/2 - p_j. \tag{21}$$

This implies that:

$$[ij][jk]/[ik] = (1/2 + \delta_j/2 - p_j)(p_j - 1/2 + \delta_j/2)$$
$$= (\delta_j)^2/4 - (p_j - 1/2)^2. \tag{22}$$

Since δ_j has to be positive, it is equal to the positive square root of

$$4([ij][jk]/[ik] + (p_j - 1/2)^2), \qquad i < j < k.$$

The value of x_j follows immediately from the equation for p_j.

All the parameters in this restricted model are identifiable. Consider item 1, for instance, when the parameters of all the intermediate items have been determined. We would find that:

$$\delta_1 x_1 = [1j]/\delta_j(1 - x_j), \qquad 2 \leq j \leq n - 1,$$

and, therefore,

$$\delta_1 = 2(p_1 + [1j]/\delta_j(1 - x_j)) - 1,$$

for any choice of j between 2 and $n - 1$. Similarly, the two parameters of item n can be calculated.

If we assumed that all the a_i were equal to a, then the marginals p_j would tell us the correct ordering of the items, since $p_i < p_j$ if and only if $x_i > x_j$. $\delta = 1 - 2a$ could be obtained by the above method, for any choice of intermediate item j, and then all of the x values would be derived from the marginals.

In this special case, we can easily handle the problem of estimating parameters using real data. There is one parameter to be determined by the cross product matrix, and so we can try to choose δ in order to get the best fit of that matrix of cross products. The x_i are removed by the relations:

$$x_i = ((1 + \delta)/2 - p_i)/\delta,$$
$$1 - x_i = ((\delta - 1)/2 + p_i)/\delta.$$

Therefore, when $i < j$, $[ij]$ can be written in terms of the single unknown:

$$[ij] = \delta^2 x_i(1 - x_j) = (\delta/2 - p_i + 1/2)(\delta/2 + p_j - 1/2)$$
$$= (\delta)^2/4 - (\delta/2)(p_i - p_j) - (p_i - 1/2)(p_j - 1/2).$$

It is not hard to find the value of δ which will minimize the total squared deviation, i.e.,

$$\sum_{i<j} \sum ([ij] - [ij]^*)^2,$$

where $[ij]^*$ is the function of δ expressed in the preceding equation and $[ij]$ is the actual sample value. To do this, we differentiate the sum of squares with respect to δ, set the result equal to 0 and solve for δ. There will be a cubic equation in δ; if there is more than a single positive root lying between 0 and 1 it would not be too difficult to ascertain which value actually provides the best fit. If no roots lie between 0 and 1, it would indicate that the model is not appropriate or that some items should be eliminated from the scale.

The actual equation for the "least squares" δ is:

$$\sum_{i<j} \sum ([ij] - \delta^2/4 + (\delta/2)(p_i - p_j)$$
$$+ (p_i - 1/2)(p_j - 1/2))(-\delta/2 + (p_i - p_j)/2) = 0.$$

Collecting terms, we have

$$n(n - 1)\delta^3/16 - (\delta^2/8) \sum_{i<j} \sum (p_i - p_j)$$
$$+ (\delta/8) \sum_{i<j} \sum (2(p_i - p_j)^2 - 4[ij] - 4(1/2 - p_i)(1/2 - p_j))$$
$$+ \sum_{i<j} \sum (p_i - p_j)([ij] + (1/2 - p_i)(1/2 - p_j))/2 = 0.$$

Keep in mind that the summations are over $n(n-1)/2$ possible arrangements with i preceding j.

The δ_i could also be estimated by least squares under the general condition that they are not all equal. Using Equation (21) to eliminate the x_i from the expressions for the cross products, we find that:

$$[ij] = (\delta_i x_i)(\delta_j - \delta_j x_j)$$
$$= (\delta_i/2 - p_i + 1/2)(\delta_j/2 + p_j - 1/2). \tag{23}$$

The least squares fitting procedure requires differentiating with respect to each of the unknowns, δ_i, in turn, and solving the resulting equations. While this can be done, using iterative methods similar to those discussed in Chapter 4 when we derived maximum likelihood estimates for the latent class model, it is not practical to go into the details here.

A simple fitting scheme can be obtained from Equation (21). Since, for any three items where $i < j < k$,

$$\delta_j^2 = 4([ij][jk]/[ik] + (p_j - 1/2)^2),$$

we suggest averaging the values obtained by different choices of i and k. Since there are $j-1$ items preceding j, and $n-j$ following j, there would be $(j-1)(n-j)$ different values to be averaged. There are, of course, many ways of averaging these data. For instance:

(i) Take the square roots, and take an arithmetic mean of the estimates of δ_j.
(ii) Take the arithmetic mean of the estimates of δ_j^2, then take the square root.
(iii) Take the geometric mean of the estimates of δ_j. (The tth root of the products of the t estimates.)

While we have not made systematic comparisons of the results of different averaging procedures, the geometric mean seems the most plausible, for errors in the estimates of δ_j or of δ_j^2 are not likely to be additive. The special case of $p_j = 1/2$ illustrates this point, for then the estimates of δ_j^2 are products: $4[ij][jk]/[ik]$; and the error would appear to be multiplicative. The final estimate of δ_j would be twice the $2(j-1)(n-j)$th root of the product, over all i less than j and all k greater than j, of

$$([ij]^{n-j}[jk]^{j-1}/[ik]).$$

3. An Application of the Latent Distance Model

The results of the analysis of the data presented below were discussed by Stouffer and Toby (1951) in their interesting comparison of Guttman scale analysis and latent distance analysis.[3] The details of the analysis of the data were not included in that article, however.

216 subjects were asked to respond to the following four items, which were designed to measure behavior in a situation of role conflict.

---

[3]Reprinted in part in Riley, M. W. *Sociological Research: A Case Approach*, New York: Harcourt, Brace and World, 1963.

1. Your close friend is riding in a car which you are driving, and you hit a pedestrian. He knows that you are going at least 35 miles an hour in a 20-mile an hour zone. There are no other witnesses. Your lawyer says that if your friend testifies under oath that the speed was only 20 miles an hour it may save you from serious consequences. What right have you to expect him to protect you?
Positive response: I have no right as a friend to expect him to testify to the lower figure.

2. Your close friend is a doctor for an insurance company. He examines you when you need insurance. He finds that you are in pretty good shape but he is doubtful on one or two minor points which are difficult to diagnose. What right do you have to expect him to shade the doubts in your favor?
Positive response: I have no right as a friend to expect him to shade the doubts in my favor.

3. Your close friend is a New York drama critic. You have sunk all your savings in a new Broadway play. He really thinks the play is no good. What right do you have to expect him to go easy on your play in his review?
Positive response: I have no right as a friend to expect him to do this.

4. Your close friend has just come from a secret meeting of the board of directors of a company. You will be ruined unless you can get out of the market before the board's decision becomes known. He happens to be having dinner at your house this same evening. What right do you have to expect him to tip you off?
Positive response: I have no right as a friend to expect him to tip me off.

The complete response pattern frequencies are given in our Table 10 below. The manifest probabilities of positive response are given in Table 8.

TABLE 8

Relative Frequencies of Positive Response
Role Conflict Example

First- and Second-Order Proportions

Item	1	2	3	4
0	0.7917	0.5000	0.5139	0.3102 (marginals)
1		0.4444	0.4398	0.2824
2			0.3241	0.2315
3				0.2361

Third- and Fourth-Order Proportions

p_{123}	p_{124}	p_{134}	p_{234}	p_{1234}
0.3009	0.2222	0.2222	0.1991	0.1944

The cross products and third order symmetric parameters were computed and are given in Table 9.

TABLE 9

Symmetric Parameters for Role Conflict Example

Item	Cross Products				Third Order Parameters
	1	2	3	4	
1	—	0.0486	0.0330	0.0368	[123] = 0.00289
2	0.0486	—	0.0671	0.0764	[124] = 0.00547
3	0.0330	0.0671	—	0.0767	[134] = 0.006136
4	0.0368	0.0764	0.0767	—	[234] = 0.02094

In order to estimate the values of the parameters x_2 and x_3 we refer back to Equation (15): x_j and $1 - x_j$ are the two roots of

$$t^2 - t + \frac{1}{Q_j + 4} = 0$$

where

$$Q_j = [ijk]^2/[ij][ik][jk]$$

and j is between items i and k. Working with actual data, we note that Q_2 may be computed in two ways, e.g., by considering items 1, 2, and 3, or items 1, 2, and 4. To take into account the sampling variation, therefore, we shall take the average of these two values; similarly in the case of estimating Q_3.

Thus we compute the estimate of Q_2:

$$\bar{Q}_2 = ([123]^2/[12][23][13] + [124]^2/[12][24][14])/2$$
$$= 0.1483.$$

The roots of
$$t^2 - t + 1/4 .1483 = 0$$

are 0.6 and 0.4 and therefore our estimate of x_2 is:

$$x_2 = 0.60.$$

In the case of item 3, the average Q_3 is:

$$\bar{Q}_3 = \tfrac{1}{2}([134]^2/[13][34][14] + [234]^2/[23][34][24])$$
$$= 0.7546$$

The roots of
$$t^2 - t + 1/4 .7546 = 0$$

are 0.7 and 0.3, leading to the estimate:

$$x_3 = 0.70.$$

With estimates of x_2 and x_3 in hand we turn to Equation (8) in order to estimate δ_2 and δ_3:

$$\delta_j^2 = [ij][jk]/[ik]x_j(1 - x_j), \text{ where } i < j < k.$$

Again, however, we see that in each case there are two possible combinations of items that can be used to estimate each parameter. We choose to average the squares before taking square roots, as indicated in the following equations. For item 2:

$$\delta_2^2 = \tfrac{1}{2}([12][23]/[13] + [12][24]/[14])/x_2(1 - x_2),$$

leading to

$$\delta_2 = 0.65.$$

For item 3:

$$\delta_3^2 = \tfrac{1}{2}([13][34]/[14] + [23][34]/[24])/x_3(1 - x_3)$$

giving the estimate

$$\delta_3 = 0.57.$$

Finally, by using Equation (3A),

$$b_j = p_j + x_j\delta_j,$$

we estimate b_2 and b_3. Substituting the marginal proportions and the previously estimated parameters, we find that

$$b_2 = 0.89 \quad \text{and} \quad a_2 = b_2 - \delta_2 = 0.24$$

and

$$b_3 = 0.91 \quad \text{and} \quad a_3 = b_3 - \delta_3 = 0.34$$

The parameters of the extreme items, 1 and 4, cannot be exactly determined in the general model, as we have pointed out above. In this example, the restricted model in which $b_1 = 1 - a_1$ and $b_4 = 1 - a_4$ was chosen. The estimating equations are:

$$b_1 = p_1 + \tfrac{1}{2}([12]/(1 - x_2)\delta_2 + [13]/(1 - x_3)\delta_3);$$
$$x_1 = (b_1 - p_1)/(2b_1 - 1);$$
$$a_4 = p_4 - \tfrac{1}{2}([24]/x_2\delta_2 + [34]/x_3\delta_3);$$
$$x_4 = (b_4 - p_4)/(1 - 2a_4).$$

The estimates are:

$$b_1 = 0.98, a_1 = 0.02, x_1 = 0.20$$
$$b_4 = 0.88, a_4 = 0.12, x_4 = 0.75$$

The estimated latent parameters are therefore:

	\multicolumn{4}{c}{Item}			
	1	2	3	4
a	0.02	0.24	0.34	0.12
b	0.98	0.89	0.91	0.88
x	0.20	0.60	0.70	0.75

There is more variation, from one item to another, in the low probabilities a_i than in the high probabilities b_i. The latter are all close to 0.9. The most convenient way of displaying these results is by a graph, as in Figure 1. In this presentation the population is assumed to be uniformly distributed along the x-axis, and the points $x_i(i = 1, 2, 3, 4)$ are the *cutting points* between those who

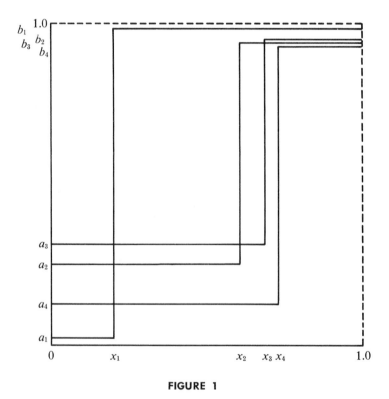

FIGURE 1

Tracelines of Four Items, Role Conflict Example

have the low probability and those who have the high probability of a positive response to item i. The step functions, which we call *tracelines*, specify what the

146

latent probability of a positive response to an item is, at every point along the latent scale which runs from 0 to 1. When the latent distance model is interpreted in this way it becomes the simplest type of model involving a continuous latent variable, x. We study these models in Chapters 6 and 7.

In this example those at the low end of the scale are dominated by *particularistic* values (friendship), and those at the high end by *universalistic* values. The major contrast among the items involves item 1: 80% of the population have the high probability of agreeing that a friend has no right to expect help in the case of the automobile accident. On the other three items a majority has the lower probability of responding positively.

Table 10 provides us with (1) the pattern of recruitment from the five latent classes for each response pattern; (2) the fit between the actual data and the

TABLE 10

Analysis of Latent Distance Structure

Response Pattern Item	Proportion of Each Pattern in Each Latent Class: P(class | s) Latent Classes					Average Scale Value	Fitted Total	Actual Total
1 2 3 4	0	1	2	3	4	$\bar{x}_s^*$	216 p_s	n_s
+ + + +	—	0.020	0.019	0.025	0.935	0.86	40.3	42
+ + − +	0.002	0.231	0.215	0.015	0.537	0.70	7.0	6
+ − + +	0.003	0.348	0.013	0.017	0.619	0.70	7.5	6
+ + + −	0.003	0.249	0.230	0.308	0.210	0.66	24.4	23
− + + +	0.335	0.013	0.013	0.077	0.622	0.60	1.2	1
+ + − −	0.005	0.489	0.454	0.031	0.021	0.53	24.1	25
+ − + −	0.009	0.841	0.081	0.041	0.028	0.44	22.9	24
+ − − +	0.090	0.816	0.029	0.002	0.073	0.42	6.3	7
+ − − −	0.010	0.952	0.034	0.002	0.002	0.41	39.3	38
− + − +	0.851	0.035	0.032	0.002	0.080	0.19	1.0	1
− + + −	0.859	0.035	0.032	0.044	0.030	0.18	2.5	4
− − + +	0.895	0.037	0.001	0.002	0.065	0.16	1.5	2
− + − −	0.923	0.038	0.035	0.002	0.002	0.13	6.4	6
− − − +	0.956	0.039	0.001	—	0.004	0.12	2.7	2
− − + −	0.957	0.039	0.001	0.002	0.001	0.11	10.1	9
− − − −	0.960	0.039	0.001	—	—	0.11	19.5	20

probabilities computed from the estimated latent probabilities; (3) average scale values, $\bar{x}_s^*$ for each response pattern. The response patterns have been ordered with respect to the values $\bar{x}_s^*$, which were computed according to the definitions in Section 2.5. Notice that we took as the locations of the five classes 0.10, 0.40, 0.65, 0.675, and 0.825, the midpoints of the five intervals formed by the cutting points x_i. Notice that the ranking inferred as a result of the latent structure analysis does not correspond exactly to what we would have if we simply used the number of "+" responses as our scale: the pattern $(+ - - -)$, with an average scale value of 0.41 falls near the middle, while three of the patterns containing two positive responses are near the lower end of the scale.

Concerning the fit of the model to these data, we computed the chi-square statistic, i.e.,

$$\chi^2 = \sum_s (216p_s - n_s)^2 / 216p_s$$

where s ranges over the 16 response patterns, and the p_s are the manifest probabilities computed from the estimates of the latent parameters. The value was found to be 1.24. The degrees of freedom appropriate to a test of goodness of fit equal the number of response patterns minus one minus the number of estimated parameters. There are four x-parameters; two probabilities for each of items 2 and 3; and one probability for each of items 1 and 4 (remember we assumed that $a_1 = 1 - b_1$ and $a_4 = 1 - b_4$); 10 in all. Thus there are 5 degrees of freedom. The value 1.24 is obviously not significant. Of course it is somewhat questionable to use chi-square test here, for we did not estimate the parameters so as to minimize the value of chi-square. But, since such an estimate would only *improve* the fit, it is quite reasonable to agree that the model adequately accounts for the observed data.

4. Located Classes

The latent distance model of the previous section is one attempt to formalize mathematically the idea of ordered classes. We emphasized in that discussion the existence of an ordering of the items, and only at the very end did we suggest that individuals might be considered to be distributed along a continuum, or one-dimensional scale.

In this section, we begin by postulating the existence of such a scale, and go on to discuss how this assumption can be used within the framework of the latent class model.

Suppose that there exist m latent classes, defined exactly as in Chapter 3. In addition, suppose that there exists a one-dimensional scale, or *latent continuum*, and that each class is located at some point on this scale. Define x_α to be the location of class α.[4]

The notion of a "located class" is not in itself contradictory even though we usually think of discrete classes and continuous scales as alternative, not complementary hypotheses about the structure of a population. For example, a theory of social class might assert that discrete ordered classes actually exist, and at the same time seek to formalize the concept of *distance* between these classes. Order and distance are the two properties which are usually associated with the term "scale" and which are the basis of our discussion of "located classes."

Sometimes, of course, a discrete distribution is an approximation to a continuous distribution. The "classes" are then simply artifacts, a means of sum-

---

[4]The notation is similar to that of Section 2, but not identical. In the latent distance model, x_α could be thought of as the location of class α in a very specific sense: the proportion of the population below class α in the ordering. Here, as yet, there is no such meaning attached to the "locations" (x_α).

marizing some of the information about the population. In latent structure analysis, however, the requirement that the classes be homogeneous makes such an interpretation invalid, for it is very hard to find good approximations to local independence.

We may assume that the usual parameters of latent class structure are known, since they can be determined by the methods of Chapters 2–4 if no restrictions are imposed on the latent probabilities. What must be done, if we take seriously the "located class" concept, is to define how the locations of the classes, the unknown $x_1, x_2, \ldots, x_n$, affect the responses to the items.

The model which we shall explore below makes the assumption that the within-class probabilities of positive response to items are *polynomial* functions of the (x_i). That is, there are numbers a_{ik} such that

$$p_i^\alpha = p_i(x_\alpha) = a_{i0} + a_{i1}x_\alpha + \cdots + a_{ir}x_\alpha^r$$

for some fixed integer r.

4.1 *Analysis of Linear Functions*

If we start by assuming that a linear function relates the points $(x_1, x_2, \ldots, x_m)$ to the latent probabilities p_i^α, we have to postulate two new parameters for each item. That is, the linear function is:

$$p_i^\alpha = p_i(x_\alpha) = a_{i0} + a_{i1}x_\alpha. \tag{24}$$

Given the $n \times m$ array of latent parameters:

$$L = (p_i^\alpha),$$

we have to determine the item parameters (a_{i0}, a_{i1}) and the class locations (x_α). Let A be the $n \times 2$ matrix (a_{i0}, a_{i1}), and let X be the $2 \times m$ matrix whose first row is ones and whose second row consists of the vector $(x_1, x_2, \ldots, x_n)$. Then the equation is

$$L = AX. \tag{25}$$

For instance, if the number of classes, $m = 3$, and the number of items, $n = 5$,

$$\begin{pmatrix} p_1^1 & p_1^2 & p_1^3 \\ p_2^1 & p_2^2 & p_2^3 \\ p_3^1 & p_3^2 & p_3^3 \\ p_4^1 & p_4^2 & p_4^3 \\ p_5^1 & p_5^2 & p_5^3 \end{pmatrix} = \begin{pmatrix} a_{10} & a_{11} \\ a_{20} & a_{21} \\ a_{30} & a_{31} \\ a_{40} & a_{41} \\ a_{50} & a_{51} \end{pmatrix} \begin{pmatrix} 1 & 1 & 1 \\ x_1 & x_2 & x_3 \end{pmatrix}.$$

This system of equations can be solved partially by considering 2×2 submatrices of L, and taking determinants. Let $L_{ab;cd}$ be the submatrix of L that consists of rows (items) a and b and columns (classes) c and d. Let A_{ab} be the submatrix consisting of rows a and b of A, and X_{cd} the matrix consisting of columns c and d of X. It is easy to see that:

$$L_{ab;cd} = A_{ab}X_{cd}.\qquad(26)$$

Taking determinants:

$$|L_{ab;cd}| = |A_{ab}|\,|X_{cd}|.$$

Because of the simple form of X, we can compute:

$$|X_{cd}| = x_d - x_c.$$

By fixing two items, a and b, and varying the classes c and d, we can solve for the locations x_1, x_2, x_3. For instance,

$$|L_{12;12}| = |A_{12}|\,|X_{12}|$$
$$|L_{12;13}| = |A_{12}|\,|X_{13}|.$$

Therefore, we obtain an equation that is free of the coefficients a_{ik}

$$\frac{|L_{12;12}|}{|L_{12;13}|} = \frac{|X_{12}|}{|X_{13}|} = \frac{x_2 - x_1}{x_3 - x_1}.\qquad(27)$$

The problem is simpler than it appears, because of a fundamental indeterminacy in the scale points x_α. There are always two arbitrary choices when constructing a scale, corresponding to the zero point and the unit of measurement. To make clear what we mean, suppose that we replace every x_α by

$$y_\alpha = d + ex_\alpha.$$

The linear function still applies if we change *all* the item coefficients accordingly:

$$p_i(x_\alpha) = a_{i0} + a_{i1}x_\alpha$$
$$= a_{i0} + a_{i1}(y_\alpha - d)/e$$
$$= (a_{i0} - a_{i1}d/e) + y_\alpha a_{i1}/e.$$

This means that two arbitrary conditions can be imposed on the points x_α. In this case, the simplest thing is to fix two of the locations. For instance, let

$$x_1 = 0 \quad \text{and} \quad x_3 = 1.$$

Substituting in Equation (27), we solve for x_2:

$$x_2 = |L_{12;12}|/|L_{12;13}| = (p_1^1 p_2^2 - p_2^1 p_1^2)/(p_1^1 p_2^3 - p_2^1 p_1^3).$$

The a_{i0} and a_{i1} can then be determined by solving Equations (24), which are simple linear equations when the x_α are given.

150

Alternatively, we may consider the first and third columns of L: call this submatrix $L_{.;13}$. If $x_1 = 0$ and $x_3 = 1$, then:

$$L_{.;13} = A \begin{pmatrix} 1 & 1 \\ 0 & 1 \end{pmatrix}.$$

Since the inverse of

$$\begin{pmatrix} 1 & 1 \\ 0 & 1 \end{pmatrix}$$

is

$$\begin{pmatrix} 1 & -1 \\ 0 & 1 \end{pmatrix},$$

we can solve for A:

$$A = L_{.;13} \begin{pmatrix} 1 & -1 \\ 0 & 1 \end{pmatrix}.$$

Thus, $a_{i0} = p_i^1$ and $a_{i1} = p_i^3 - p_i^1$.

The linear traceline implies the following relations. There must be a consistent ordering of the classes: if $x_1 < x_2 < x_3$, then

$$p_i^1 < p_i^2 < p_i^3$$

for all i, if a_{i1} is positive. More specifically, since

$$x_2 = (p_i^2 - p_i^1)/(p_i^3 - p_i^1)$$

for every i, the ratios

$$(p_i^2 - p_i^1)/(p_i^3 - p_i^1) = (p_j^2 - p_j^1)/(p_j^3 - p_j^1)$$

must remain constant for any items i and j.

In assuming the within-class probabilities (p_i^α) are known, and considering only the question of whether they satisfy the linear traceline assumption, we have bypassed the question of how to compute them from the *manifest* probabilities. This turns out to be an important question, for the assumption of a linear traceline precludes the use of the "basic" solution of the accounting equations of the latent class model (Theorem 1, Chapter 3). Recall that this approach requires that the unstratified basic matrix B_{hv}, which has m rows and columns, have an inverse. The equation linking manifest and latent matrixes is, of course,

$$B_{hv} = L_h V L_v'.$$

The assumption of linear tracelines is expressed by Equation (25), and when this is substituted, we have:

$$B_{hv} = A_h X V X' A_v'.$$

No matter how many classes there are, the rank of B_{hv} cannot be greater than two, because X has only two rows. Thus when m is greater than two, B_{hv} does not have an inverse. The way to solve this model is to consider *ascending* matrices, and to use the solution discussed in Section 4.1 of Chapter 3.

An ascending matrix, P_{hv}, has signatures which involve combinations of items. The following illustration shows how such a matrix can have an inverse. Suppose that there are 3 classes, with $x_1 = 0$ and $x_3 = 1$ as above. Let the signatures be $h = (0, 2, 24)$ and $v = (0, 3, 35)$.

$$P_{hv} = \begin{pmatrix} 1 & p_3 & p_{34} \\ p_2 & p_{23} & p_{234} \\ p_{25} & p_{235} & p_{2345} \end{pmatrix}.$$

The matrix of latent probabilities L_h is, remembering that $x_1 = 0$ and $x_3 = 1$,

$$\begin{pmatrix} 1 & 1 & 1 \\ p_2^1 & p_2^2 & p_2^3 \\ p_2^1 p_5^1 & p_2^2 p_5^2 & p_2^3 p_5^3 \end{pmatrix}$$

$$= \begin{pmatrix} 1 & 1 & 1 \\ a_{20} & a_{20} + a_{21}x_2 & a_{20} + a_{21} \\ a_{20}a_{50} & (a_{20} + a_{21}x_2)(a_{50} + a_{51}x_2) & (a_{20} + a_{21})(a_{50} + a_{51}) \end{pmatrix}.$$

We can show directly, by evaluating the determinant, that L_h will have an inverse as long as x_2, the location of class 2, is different from 0 and 1, locations of the other two classes. Instead, we consider the following matrix product, which, the reader can verify, is equal to the matrix L_h.

$$\begin{pmatrix} 1 & 0 & 0 \\ a_{20} & a_{21} & 0 \\ a_{20}a_{50} & a_{20}a_{51} + a_{21}a_{50} & a_{21}a_{51} \end{pmatrix} \begin{pmatrix} 1 & 1 & 1 \\ 0 & x_2 & 1 \\ 0 & x_2^2 & 1 \end{pmatrix}.$$

The determinant of the triangular matrix of "a" parameters is $a_{51}(a_{21})^2$, and the determinant of the matrix of "x" parameters is $x_2(1 - x_2)$, so we see that the matrix L_h will have an inverse in all but the trivial cases.

Notice the similarity between these matrices and the A and X defined previously. The entry in row i and column j of A is the coefficient of x^j in the polynomial expression of the ith element of the signature h. That is exactly the case here, where we recognize that the polynomial expression for the "25" entry of h is of degree 2, requiring three columns rather than the two in A. Similarly, the X matrix is merely extended to include the necessary squared terms. A column of X still represents a class, and a row a particular power of the location parameters x.

In Chapter 7, when we discuss the polynomial traceline models in greater generality, we shall carry this analysis of the relation between the manifest probabilities and the coefficients of the latent polynomials further. Our purpose at this point was simply to point out that the ascending matrix solution of the latent class model is required when the polynomial relationship exists among the latent probabilities.

4.2 Quadratic Tracelines

Adding more latent parameters by specifying a higher-degree polynomial will permit us more freedom in fitting the data. Suppose that the quadratic functions are chosen, i.e.:

$$p_i^\alpha = p_i(x_\alpha) = a_{i0} + a_{i1}x_\alpha + a_{i2}x_\alpha^2.$$

Just as before, we have the matrix equality

$$L = AX,$$

where now A has 3 columns and X has 3 rows. If we take care of the arbitrary conditions by setting $x_1 = 0$ and $x_2 = 1$, then:

$$X = \begin{pmatrix} 1 & 1 & 1 & \cdots & 1 \\ 0 & 1 & x_3 & \cdots & x_m \\ 0 & 1 & x_3^2 & \cdots & x_m^2 \end{pmatrix}.$$

If we choose three rows (items) of L, summarized by the symbol "r" and three columns (classes) "c" then

$$L_{r;c} = A_r X_c. \tag{28}$$

Rather than taking determinants of both sides, as in the linear case, we shall let d stand for another set of three classes and consider the matrix product:

$$L_{r;d}^{-1} L_{r;c},$$

for different choices of columns of X, c and d.

$$L_{r;d}^{-1} L_{r;c} = X_d^{-1} A_r^{-1} A_r X_c$$
$$= X_d^{-1} X_c. \tag{29}$$

Suppose that $d = (1, 2, 3)$ and $c = (1, 2, 4)$:

$$X_d^{-1} X_c = \begin{pmatrix} 1 & 1 & 1 \\ 0 & 1 & x_3 \\ 0 & 1 & x_3^2 \end{pmatrix}^{-1} \begin{pmatrix} 1 & 1 & 1 \\ 0 & 1 & x_4 \\ 0 & 1 & x_4^2 \end{pmatrix}.$$

Let $x_3 = x$ and $x_4 = y$, for convenience in what follows:

$$\begin{pmatrix} 1 & 1 & 1 \\ 0 & 1 & x \\ 0 & 1 & x^2 \end{pmatrix}^{-1} \begin{pmatrix} 1 & 1 & 1 \\ 0 & 1 & y \\ 0 & 1 & y^2 \end{pmatrix}$$

$$= \frac{1}{x(1-x)} \begin{pmatrix} x(1-x) & x^2-1 \\ 0 & -x^2 \\ 0 & 1 \end{pmatrix} \begin{pmatrix} 1-x & 1 & 1 & 1 \\ x & 0 & 1 & y \\ -1 & 0 & 1 & y^2 \end{pmatrix}$$

$$= \begin{pmatrix} 1 & 0 & (1-y)(x-y)/x \\ 0 & 1 & y(y-x)/(1-x) \\ 0 & 0 & y(1-y)/x(1-x) \end{pmatrix}. \tag{30}$$

Let (a, b, c) stand for the elements of the third column of $L_{r;d}^{-1}L_{r;c}$, which are supposed to be known. There are three equations in the unknowns x and y:

$$\begin{aligned} a &= (1-y)(x-y)/x, \\ b &= y(y-x)/(1-x), \\ c &= y(1-y)/x(1-x). \end{aligned} \tag{31}$$

It is easy to see that $a + b + c = 1$, however.

These equations can be combined in a way that simplifies the analysis considerably:

$$\begin{aligned} b + cx &= y, \\ b + cx^2 &= y^2. \end{aligned} \tag{32}$$

Substituting for y, and solving for x, we have the quadratic:

$$x^2c(1-c) - x(2bc) + b(1-b) = 0,$$

and, solving for x:

$$x = b/(1-c) \pm (-abc)^{1/2}/c(1-c). \tag{33}$$

If the assumptions of the model were satisfied so that Equations (31) held exactly, the product $(-abc)$ would be positive and, therefore, the square root would be real. The fact that the quadratic equation has two roots, however, is troublesome. It means that if we had begun with two locations, x and y, and generated the accounting equations, the solution (24) would give us an alternative pair of locations, say (x_*, y_*), which would also satisfy the accounting equations.

It is not hard to show that if one root of Equation (33) is the true value x, then the other value is:

$$x_* = x(y - x + 1)/(x + y - 1) = x + 2x(1 - x)/(x + y - 1),$$

and
$$\tag{34}$$
$$y_* = y(x - y + 1)/(x + y - 1) = y + 2y(1 - y)/(x + y - 1).$$

It is necessary to substitute from Equations (31) into (33) to show that the alternate solution is as given here. Notice, in particular, that $(x_* - y_*) = (y - x)$. In other words, the distance between the two points remains constant in absolute value, but the order of the points is reversed.

If we had a fifth class, with $x_5 = z$, say, we would be able to determine x, y, and z exactly by repeating the analysis of Equations (30)–(33) for the pairs (x, y), and (x, z) in turn. In the first case, as above, the two roots (33) would be x and x_*; in the second case, they would be x and x_{**}, say; and x_* and x_{**} must be different if all of the five locations, x_1, x_2, x_3, x_4, x_5 are distinct. This can be seen by setting $x_* = x_{**}$, using Equations (34).

$$x(y - x + 1)/(x + y - 1) = x(z - x + 1)/(z + x - 1)$$

implies that:

$$(z + x - 1)(y - x + 1) = (z - x + 1)(x + y - 1),$$
$$z(1 - x) = y(1 - x),$$
$$(z - y)(1 - x) = 0.$$

The parameters of the located class model, with quadratic tracelines $p_i(x)$ for each item, can be specified exactly if there are five latent classes, as long as there are three items i, j, k whose coefficient matrix:

$$A_r = A_{(i,j,k)}$$

has an inverse.

4.3 Summary

Finally, we consider the case of cubic tracelines, and show what the general case will look like.

As before, given two matrices of latent probabilities, $L_{r;c}$ and $L_{r;d}$, we have

$$L_{r;d}^{-1} L_{r;c} = X_d^{-1} X_c, \tag{35}$$

assuming that the matrix A_r of coefficients has an inverse. Now, in the cubic case, let $c = (1, 2, 3, 5)$ and $d = (1, 2, 3, 4)$ and suppose that $x_1 = 0$ and $x_2 = 1$. The product (35) will be an identity matrix, except for the last column:

$$L_{r;d}^{-1} L_{r;c} = \begin{pmatrix} 1 & 0 & 0 & b_0 \\ 0 & 1 & 0 & b_1 \\ 0 & 0 & 1 & b_2 \\ 0 & 0 & 0 & b_3^3 \end{pmatrix}.$$

This implies that:

$$\begin{pmatrix} 1 & 1 & 1 & 1 \\ 0 & 1 & x_3 & x_4 \\ 0 & 1 & x_3^2 & x_4^2 \\ 0 & 1 & x_3^3 & x_4^2 \end{pmatrix} \begin{pmatrix} b_0 \\ b_1 \\ b_2 \\ b_3 \end{pmatrix} = \begin{pmatrix} 1 \\ x_5 \\ x_5^2 \\ x_5^3 \end{pmatrix}. \tag{36}$$

Equation (36) can be rewritten with all the unknowns on the same side:

$$\begin{pmatrix} x_3 & x_4 & x_5 \\ x_3^2 & x_4^2 & x_5^2 \\ x_3^3 & x_4^3 & x_5^3 \end{pmatrix} \begin{pmatrix} b_2 \\ b_3 \\ -1 \end{pmatrix} = \begin{pmatrix} -b_1 \\ -b_1 \\ -b_1 \end{pmatrix},$$

or,

$$\begin{pmatrix} x_3 & x_4 & x_5 \\ x_3^2 & x_4^2 & x_5^2 \\ x_3^3 & x_4^3 & x_5^3 \end{pmatrix} \begin{pmatrix} -b_2/b_1 \\ -b_3/b_1 \\ 1/b_1 \end{pmatrix} = \begin{pmatrix} 1 \\ 1 \\ 1 \end{pmatrix}. \tag{37}$$

Equation (37) will not have a unique solution, of course. In the quadratic case, the corresponding equation (32), involving the locations of two classes, had two different solutions. Uniqueness was specified only if there were another latent class, for a total of five in all. We do not know how many different classes would be needed to obtain a unique specification of these location parameters in the cubic model. Statements about the general polynomial of degree r also remain as unsolved problems.

The extension to the polynomial of order r should be clear. We choose $d = (1, 2, 3, \ldots, r + 1)$ and $c = (1, 2, 3, \ldots, r, r + 2)$; the vector (b_i) is defined to be the last column of the product $L_{r;d}^{-1} L_{r;c}$, and we end up with equations of the form of Equation (37).

Models that involve high order polynomial restrictions require complicated computations, as evidenced by Equation (37) and its generalizations. Furthermore, the statistical problems associated with the estimation of the latent parameters in actual data analysis will require that very large samples be available: otherwise sampling variations will cause the estimates to be unreliable. The quadratic model, with five located classes, may become empirically useful, however, if we are successful in programming a computer to handle the estimation procedures. As an example, consider the perennial problem of social stratification. The only empirical evidence for the number of social classes and their relative locations is data indicating the attitudes of individuals, their positions in social organizations, and their roles in various decision processes. Classification will vary, depending on what items are used as indicators. The differences in such classifications could best be assessed by comparing the kind of ordered, located class models to which they lead. If the data do not fit this sort of simple model well, the deviations may give rise to more refined theoretical statements. In an unpublished Columbia dissertation Peter Rossi (1951) began the examination of empirical data and latent class analysis. The quadratic traceline, located class model presented in this chapter might become an important instrument for coordinating the frequent studies of social stratification.

6

Latent Structure Models with Continuous Latent Space: I

1. Continuous Latent Variables

In the initial chapters of this book, we have assumed that the latent space was discrete, since the idea of a finite number of latent classes is attractive in a number of sociological applications. Also, of course, much more work has been done in the mathematical and statistical development of the latent class models than in the so-called traceline models which we introduce in this section.

It is very common, especially in psychological applications, to think of a latent variable as though it could be measured on an interval scale and represented mathematically by a real number. Concepts such as "ability," "intelligence," and "prejudice" are usually supposed to have the characteristic of ordering the population, and, also, to be infinitely divisible (that is, between any two different values, we can conceive of an intermediate value). There may or may not be a "zero point" on these hypothetical scales, but this is not relevant to our approach. We are going to consider in some detail latent structure models where the latent variable ranges over some interval of the real line.

Suppose, then, that the latent variable takes on real values x within some closed interval X, and that there is some probability distribution $F(x)$ over this interval. $F(x) = $ Prob [an individual chosen at random has a value less than x]. To take an example, if X were the interval from zero to one, $F(x)$ might be the uniform distribution, $F(x) = x$.

For each value x of the latent variable, and for each item i, we must define a function $p_i(x)$ which gives the probability of a positive response to item i, given a value x of the latent quality. These functions are called the *item characteristic curves*, or *item tracelines*. If they are specified, the model is completely defined as soon as we note that the axiom of local independence is to hold, just as in the latent class models. That is, the probability of a positive response to one item is independent of responses to other items when x is given.

Let's take a simple example, where the tracelines are all straight lines. Then the functions $p_i(x)$ are linear functions of x, say

$$p_i(x) = a_i + b_i x,$$

and a_i and b_i are latent parameters of the model. The latent probability of a positive response to both items 1 and 2, given x, would be:

$$p_{12}(x) = p_1(x)p_2(x) = a_1 a_2 + (a_1 b_2 + a_2 b_1)x + b_1 b_2 x^2.$$

The *manifest* or unconditional probabilities are obtained by taking the expected values of these latent probabilities over the interval X. Where we had sums in the discrete class case, we have integrals to express these expectations in the continuous traceline models. Thus, in our general notation, if s stands for some particular response pattern, and $p_s(x)$ is the conditional probability of s, given x, then the manifest probability will be

$$p_s = E[p_s(x)] = \int_X p_s(s)F'(x)\,dx$$

where $\int_X$ stands for the integral over the interval X, and $F'(x)$ is the derivative of the distribution function $F(x)$, called the *probability density* function of x.[1]

There may be parameters in the model identified with the items, as the a_i and b_i above, and parameters identified with the distribution F, as for instance the mean and variance of the latent distribution. It will be part of the analysis of a proposed model to show whether the latent parameters are identifiable, i.e., whether or not they can be determined uniquely from the manifest probabilities, and to indicate how they may be estimated from observed data.

Let the density function $F'(x)$ be denoted by $f(x)$, and suppose that the interval X consists of all points between α and β. Then, from basic principles of probability we know that

$$\int_\alpha^\beta f(x)\,dx = 1.$$

The moments of the latent distribution are defined to be

$$M(1) = \int_\alpha^\beta x f(x)\,dx,$$

$$M(2) = \int_\alpha^\beta x^2 f(x)\,dx,$$

$$M(t) = \int_\alpha^\beta x^t f(x)\,dx.$$

$M(1)$ is, of course, the mean, or expected value of x; the second moment is related to the variance of x by the relation:

$$\sigma^2 = M(2) - M(1)^2.$$

[1] Anyone who is unfamiliar with these notions should turn to the discussion of distribution functions in any text on probability, for instance, Parzen (1960), Ch. 4.

We shall have occasion to use this notation when we consider specific traceline functions. Notice, for instance, what happens in the case of linear tracelines:

$$p_1 = \int_\alpha^\beta (a_1 + b_1 x) f(x)\, dx$$

$$= a_1 \int_\alpha^\beta f(x)\, dx + b_1 \int_\alpha^\beta x f(x)\, dx$$

$$= a_1 + b_1 M(1).$$

If we assume that a real-valued latent variable x exists, then a particular latent structure model is defined whenever we specify the functional form of the traceline functions $p_i(s)$. This will generally involve several *latent parameters*, which can be determined by the manifest probabilities if the model is identifiable. x will have some cumulative distribution function, $F(x)$. Sometimes F will be specified completely, and sometimes only its functional form will be specified, involving one or more free parameters. Usually we shall assume that the derivative of F exists: $F'(x) = f(x)$.

Consider the following two examples of distribution functions:

(a) $\qquad\qquad\qquad F(x) = x, f(x) = 1, 0 \leq x \leq 1.$

Here there are no parameters to determine. This distribution is particularly useful, and not only because of its simple form. Since $x = F(x)$, an individual's value of the latent variable tells what proportion of the population has less of the attribute than he. In coupling this distribution with some traceline functions $p_i(x)$, we are supposing that the *rank order* of the attribute is important in determining responses, rather than the actual value of the variable on some scale. In a sense, this would be a *non-parametric* model, in which we never really uncover a *value* for the latent variable, but only the ordering of the population on it.

(b) $\qquad\quad f(x) = (\alpha + 1)(\alpha + 2)(1 - x)(x)^\alpha, \qquad 0 \leq x \leq 1.$

This distribution involves one latent parameter, α.

It is not hard to verify that this function satisfies the basic requirement, that $\int_0^1 f(x)\, dx = 1$, as long as the parameter α is greater than or equal to zero. It has a single maximum, located at the point $x = \alpha/(\alpha + 1)$, and its mean is $(\alpha + 1)/(\alpha + 3)$.

ASIDE: To find the modal value of x, we must differentiate $f(x)$, set the result equal to zero, and solve for x:

$$f'(x) = (\alpha + 1)(\alpha + 2)[\alpha x^{\alpha-1}(1 - x) - x^\alpha],$$
$$0 = (\alpha + 1)(\alpha + 2)x^{\alpha-1}[\alpha - \alpha x - x],$$
$$0 = \alpha - x(\alpha + 1),$$
$$x = \alpha/(1 + \alpha).$$

159

Since we have not restricted α other than to be non-negative, we see that the peak of the distribution can occur anywhere in the interval $[0, 1]$ depending on the value of α.

To find the mean, the expected value of x, we must integrate:

$$M(1) = E(x) = \int_0^1 xf(x) = \int_0^1 (\alpha + 1)(\alpha + 2)x^{\alpha+1}(1 - x)\,dx$$

$$= (\alpha + 1)(\alpha + 2)\left[\int_0^1 x^{\alpha+1}\,dx - \int_0^1 x^{\alpha+2}\,dx\right]$$

$$= (\alpha + 1)(\alpha + 2)[1/(\alpha + 2) - 1/(\alpha + 3)]$$

$$= (\alpha + 1)/(\alpha + 3). \quad\blacksquare$$

EXERCISE. Find the second moment, $M(2)$, and the variance, σ^2, of this distribution.

2. The Latent Content Model[2]

The first of the latent structure models involving a single continuous valued latent variable x that we shall study is the latent content model. We suppose that x can take on values between 0 and 1. The traceline function is:

$$p_i(x) = a_i + b_i x^{d_i}. \tag{1}$$

There are some restrictions on the item parameters.

(i) $d_i \geq 0$.
(ii) $0 < a_i < 1$.
(iii) $0 < a_i + b_i < 1$.

The first restriction is necessary in order that $p_i(x)$ remain less than 1 in the vicinity of $x = 0$. The second two restrictions are also implied by the necessity of the bound

$$0 \leq p_i(x) \leq 1$$

since $a_i = p_i(0)$ and $a_i + b_i = p_i(1)$. We shall add a fourth restriction, namely;

(iv) $b_i > 0$.

This is not strictly required by the model, but it is equivalent to the statement that "as x increases the chance of a positive response to any item increases." The type of data to which the latent content model will be applied will be of this type, wherein a positive response will be associated with larger values of the underlying variable, x. This choice of traceline function is plausible in many instances, since it permits the items to vary in how fast their tracelines increase

---

[2]Some applications of the latent model have been published by Lazarsfeld (1959b), and Somers (1961); the latter contains a more detailed discussion of some aspects of the model.

with x. In Figure 1 we show three tracelines, with d's less than, equal to, and greater than 1.

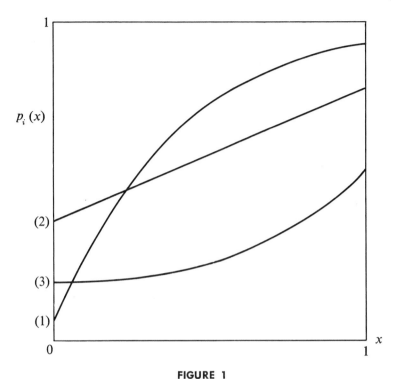

FIGURE 1

Three Latent Content Tracelines
(1) $d < 1$; (2) $d = 1$; (3) $d > 1$

Under the restrictions (i)–(iv) the function

$$p(x) = a + bx^d \tag{2}$$

is steadily increasing with x. The rate of increase increases if d is bigger than 1, and decreases if d is less than 1. The derivative

$$p'(x) = dbx^{d-1}$$

is always positive, and is constant, of course, only if $d = 1$, i.e., the traceline is linear.

We have paid special attention to this model for several reasons. First, the continuous traceline, with its three latent parameters, seems to be an interesting generalization from the step-functions of the latent distance model. The probability of a positive response increases with x, but at different rates for each item. Second, the data to which this model may be applied must show radically different patterns from those of the latent class models. That is, the conditions which manifest probabilities must satisfy in this model are not similar to those previously discussed. The latent class models imposed rank conditions on the cross product matrices, in a way quite similar to those imposed by factor analysis models. Here, there is little similarity to factor analysis. Thus the model requires some unique mathematical contributions; in particular the analysis of the "rotation" of points in a plane along a hyperbola. As a consequence we have occasionally to point out unsolved problems, both of a theoretical and a computational nature. We hope that this will stimulate readers to further work.

2.1 *The Accounting Equations*

If x has the density $f(x)$ on the unit interval, then the latent parameters determine the manifest probabilities according to the following accounting equations:

$$p_i = \int_0^1 p_i(x)f(x)\,dx$$

$$= a_i + b_i \int x^{d_i} f(x)\,dx = a_i + b_i M(d_i). \tag{3a}$$

$$p_{ij} = \int p_i(x)p_j(x)f(x)\,dx = a_i a_j M(d_j) + a_j b_i M(d_i) + b_i b_j M(d_i + d_j). \tag{3b}$$

$$
\begin{aligned}
p_{ijk} = {} & a_i a_j a_k + a_i a_j b_k M(d_k) + a_i a_k b_j M(d_j) + a_j a_k b_i M(d_i) \\
& + a_i b_j b_k M(d_j + d_k) + a_j b_i b_k M(d_i + d_k) + a_k b_i b_j M(d_i + d_j) \\
& + b_i b_j b_k M(d_i + d_j + d_k),
\end{aligned} \tag{3c}
$$

and so on for positive probabilities of any order.

In trying to simplify these expressions so that a solution of the model may be found, we construct the cross products, $[ij] = p_{ij} - p_i p_j$, and find that the a's drop out:

$$[ij] = b_i b_j M(d_i + d_j) - b_i b_j M(d_i)M(d_j) = b_i b_j[M(d_i + d_j) - M(d_i)M(d_j)]. \tag{4}$$

The symmetric third-order parameter,

$$[ijk] = p_{ijk} - p_i p_j p_k - p_i[jk] - p_j[ik] - p_k[ij]$$

can also be evaluated, using (3a), (3c), and (4):

$$
\begin{aligned}
[ijk] = b_i b_j b_k [& M(d_i + d_j + d_k) - M(d_i)M(d_j + d_k) - M(d_j)M(d_i + d_k) \\
& - M(d_k)M(d_i + d_j) + 2M(d_i)M(d_j)M(d_k)].
\end{aligned} \tag{5}
$$

We arrived at this result by the following steps. The symmetric parameters $[ij]$ and $[ijk]$ have been defined in earlier chapters, where we have noted (in Chapter 3) that $[ij]$ is the covariance of items i and j while $[ijk]$ is the *third-order covariance* (or central moment) of items $i, j,$ and k. Thus, it is possible for us to

162

calculate $[ij]$ and $[ijk]$ by using the equations:

$$[ij] = \int (p_i(x) - p_i)(p_j(x) - p_j)f(x)\,dx$$

and,

$$[ijk] = \int (p_i(x) - p_i)(p_j(x) - p_j)(p_k(x) - p_k)f(x)\,dx.$$

Since

$$(p_i(x) - p_i) = a_i + b_i x^{d_i} - a_i - b_i M(d_i) = b_i(x^{d_i} - M(d_i)),$$

and the various terms $M(d)$ do not depend on x, the integrals are easy to evaluate:

$$[ij] = b_i b_j \int (x^{d_i} - M(d_i))(x^{d_j} - M(d_j))f(x)\,dx$$

$$= b_i b_j \int (x^{d_i+d_j} - M(d_i)x^{d_j} - M(d_j)x^{d_i} + M(d_i)M(d_j))f(x)\,dx$$

$$= b_i b_j (M(d_i + d_j) - M(d_i)M(d_j)).$$

$$[ijk] = b_i b_j b_k \int (x^{d_i} - M(d_i))(x^{d_j} - M(d_j))(x^{d_k} - M(d_k))f(x)\,dx.$$

Equation (5) is a straightforward expansion of this last expression.

We shall not manipulate these expressions any further. The reader can see that there is little hope of obtaining a general solution, without specifying the density function $f(x)$ (or its moments) in more detail. We choose to look first at the uniform distribution, $f(x) = 1$, for all x between 0 and 1. This density function is the simplest, algebraically, and, as noted above, allows us to interpret the latent variable, x, as the proportion of the population which ranks *below* an individual having that value. (Recall our discussion of scales in the previous chapter.) The moment functions $M(t)$ of the uniform distribution are:

$$M(t) = \int_0^1 x^t\,dx = 1/(t + 1). \tag{6}$$

The expressions for the cross product and the symmetric parameter of third order become:

$$[ij] = b_i b_j d_i d_j / (1 + d_i)(1 + d_j)(1 + d_i + d_j) \tag{7}$$

and

$$[ijk] = \frac{b_i b_j b_k d_i d_j d_k ((d_i + d_j)(d_i + d_k)(d_j + d_k) - 2(1 + d_i + d_j + d_k))}{(1 + d_i)(1 + d_j)(1 + d_k)(1 + d_i + d_j)(1 + d_i + d_k)(1 + d_j + d_k)(1 + d_i + d_j + d_k)}. \tag{8}$$

ASIDE: An interesting special case arises if we suppose that all of the d's are equal to 1, i.e., that all tracelines are linear functions of x. Then the b_i can be determined from the cross products, since

$$\frac{[ik][jk]}{[ij]} = b_k^2/12,$$

and the a_i follow from $p_i = a_i + b_i/2$. Notice that all third-order co-variances, $[ijk]$, are zero in this case.

Later in this chapter, we shall consider other special cases, including (a) all d_i equal, but unspecified; (b) all $a_i = 0$, and (c) all b_i equal but unspecified. ∎

2.2 *The Reciprocals of the Cross Products*

In this section we shall investigate an interesting necessary condition on the manifest probabilities generated by the latent content model. The condition is that the matrix of *reciprocals* of the cross products has rank two.

We begin by defining

$$q_{ij} = 1/[ij], \qquad i \neq j. \tag{9}$$

From Equation (7) we know that

$$q_{ij} = (1 + d_i)(1 + d_j)(1 + d_i + d_j)/b_i b_j d_i d_j, \qquad i \neq j. \tag{10}$$

For our purposes this expression can be simplified by defining

$$r_i = (1 + d_i)/b_i d_i \tag{11}$$

and

$$s_i = (1 + d_i)(1 + 2d_i)/b_i d_i, \qquad \text{for all } i. \tag{12}$$

We then find the useful formula

$$q_{ij} = (r_i s_j + s_i r_j)/2, \qquad \text{for } i \neq j. \tag{13}$$

There is a one-to-one correspondence between the pair (b_i, d_i) and the pair (r_i, s_i); it is quite easy to show from the defining equations (11) and (12) that:

$$d_i = (s_i - r_i)/2r_i \tag{14}$$

and

$$b_i = (s_i + r_i)/r_i(s_i - r_i). \tag{15}$$

The latent content model required that certain conditions be placed on the parameters b_i and d_i. These, in turn, imply that the r_i and s_i satisfy some conditions, which we list below for easy reference. The conditions on b_i and d_i are:

$$0 < b_i < 1$$

and

$$0 < d_i.$$

It then follows from Equation (11) that

$$r_i > 1 \qquad \text{for all } i. \tag{16}$$

Also, by comparing Equations (11) and (12) we see that

$$s_i = r_i(1 + 2d_i), \tag{17}$$

which implies that

$$s_i > r_i \qquad \text{for all } i. \tag{18}$$

The equation for the marginal probability, p_i, is

$$p_i = a_i + b_i/(1 + d_i),$$

which implies that $b_i/(1 + d_i)$ must be between 0 and p_i:

$$0 < b_i/(1 + d_i) < p_i.$$

When we substitute from (14) and (15), we get

$$b_i/(1 + d_i) = 2/(s_i - r_i),$$

so that a more restrictive condition is evident:

$$2/(s_i - r_i) < p_i,$$

or

$$s_i - r_i > 2/p_i. \tag{19}$$

This is a different type of condition from those (16–18) which follow from the restriction of the tracelines, $p_i(x)$, to values between 0 and 1. Geometrically, the inequality (19) follows from the restriction of the *area* under the traceline to values between 0 and 1.

Our strategy is to try to solve the accounting equations for the unknown values of r_i and s_i, and then to use Equations (14) and (15) to determine the original traceline parameters b_i and d_i. The first step in our solution is to note that Equation (13) requires the matrix Q to have rank two, as we show in the following theorem.

THEOREM 1: *In the latent content model any submatrix of Q which does not include any diagonal entries has rank no larger than two.*

PROOF: We can write q_{ij} as the product of two vectors:

$$q_{ij} = (r_i, s_i) \begin{pmatrix} s_j \\ r_j \end{pmatrix} \Big/ 2$$

$$= (r_i, s_i) \begin{pmatrix} 0 & 1/2 \\ 1/2 & 0 \end{pmatrix} \begin{pmatrix} r_j \\ s_j \end{pmatrix}, \qquad \text{for } i \neq j.$$

Let R_h be a column vector containing the r_i for all items in a signature h, and let S_h be the column vector of the s_i for i in h. Define Q_{hv} to be the matrix of q_{ij} with i belonging to the set h, and j to the set v. As long as the two signatures, h and v, do not have any items in common we can write:

$$Q_{hv} = (R_h, S_h) \begin{pmatrix} 0 & 1/2 \\ 1/2 & 0 \end{pmatrix} \begin{pmatrix} R'_v \\ S'_v \end{pmatrix}. \tag{20}$$

The rank of Q_{hv} cannot exceed two, since the minimum dimension in the product (20) is two. (This definition of rank has been used in earlier chapters, and is defined in Appendix A.) Any determinant of a submatrix of Q that is of order greater than two will therefore equal zero. ∎

The diagonal entries of Q are not manifest quantities, but Equation (13) serves to define them in terms of the latent parameters:

$$q_{ii} = r_i s_i \tag{21}$$

We can solve for the q_{ii}, in terms of the off-diagonal entries of Q, however, since the rank two condition applies to the complete matrix as defined by (13) and (21). The 3×3 determinant

$$\begin{vmatrix} q_{ii} & q_{ij} & q_{ik} \\ q_{mi} & q_{mj} & q_{mk} \\ q_{ni} & q_{nj} & q_{nk} \end{vmatrix}$$

must equal zero. The items i, j, k, m, and n being distinct, all the other entries in this determinant *are* manifest, and so we can solve for q_{ii}. Expanding the determinant by elements of the first column gives:

$$q_{ii} \begin{vmatrix} q_{mj} & q_{mk} \\ q_{nj} & q_{nk} \end{vmatrix} - q_{mi} \begin{vmatrix} q_{ij} & q_{ik} \\ q_{nj} & q_{nk} \end{vmatrix} + q_{ni} \begin{vmatrix} q_{ij} & q_{ik} \\ q_{mj} & q_{mk} \end{vmatrix}.$$

Setting it equal to zero and solving for q_{ii},

$$q_{ii} = \frac{q_{mi}(q_{ij}q_{nk} - q_{nj}q_{ik}) - q_{ni}(q_{ij}q_{mk} - q_{mj}q_{ik})}{(q_{mj}q_{nk} - q_{nj}q_{mk})}. \tag{22}$$

From here on we shall assume that *all* entries of Q are known, supposing that all the diagonal entries have been computed according to equations similar to (14). Of course, the denominator must be different from zero, and there must be at least five items available in order to do this.

EXERCISE: Show that $q_{mj}q_{nk} - q_{mk}q_{nj}$ is different from zero if and only if $d_n \neq d_m$ and $d_k \neq d_j$. Use the fact that

$$q_{ij} = r_i r_j (1 + d_i + d_j).$$

Now that we can consider the diagonal entries of Q as known, computed from the other manifest parameters, we can eliminate half of the unknown latent parameters from our equations. From (21), we can say

$$s_i = q_{ii}/r_i$$

for all i. Substitution into Equation (13) would leave only r_i and r_j as unknowns:

$$2q_{ij} = q_{jj}(r_i/r_j) + q_{ii}(r_j/r_i) \tag{23}$$

We will continue along the lines suggested by the interesting form of Equation (23) in Section 3.

2.3 *An Intermediate Step*

Let us review briefly where we stand in the development of a solution of the latent content model. The accounting equations (3) linked the manifest marginals and joint probabilities to the parameters of the traceline functions (1). Then a number of transformations were made. On the manifest side, the reciprocals of the cross products (q_{ij}) seemed important. On the latent side, the parameters (r_i) and (s_i) provided us with a new and much simpler set of accounting equations, (13). They only involve first- and second-order information; we may have to use higher order manifest probabilities for a full identification of the latent parameters. The answers to two intermediate questions guide us through the next part of our analysis.

Can the latent parameters (r_i, s_i) be uniquely determined if the matrix Q is known?

The answer to this question is *no*. This fact is easily exhibited. Suppose that (r_i, s_i) satisfy the equation

$$2q_{ij} = r_i s_j + s_i r_j.$$

Let another set of parameters be defined by:

$$r_i^* = t r_i$$

and

$$s_i^* = s_i/t$$

for every i, where t is a positive number. The set (r_i^*, s_i^*) also satisfy the equations for the given Q matrix:

$$r_i^* s_j^* + s_i^* r_j^* = t r_i s_j/t + t r_j s_i/t = q_{ij}.$$

How much freedom is left, after all the information in the matrix Q has been used?

There are two aspects to this problem, one being the determination of a *single* parameter, and the second being the way in which this parameter is used to specify the solution. Theorem 2 explains why this is so.

THEOREM 2: *Let Q be a matrix of rank two. Let R and S be column vectors satisfying the equation:*

$$2Q = (R, S)\begin{pmatrix} S' \\ R' \end{pmatrix}.$$

If R^* and S^* also satisfy the same equation, then either

(i) *there is a $t \neq 0$ so that $r_i^* = r_i t$ and $s_i^* = s_i/t$ for all i; or*
(ii) *there is a $t \neq 0$ so that $r_i^* = s_i t$ and $s_i^* = r_i/t$ for all i.*

PROOF: By assumption

$$(R, S)\begin{pmatrix} 0 & 1 \\ 1 & 0 \end{pmatrix}\begin{pmatrix} R' \\ S' \end{pmatrix} = 2Q = (R^*, S^*)\begin{pmatrix} 0 & 1 \\ 1 & 0 \end{pmatrix}\begin{pmatrix} R^{*\prime} \\ S^{*\prime} \end{pmatrix}.$$

Because Q has rank two there exists some 2×2 matrix T such that $(R^*, S^*) = (R, S)T$. When this is substituted, the result is

$$(R, S)\begin{pmatrix} 0 & 1 \\ 1 & 0 \end{pmatrix}\begin{pmatrix} R' \\ S' \end{pmatrix} = (R, S)T\begin{pmatrix} 0 & 1 \\ 1 & 0 \end{pmatrix}T'\begin{pmatrix} R' \\ S' \end{pmatrix}.$$

For this equation to hold, we must have

$$\begin{pmatrix} 0 & 1 \\ 1 & 0 \end{pmatrix} = T \begin{pmatrix} 0 & 1 \\ 1 & 0 \end{pmatrix} T',$$

which leads to

$$\begin{pmatrix} 0 & 1 \\ 1 & 0 \end{pmatrix} = \begin{pmatrix} t_{11}t_{12} & t_{11}t_{22} + t_{12}t_{21} \\ t_{11}t_{22} + t_{12}t_{21} & t_{21}t_{22} \end{pmatrix}.$$

There are two possible solutions, either

(i) $t_{12} = t_{21} = 0$ and $t_{22} = 1/t_{11}$; or
(ii) $t_{11} = t_{22} = 0$ and $t_{12} = 1/t_{21}$.

These two solutions correspond to the two alternative transformations specified in the statement of the Theorem.

3. A Solution for the Latent Content Model

In this section we show how to express all the unknown latent parameters in terms of the given values of the manifest parameters and *one* unknown. This derivation will permit us to obtain an equation in this unknown by substitution into accounting equations of third order.

The geometric interpretation of the points (r_i, s_i) is helpful for understanding the algebraic derivations. Let (r_i, s_i) be a point in the plane, with the horizontal axis identifying r and the vertical axis s. The restriction to parameter values for which

$$1 < r_i < s_i$$

which we noted above, requires that the points lie in the upper right quadrant, and above the line $r = s$. The equation

$$q_{ii} = r_i s_i$$

tells us that the point (r_i, s_i) lies on an hyperbola whose asymptotes are the r- and s-axes. Figure 2 illustrates this property. The value of q_{ii} thus specifies a restricted set of possible values for r_i and s_i.

From Equation (17) we know that

$$s_i/r_i = 1 + 2d_i.$$

Geometrically, the ratio s_i/r_i is equal to the tangent of the angle which the vector (r_i, s_i) makes with the r-axis. (Call this angle θ_i.) The *orientation* of this vector depends only on the value of the traceline parameter d_i, therefore, while the *length* of the vector depends on both d_i and b_i.

Each value of q_{ij} tells us something about the *relative* position of the two points (r_i, s_i) and (r_j, s_j). This information is closely related to the area of the triangle formed by the two points, and the origin, shown in Figure 3. This

168

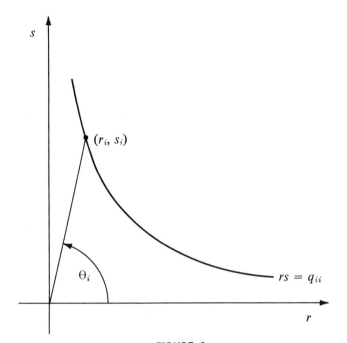

FIGURE 2

The Location of Item i in the r−s Plane

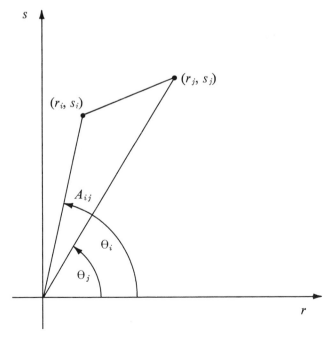

FIGURE 3

The Locations of Items i and j in the r−s Plane, with the Area between the Vectors area is equal to the absolute value of:

$$A_{ij} = (r_i s_j - r_j s_i)/2.$$

The value of q_{ij} is, of course,

$$(r_i s_j + r_j s_i)/2.$$

We can therefore derive the following relation between the area A_{ij} and the value of q_{ij}:

$$q_{ij}^2 - A_{ij}^2 = r_i s_j r_j s_i = q_{ii} q_{jj}.$$

The exact position of the two vectors (r_i, s_i) and (r_j, s_j) cannot be determined from this information alone, of course. The pair are free to move along their respective hyperbolae, subject to the constraint that the area between the vectors remain constant. The interesting thing about two such configurations is that, although the area of the triangle remains constant, the shape of the triangle changes drastically. This property is contrasted with the familiar rotation of vectors along circular paths: in that case, when the area of a triangle remains constant the shape must stay exactly the same.

A_{ij} can be either positive or negative, depending on which of the two vectors lies above the other (i.e., on whether r_i/s_i is greater or less than r_j/s_j), but q_{ij} is always positive. This means that if we are restricted to knowledge of q_{ij}, q_{ii}, and q_{jj}, we know the *absolute value* of the area between the two vectors, but we do not know which vector makes the larger angle with the r-axis. We next show *algebraically* that if one of the points is known, the given value of q_{ij} permits two possible positions for the second point, and then that if *two* different points are fixed, any other point can be uniquely located.

3.1 Analysis of a Pair of Items

Our plan is to solve for the latent parameters, in terms of the r-value of one particular item, which we choose to call item 1. When we take a second item, we know from Equation (23) that q_{12} depends on the values of r_1 and r_2.

$$2q_{12} = q_{22}(r_1/r_2) + q_{11}(r_2/r_1). \tag{24}$$

Multiplying by $r_1 r_2$, and rearranging terms, we obtain the quadratic equation (25):

$$q_{11}r_2^2 - 2q_{12}r_1r_2 + q_{22}r_1^2 = 0. \tag{25}$$

We solve for r_2, as a function of r_1, and obtain two roots.

$$r_2 = r_1(q_{12} \pm \sqrt{q_{12}^2 - q_{11}q_{22}})/q_{11}. \tag{26}$$

If r_1 were known to be a certain number, Equation (26) would offer two possible values for r_2. Both values would be positive, real numbers, as long as the given values of q_{12}, q_{11} and q_{22} were actually manifest parameters of a latent content model. By examining some of the conditions which the r_i must satisfy, such as listed above ((16)–(19)), it might be possible to rule out one of the roots as a permissible value of r_2. There is no reason to think that this would be generally possible, however. We are going to substitute one or the other of the two roots of Equation (25) for r_2, when it arises in other equations. A new notation will help simplify much of the algebra that is to follow.

DEFINITIONS.

$$u_{ij} = q_{ij}/(q_{ii}q_{jj})^{1/2} \qquad \text{for all } i, j \tag{27}$$

and

$$\rho_i = r_i/(q_{ii})^{1/2} \qquad \text{for all } i. \tag{28}$$

The u_{ij} are known, and the ρ_i are unknown. Notice that it follows from the definition (28) that

$$s_i/(q_{ii})^{1/2} = 1/\rho_i. \tag{29}$$

The effect of using these parameters in place of the q_{ij} and r_i can be seen by substituting in Equation (25).

$$q_{11}q_{22}\rho_2^2 - 2u_{12}q_{11}q_{22}\rho_1\rho_2 + q_{22}q_{11}\rho_1^2 = 0.$$

Dividing out the product $q_{11}q_{22}$ leaves

$$\rho_1^2 + \rho_2^2 = 2u_{12}\rho_1\rho_2.$$

This, of course, can be extended to any pair of items:

$$\rho_i^2 + \rho_j^2 = 2u_{ij}\rho_i\rho_j, \qquad \text{for any } i \text{ and } j. \tag{30}$$

Equation (26) can also be simplified by this change of variable. As it stands, the equation can be factored:

$$r_2 = r_1(q_{12}/q_{11})(1 \pm \sqrt{1 - q_{11}q_{22}/q_{12}^2}).$$

The substitution leads to Equation (31).

$$\rho_2 = \rho_1(u_{12} \pm \sqrt{u_{12}^2 - 1}). \tag{31}$$

Notice that the same result can be obtained by solving Equation (30), with $i = 1$ and $j = 2$, for ρ_2. (We could have defined the parameters ρ_i in the previous section, and bypassed the (r_i, s_i) notation entirely. It aids the exposition to be able to go back and forth between these two notations.)

Let us now define

$$w_{12} = u_{12} + \sqrt{u_{12}^2 - 1}. \tag{32}$$

One possibility then is that

$$\rho_2 = \rho_1 w_{12}. \tag{33}$$

On the other hand,

$$(u_{12} + \sqrt{u_{12}^2 - 1})(u_{12} - \sqrt{u_{12}^2 - 1}) = 1,$$

and therefore

$$u_{12} - \sqrt{u_{12}^2 - 1} = 1/w_{12}.$$

Thus the *other* possibility is that

$$\rho_2 = \rho_1/w_{12}. \tag{34}$$

The reciprocal form of the two possible roots of Equation (31), as shown in Equations (33) and (34) is very convenient. For instance, it is easy to show that one of the two roots gives a point (r_2, s_2) which lies above (r_1, s_1), while the other root leads to a point that lies below the point (r_1, s_1). We have noted that the tangent made by a vector (r, s) and the r axis is equal to the ratio s/r. Hence

$$\tan \theta_2 = s_2/r_2$$
$$= q_{22}/r_2^2.$$

Referring to Equation (28), and replacing r_2 by ρ_2, we have

$$\tan \theta_2 = 1/\rho_2^2. \tag{35}$$

Using the root (33),

$$\tan \theta_2 = 1/(\rho_1^2 w_{12}^2), \tag{36}$$

while if θ_2' is the angle made by the point defined by the second root, (34), we have

$$\tan \theta_2' = w_{12}^2/\rho_1^2. \tag{37}$$

Since $1/\rho_1^2$ is equal to the tangent of θ_1, the following sequence of relations hold:

$$\tan \theta_2 = (\tan \theta_1)/w_{12}^2 < \tan \theta_1 < (\tan \theta_1)w_{12}^2 = \tan \theta_2'. \tag{38}$$

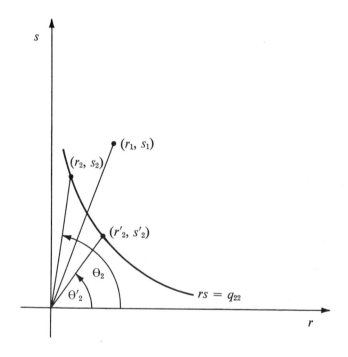

FIGURE 4

The Two Possible Locations of Item 2, in the $r-s$ Plane, when the Location of Item 1 Is Fixed

(The reader should satisfy himself that w_{12}, as defined by (32), must be larger than 1.) The geometry of the relationship (38) is shown in Figure 4.

ASIDE: We could define a second "standardized" parameter for each item to go with ρ_i by letting $\sigma_i = s_i/(q_{ii})^{1/2}$. The geometry of the "$\rho - \sigma$" space is simpler than that of the "$r - s$" space, since all of the points (ρ_i, σ_i) lie on the same hyperbola, namely $\rho\sigma = 1$. In these terms it is clearer that the problem is one of solving for the orientation of the points, i.e., determining the various angles θ_i or, equivalently, the tangents of those angles. Algebraically, of course, the parameters σ_i are superfluous, since we can write everything in terms of ρ_i. For this reason we will *not* make use of such parameters in what follows. ∎

3.2 *Extension to More Than Two Items*

Now we consider the entire set of items, and the indeterminancy involved in the computation of the set of parameters $(\rho_j, j > 2)$. We show first, in Theorem 3, that when the two parameters, ρ_1 and ρ_2, are fixed, a unique ρ_j is determined for all the items $j > 2$. In the previous section, however, we have shown that when ρ_1 is fixed there are only two possible values of ρ_2 consistent with the manifest information. We therefore can conclude that, given the manifest information, and a particular ρ_1, there will be exactly two different *sets* of parameters ρ_j possible, where $j > 1$. The equations by which these two sets are computed are derived in Theorem 4.

THEOREM 3: *For any item $j > 2$, ρ_j can be expressed uniquely in terms of manifest parameters and ρ_1 and ρ_2, if $\rho_2 \neq \rho_1$.*

PROOF: From Equation (30) we have

and also

$$\rho_1^2 + \rho_j^2 = 2\rho_1\rho_j u_{1j}$$

$$\rho_2^2 + \rho_j^2 = 2\rho_2\rho_j u_{2j}.$$

Since both these equations must hold at once, they may be subtracted. The resulting equation is linear in ρ_j, and the solution is

$$\rho_j = \frac{\rho_2^2 - \rho_1^2}{2(\rho_2 u_{2j} - \rho_1 u_{1j})}.$$

The condition $\rho_1 \neq \rho_2$ is all that is needed to insure that the denominator will be different from zero. ∎

THEOREM 4: *Let j be any item, and let w_{1j} and w'_{1j} be defined implicitly by (39) and (40). ρ_2 can take on two values, namely, $\rho_1 w_{12}$ and ρ_1/w_{12}.*

(i) *If we set $\rho_2 = \rho_1 w_{12}$, then*

$$\rho_j = \rho_1 \frac{u_{12}w_{12} - 1}{u_{2j}w_{12} - u_{1j}} = \rho_1 w_{1j}; \tag{39}$$

(ii) *If we set* $\rho_2 = \rho_1/w_{12}$, *then*

$$\rho_j = \rho_1 \frac{u_{12} - w_{12}}{u_{2j} - w_{12}u_{1j}} = \rho_1 w'_{1j}; \tag{40}$$

(iii)
$$w'_{1j} = 1/w_{1j}. \tag{41}$$

PROOF: (i) Substitute $\rho_1 w_{12}$ for ρ_2, in Theorem 3.

$$\rho_j = \rho_1^2(w_{12}^2 - 1)/2\rho_1(w_{12}u_{2j} - u_{1j}).$$

The same substitution in (30) gives us:

$$\rho_1^2 + \rho_1^2 w_{12}^2 = 2u_{12}w_{12}\rho_1^2.$$

Therefore

$$w_{12}^2 = 2u_{12}w_{12} - 1.$$

The equation for ρ_j becomes:

$$\rho_j = \rho_1(2u_{12}w_{12} - 2)/2(w_{12}u_{2j} - u_{1j}),$$
$$\rho_j = \rho_1 w_{1j},$$

as defined in (39).

(ii) The proof of part (i) should now be applied with w_{12} replaced by $1/w_{12}$ everywhere it appears. The final result will be:

$$\rho_j = \rho_1(u_{12}/w_{12} - 1)/(u_{2j}/w_{12} - u_{1j}).$$

Multiply numerator and denominator by w_{12}:

$$\rho_j = \rho_1(u_{12} - w_{12})/(u_{2j} - w_{12}u_{1j})$$
$$= \rho_1 w'_{1j}$$

as defined in (40).

(iii) The product $w_{1j}w'_{1j}$ equals:

$$\frac{w_{12}(u_{12}^2 + 1) - u_{12}(w_{12}^2 + 1)}{w_{12}(u_{2j}^2 + u_{1j}^2) - u_{1j}u_{2j}(w_{12}^2 + 1)}.$$

Once again we shall use the fact that

$$w_{12}^2 + 1 = 2u_{12}w_{12}.$$

When this is substituted, w_{12} can be cancelled, leaving

$$w_{1j}w'_{1j} = \frac{1 - u_{12}^2}{u_{2j}^2 + u_{1j}^2 - 2u_{1j}u_{2j}u_{12}}.$$

That this ratio equals 1 follows from the fact that the matrix U has rank 2, just as the Q matrix has. Therefore the determinant

$$\begin{vmatrix} 1 & u_{12} & u_{13} \\ u_{12} & 1 & u_{23} \\ u_{13} & u_{23} & 1 \end{vmatrix} = 0.$$

By expanding the determinant by its third row, we see that it equals:

$$u_{13} \begin{vmatrix} u_{12} & u_{13} \\ 1 & u_{23} \end{vmatrix} - u_{23} \begin{vmatrix} 1 & u_{13} \\ u_{12} & u_{23} \end{vmatrix} + \begin{vmatrix} 1 & u_{12} \\ u_{12} & 1 \end{vmatrix} = 0,$$

which implies that

$$1 - u_{12}^2 = u_{2j}(u_{2j} - u_{1j}u_{12}) + u_{1j}(u_{1j} - u_{2j}u_{12}).$$

Thus $w_{1j}w'_{1j} = 1$. ∎

It is interesting to note that the Equations (39) and (40) actually hold for any item j, even for $j = 1$ or $j = 2$. That is, by direct substitution it can be shown that $w_{11} = 1 = w'_{11}$, and $w_{12} = w_{12}$ and $w'_{12} = 1/w_{12}$. A proof is left to the reader.

3.3 *Analysis of Third Order Parameters*

The formula for the third-order symmetric parameter $[ijk]$ was derived in Section 2.1. There, of course, it was expressed in terms of the original traceline parameters.

$$[123] = \frac{b_1 b_2 b_3 d_1 d_2 d_3 [(d_1 + d_2)(d_1 + d_3)(d_2 + d_3) - 2(1 + d_1 + d_2 + d_3)]}{(1 + d_1)(1 + d_2)(1 + d_3)(1 + d_1 + d_2)(1 + d_1 + d_3)(1 + d_2 + d_3)(1 + d_1 + d_2 + d_3)}. \tag{42}$$

In order to continue the solution we have to write $[123]$ as a function of the standardized parameters ρ_1, ρ_2 and ρ_3. We need to derive some formulas for the b_i and d_i in terms of the ρ_i.

First, we know that r_i and ρ_i are defined by:

$$r_i = (1 + d_i)/b_i d_i$$

and

$$\rho_i = r_i/(q_{ii})^{1/2}.$$

The first few terms in (42) can therefore be written:

$$\frac{b_1 b_2 b_3 d_1 d_2 d_3}{(1 + d_1)(1 + d_2)(1 + d_3)} = \frac{1}{r_1 r_2 r_3} = \frac{1}{\rho_1 \rho_2 \rho_3 (q_{11} q_{22} q_{33})^{1/2}}. \tag{43}$$

Another of our early equalities was:

$$q_{ij} = r_i r_j (1 + d_i + d_j).$$

When we divide both sides by the square root of $q_{ii} q_{jj}$, we get:

$$u_{ij} = \rho_i \rho_j (1 + d_i + d_j). \tag{44}$$

Equation (44) enables us to substitute for all the remaining factors in (42):

$$(1 + d_1 + d_2)(1 + d_1 + d_3)(1 + d_2 + d_3) = u_{12} u_{13} u_{23}/(\rho_1 \rho_2 \rho_3)^2; \tag{45}$$

$$1 + d_1 + d_2 + d_3 = (u_{12}/\rho_1 \rho_2 + u_{13}/\rho_1 \rho_3 + u_{23}/\rho_2 \rho_3 - 1)/2. \tag{46}$$

175

Even the more complicated factor that remains in the numerator takes a manageable form.

$$
\begin{aligned}
(d_1 + d_2)&(d_1 + d_3)(d_2 + d_3) - 2(1 + d_1 + d_2 + d_3) \\
&= (u_{12}/\rho_1\rho_2 - 1)(u_{13}/\rho_1\rho_3 - 1)(u_{23}/\rho_2\rho_3 - 1) \\
&\quad - (u_{12}/\rho_1\rho_2 + u_{13}/\rho_1\rho_3 + u_{23}/\rho_2\rho_3 - 1) \\
&= u_{12}u_{13}u_{23}(1 - \rho_1\rho_2/u_{12} - \rho_1\rho_3/u_{13} - \rho_2\rho_3/u_{23})/(\rho_1\rho_2\rho_3)^2. \quad (47)
\end{aligned}
$$

When the terms (43), (45), (46) and (47) are substituted in (42) the result is:

$$
[123] = \frac{2(1 - \rho_1\rho_2/u_{12} - \rho_1\rho_3/u_{13} - \rho_2\rho_3/u_{23})}{\rho_1\rho_2\rho_3(q_{11}q_{22}q_{33})^{1/2}(u_{12}/\rho_1\rho_2 + u_{13}/\rho_1\rho_3 + u_{23}/\rho_2\rho_3)}.
$$

A standardization of the third order symmetric parameter is thus indicated by Equation (48).

$$
\frac{[123](q_{11}q_{22}q_{33})^{1/2}}{2} = \frac{1 - \rho_1\rho_2/u_{12} - \rho_1\rho_3/u_{13} - \rho_2\rho_3/u_{23}}{\rho_1\rho_2\rho_3(u_{12}/\rho_1\rho_2 + u_{13}/\rho_1\rho_3 + u_{23}/\rho_2\rho_3 - 1)}. \quad (48)
$$

This standardization becomes more familiar when we recall that the q's are reciprocals of cross products,

$$
q_{ii} = 1/[ii].
$$

The left side of (48) is, therefore (defining a new parameter h_{123}),

$$
h_{123} = [123]/2([11][22][33])^{1/2}. \quad (49)
$$

Now we are ready to apply the results of the previous section. We know how to write ρ_2 and ρ_3 in terms of ρ_1, and so Equation (48) can be reduced to an equation involving only one unknown parameter, ρ_1. For the one solution, with

$$
\rho_2 = \rho_1 w_{12}, \quad \text{and} \quad \rho_3 = \rho_1 w_{13},
$$

substituted in Equation (48), we find that

$$
\begin{aligned}
h_{123} &= \frac{1 - \rho_1^2(w_{12}/u_{12} + w_{13}/u_{13} + w_{12}w_{13}/u_{23})}{[\rho_1(u_{12}/w_{12} + u_{13}/w_{13} + u_{23}/w_{12}w_{13}) - \rho_1^3]w_{12}w_{13}} \\
&= \frac{1 - \rho_1^2 A}{(\rho_1 B - \rho_1^3)w_{12}w_{13}} \quad (50)
\end{aligned}
$$

where A and B are coefficients, depending only on manifest parameters, defined implicitly by Equation (50).

The alternative solution, from Theorem 4, was

$$
\rho_2 = \rho_1/w_{12} \quad \text{and} \quad \rho_3 = \rho_1/w_{13}.
$$

This implies that, in (50), we should replace each w_{ij} by $1/w_{ij}$. The result of this substitution is shown in Equation (51).

$$h_{123} = \frac{1 - \rho_1^2(1/u_{12}w_{12} + 1/u_{13}w_{13} + 1/u_{23}w_{12}w_{13})}{[\rho_1(u_{12}w_{12} + u_{13}w_{13} + u_{23}w_{13}w_{12}) - \rho_1^3]/w_{12}w_{13}}$$

$$= \frac{(1 - \rho_1^2 A')w_{12}w_{13}}{(\rho_1 B' - \rho_1^3)}. \tag{51}$$

The coefficients A' and B' are defined implicitly by the Equation (51).

It is important to remember how these two equations ((50) and (51)) were derived: the unknowns, ρ_1, ρ_2 and ρ_3 must *either* satisfy

         (i) $\rho_2 = \rho_1 w_{12}$ and $\rho_3 = w_{13}\rho_1$

or   (ii) $\rho_2 = \rho_1/w_{12}$ and $\rho_3 = \rho_1/w_{13}$.

If (i) holds, ρ_1 will satisfy Equation (50), while if (ii) holds, ρ_1 will satisfy Equation (51). The equations *do not have a common root*, so that we should not attempt to solve them simultaneously. If we think of the *true* value of ρ_1, we can say that it is either a root of (50), or a root of (51); at this point, given only the manifest probabilities, we cannot say which equation, or which root, will give us the true value.

The problem now remains to discover conditions under which there may be found a unique solution which unequivocally specifies the latent parameters that actually generated the given set of manifest parameters. The possibility of *extraneous solutions* to the accounting equations arises at two points. First, we have two equations (50 and 51), and do not know which is the proper one in any particular situation. Second, each of these equations, being of third degree, will have more than one root. In the next section we shall attempt to suggest ways of eliminating the extraneous roots, of determining the true latent parameters. In conclusion we summarize the steps in the solution, up to this point.

(1) Compute the diagonal entries of the Q matrix, according to Equation (22).
(2) Choose a pair of items, denoted here by "1" and "2", and compute w_{12}, defined in Equation (32).
(3) Compute w_{1j}, for any other item j, according to Equation (39).
(4) Compute the roots of Equations (50) and (51).
(5) If z is positive, less than 1, and a root of (50), then it may be true that $\rho_1 = z$, and $\rho_j = zw_{1j}$, for all j.
(6) If z' is positive, less than 1, and a root of (51), then it may be true that $\rho_1 = z'$ and $\rho_j = z'/w_{1j}$, for all j.

3.4   *Identification of Latent Parameters*

It is known that the latent parameters ρ_j must lie between 0 and 1. (In fact, ρ_j equals the square root of $1/(1 + 2d_j)$.) We used this fact in stating points (5) and (6) of the summary in Section 3.3: we can rule out as possible values of ρ_1 any roots of Equations (50) and (51) which fall outside the unit interval.

Furthermore, even if $0 < z < 1$, for instance, the solution of (50) can be rejected if, for any j,

$$zw_{1j} > 1,$$

and the analogous statement can be made for any root z' of (51).

A more systematic statement about the roots of those cubic equations can be made, however, by examining the signs of the coefficients of the equations. The conclusion is that if the third-order parameter [123] is negative, each equation will have one, and only one, positive root. This is demonstrated in the proof of Theorem 5. Let us first write these two equations in the standard form. (50) becomes (substituting t for the unknown parameter):

$$f(t) = t^3 - t^2 A/h_{123}w_{12}w_{13} - tB + 1/h_{123}w_{12}w_{13} = 0. \qquad (52)$$

and (51) becomes:

$$g(t) = t^3 - t^2 A'w_{12}w_{13}/h_{123} - tB' + w_{12}w_{13}/h_{123} = 0. \qquad (53)$$

All w_{1j} are positive, by definition, as are all q_{ij}; A, B and A' and B' are also positive, since they are sums of products or ratios of w's and q's. Only the sign of h_{123}, which is the same as the sign of [123], is permitted to be either positive or negative.

THEOREM 5: *If* [123] *is negative, Equation* (52) *has only one positive root, and Equation* (53) *has only one positive root. If* [123] *is positive, both equations may have as many as two positive roots.*

PROOF: When $h_{123} < 0$, Equation (52) has the form

$$f(t) = t^3 + c_2 t^2 - c_1 t - c_0 = 0$$

where the coefficients c_0, c_1 and c_2 are positive. When $t = 0$ the function $f(t)$ has a negative value, $-c_0$, and its *slope* at that point is also negative, $-c_1$. In addition, $f(t)$ must approach $+\infty$ as t gets large, and $-\infty$ as t gets small.

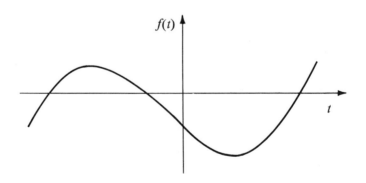

FIGURE 5

Graph of the Function:
$$f(t) = t^3 + c_2 t^2 - c_1 t - c_0$$

The shape of such a curve is illustrated in Figure 5. There can be only one crossing of the positive part of the t-axis.

Equation (53), $g(t) = 0$, has exactly the same sign pattern, and so the same argument holds.

When $h_{123} > 0$, we get

$$f(t) = t^3 - c_2t^2 - c_1t + c_0 = 0.$$

Here, at the intercept $t = 0$, the slope is still negative $(-c_1)$, but the value of $f(t)$ is positive $(+c_0)$. The function has the form shown in Figure 6, which crosses the positive t-axis twice, once, or not at all, depending on the values of the three coefficients. ▌

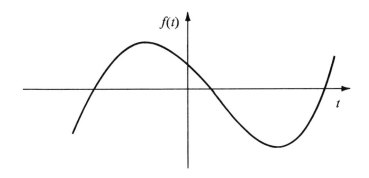

FIGURE 6

Graph of the Function:
$$f(t) = t^3 - c_2t^2 - c_1t + c_0$$

Notice that the sign of $[ijk]$ depends on the parameters d_i, d_j and d_k. Equation (42) indicates that the sign of

$$(d_i + d_j)(d_i + d_k)(d_j + d_k) - 2(1 + d_i + d_j + d_k)$$

determines the sign of $[ijk]$. Thus, if all the d's are smaller than one, $[ijk]$ is negative, while if they are all larger than one, $[ijk]$ will be positive. This fact is not hard to prove, but we simply indicate what happens if all the d's are equal. Then the term is:

$$(2d)^3 - 2(1 + 3d) = (d - 1)(8d^2 + 8d + 2),$$

which is positive, negative, or zero according as d is greater than, less than, or equal to one. Of course, if some of the d parameters are greater than one, and others are less than one, determining the sign of the $[ijk]$ becomes a question of their relative magnitudes.

As long as there is some third-order parameter which is negative, there will be only two possible sets of latent parameters. One is obtained by setting ρ_1 equal to the positive root of (52), and the other by setting ρ_1 equal to the positive root of (53). After obtaining these, we can then check whether the various conditions are satisfied, hoping to be able to eliminate one of them. On the other hand, if *all* third-order parameters are positive, there may be as many as four different solutions of those cubic equations, and the process of checking becomes more tedious.

There is another way of ascertaining the true latent parameters, and that is to look at several different third-order parameters. For example, if we take the triplet (1, 2, 4), we can construct two more cubic equations one root of which is the true value of ρ_1. Letting Equation (52) read:

$$f_{1;23}(t) = 0 \tag{54}$$

and (53) be:

$$g_{1;23}(t) = 0 \tag{55}$$

the extension to the triplet (1, 2, 4) gives us additional equations

$$f_{1;24}(t) = 0 \tag{56}$$

and

$$g_{1;24}(t) = 0. \tag{57}$$

Assume for the moment that both [123] and [124] are negative; then each equation has one positive root. If the true value ρ_1 is the root of (54), it must also be the root of (56) (because both equations rest on the same assumption, i.e., that $\rho_j = \rho_1 w_{1j}$), but the roots of Equations (55) and (57) need not be the same. The reverse is true, of course, if the true value is the root of (55).

When the third-order parameters are positive, the four equations may each have two positive roots, but there is no reason to believe that the extraneous roots will appear as roots of more than one equation. Thus, by matching the equal roots, for different triples of items, we can determine the true value of ρ_1.

Note that we do not have to solve all of those equations, merely (54) and (55). The various roots obtained can be checked by just substituting them in (56) and (57), as appropriate.

The important result which we have *not* obtained would be to state explicitly the conditions under which the two "false" equations in the set (54–57) have different roots, because when this is the case the procedure will reveal which root is the true parameter value. We conjecture, however, that $d_3 \neq d_4$ would be a sufficient condition.

ASIDE: Let us give a few more details to the above argument. Suppose that [123] is positive. Let z be the positive root of (54), and let z' be the positive root of (55). Then either $\rho_1 = z$ or $\rho_1 = z'$. Now substitute z into (56) and z' into (57). If

$$f_{1;24}(z) = 0 \quad \text{and} \quad g_{1;24}(z') \neq 0$$

then $\rho_1 = z$ and $\rho_j = zw_{1j}$ for all j.
   If

$$f_{1;24}(z) \neq 0 \quad \text{and} \quad g_{1;24}(z') = 0$$

then $\rho_1 = z'$ and $\rho_j = z'/w_{1j}$ for all j.

If

$$f_{1;24}(z) = 0 \quad \text{and} \quad g_{1;24}(z') = 0$$

then we have no new information, and can draw no further conclusions about ρ_1. (The fourth logical alternative, i.e., that both $f_{1;24}(z)$ and $g_{1;24}(z')$ are different from zero, cannot occur unless the model does not apply, for we have assumed that there really is some true set of latent parameters.) ∎

After the ρ_j have been determined, for every item j, straightforward substitutions in equations that have been derived previously permit the calculation of the traceline parameters, a_j, b_j, and d_j. The necessary equations include:

$$(\rho_j)^2 = 1/(1 + 2d_j),$$
$$d_j = (1/\rho_j^2 - 1)/2;$$
$$q_{jj} = (1 + d_j)^2(1 + 2d_j)/(b_j d_j)^2,$$
$$(b_j)^2 = (1 + d_j)^2(1 + 2d_j)/q_{jj}(d_j)^2;$$
$$a_j = p_j - b_j/(1 + d_j).$$

In Section 4 we shall briefly discuss the difficulty in estimating these latent parameters when there is sampling error, or deviation from the model, present in the manifest data. In Section 5 some special cases are discussed.

4. Examples, and the Analysis of Real Data

4.1 *Example*

Let us now illustrate some of the derivations of the previous sections, by considering a hypothetical latent structure. We suppose that we have a model whose latent parameters are given in Table 1. The manifest parameters were computed according to the accounting Equations, (10), (42). The marginal probabilities, the Q matrix, and the third order parameters $[ijk]$ are given in Table 2.

TABLE 1

Latent Parameters of a Hypothetical
Latent Content Model

Latent Parameters	Item 1	Item 2	Item 3	Item 4	Item 5
a_i	0.2	0.2	0.2	0.2	0.2
b_i	0.4	0.6	0.8	0.4	0.6
d_i	0.2	0.5	1.0	3.0	5.0

TABLE 2

*Manifest Data Generated by the Latent Content
Model with Parameters given in Table 1.*

	Item				
	1	2	3	4	5
Marginal Probabilities	8/15	3/5	3/5	3/10	3/10

Matrix Q of Reciprocals of Cross Products

Item	Item				
	1	2	3	4	5
1	315	255/2	165/2	210	186
2		50	125/4	75	65
3			75/4	125/3	35
4				700/9	60
5					44

Some Third-Order Symmetric Parameters

$$[123] = -184/(33)(17)(375) = -184/(210,375)$$
$$[124] = -52/(47)(17)(63)(25) = -52/(1,258,425)$$
$$[125] = 662/(67)(17)(39)(155) = 662/(6,885,255)$$

From the data in Table 2 we first compute the various

$$u_{ij} = q_{ij}/(q_{ii}q_{jj})^{1/2}.$$

The solution will begin by determining ρ_1, and so we must compute w_{12} according to Equation (32).

$$w_{12} = u_{12} + (u_{12}^2 - 1)^{1/2}$$
$$= 17/2(70)^{1/2} + (9/280)^{1/2}$$
$$= 10/(70)^{1/2}.$$

Next w_{13}, w_{14} and w_{15} are computed from Equation (39):

$$w_{1j} = (u_{12}w_{12} - 1)/(u_{2j}w_{12} - u_{1j}).$$

182

Intermediate computations include:

$$u_{12}w_{12} - 1 \;\; = 170/140 - 1 = 3/14;$$
$$u_{23}w_{12} - u_{13} = 25/2(105)^{1/2} - 11/(105)^{1/2} = 3/2(105)^{1/2};$$
$$u_{24}w_{12} - u_{14} = 45/14(5)^{1/2} - 3/(5)^{1/2} = 3/14(5)^{1/2};$$
$$u_{25}w_{12} - u_{15} = 65/2(385)^{1/2} - 31/(385)^{1/2} = 3/2(385)^{1/2}.$$

These lead to the following:

$$w_{13} = \sqrt{105}/7 = \sqrt{15/7}$$
$$w_{14} = \sqrt{5}$$
$$w_{15} = \sqrt{385}/7 = \sqrt{55/7}.$$

The value of [123] is negative, so we choose to construct the cubic equations for this triplet of items, knowing in advance that each of the two equations will have only one positive root. Referring to Equations (50) and (51), we need to compute:

$$h_{123} = [123](q_{11}q_{22}q_{33})^{1/2}/2$$
$$= \frac{-46(210)^{1/2}}{(33)(85)};$$

$$A = w_{12}/u_{12} + w_{13}/u_{13} + w_{12}w_{13}/u_{23}$$
$$= 20/17 + 15/11 + 12/7 = 5554/(7)(\dot{1}1)(17).$$
$$B = u_{12}/w_{12} \dotplus u_{13}/w_{13} + u_{23}/w_{12}w_{13}$$
$$= 17/20 + 11/15 + 7/12 = 13/6.$$
$$A' = 1/u_{12}w_{12} + 1/u_{13}w_{13} + 1/u_{23}w_{12}w_{13}$$
$$= 14/17 + 7/11 + 14/25 = 7(1349)/(11)(17)(25).$$
$$B' = u_{12}w_{12} + u_{13}w_{13} + u_{23}w_{12}w_{13}$$
$$= 17/14 + 11/7 + 25/14 = 32/7.$$

Under the assumption that $\rho_j = \rho_1 w_{1j}$, we have the cubic equation (50), which in its standard form, (52), is:

$$f_{1;23}(t) = t^3 - t^2 A/h_{123}w_{12}w_{13} - tB + 1/h_{123}w_{12}w_{13} = 0.$$

Substituting,

$$f_{1;23}(t) = t^3 + t^2(2777/46(35)^{1/2}) - t(13/6) - (77)(85)/460(35)^{1/2} = 0.$$

Under the alternative assumption, that $\rho_j = \rho_1/w_{1j}$, the equation, (53), is:

$$g_{1;23}(t) = t^3 - t^2 A'w_{12}w_{13}/h_{123} - tB' + w_{12}w_{13}/h_{123} = 0.$$

Substituting,

$$g_{1;23}(t) = t^3 + t^2(4047/46(35)^{1/2}) - t(32/7) - (5)(33)(85)/7(46)(35)^{1/2} = 0.$$

Since this is a constructed example, we actually know what the true value of ρ_1 is, namely

$$\rho_1 = 1/(1 + 2d_1)^{1/2} = 1/(1.4)^{1/2} = 5/(35)^{1/2}.$$

We can easily check that this is a root of $g_{1;23}(t) = 0$, but not a root of $f_{1;23}(t) = 0$. That is,

$$f_{1;23}\big(5/(35)^{1/2}\big) \neq 0$$

and

$$g_{1;23}\big(5/(35)^{1/2}\big) = 0.$$

For instance,

$$\begin{aligned}
g_{1;23}\big(5/(35)^{1/2}\big) &= [5/(35)^{1/2}][25/35 + (5)(4047)/(46)(35) \\
&\quad - 32/7 - (33)(85)/(7)(46)] \\
&= [5/(35)^{1/2}][-27/7 + 1242/(7)(46)] = 0.
\end{aligned}$$

The positive root of the equation $f_{1;23}(t) = 0$ is approximately equal to 0.58.

In order to illustrate how, in practice, we could determine the actual value of ρ_1, we look at another triple of items. We choose items 1, 2 and 4, noting that [124] is also negative. Therefore the equations $f_{1;24}(t) = 0$ and $g_{1;24}(t) = 0$ each have one positive root. In order to write these equations we need to compute:

$$\begin{aligned}
h_{124} &= \big(-52/(47)(17)(63)(25)\big)(350\sqrt{10})/2 \\
&= \frac{-52\sqrt{10}}{(47)(17)(9)};
\end{aligned}$$

$$\begin{aligned}
A &= w_{12}/u_{12} + w_{14}/u_{14} + w_{12}w_{14}/u_{24} \\
&= 20/17 + 5/3 + 4/3 = 71/17; \\
B &= u_{12}/w_{12} + u_{14}/w_{14} + u_{24}/w_{12}w_{14} \\
&= 17/20 + 3/5 + 3/4 = 11/5; \\
A' &= 1/u_{12}w_{12} + 1/u_{14}w_{14} + 1/u_{24}w_{12}w_{14} \\
&= 14/17 + 1/3 + 14/45 = 1123/(17)(45); \\
B' &= 17/14 + 3 + 45/14 = 52/7.
\end{aligned}$$

The two equations turn out to be:

$$\begin{aligned}
f_{1;24}(t) &= t^3 + t^2(47)(639)(\sqrt{35})/2600 - t(11/5) \\
&\quad - (47)(17)(9)(\sqrt{35})/2600 = 0
\end{aligned}$$

and

$$g_{1;24}(t) = t^3 + t^2(47)(1123)/(52\sqrt{35}) - t(52/7) - (47)(17)(45)/(52\sqrt{35}) = 0.$$

It is quite easy to check that $5/(35)^{1/2}$ is a root of the latter equation, and a bit more tedious to show that the positive root of $f_{1;24}(t) = 0$ is approximately 0.503. This verifies that ρ_1 does indeed equal $\sqrt{5/7}$: there is no other alternative.

It is actually unnecessary to use the equation involving items 1, 2, and 4 to eliminate the root of $f_{1;23}(t) = 0$ as a possible value of ρ_1, for the condition that every ρ_j must be less than 1 eliminates this root. The root is, as we noted, approximately

$$z = 0.58.$$

If $z = \rho_1$, then $\rho_j = zw_{1j}$. Substituting, we would have

$$\rho_2 = (0.58)(10/7)^{1/2};$$
$$\rho_3 = (0.58)(15/7)^{1/2};$$
$$\rho_4 = (0.58)(5)^{1/2} > (0.58)(2.0) > 1;$$
$$\rho_5 = (0.58)(55/7)^{1/2} > (0.58)(2.0) > 1.$$

The indicated values of ρ_4 and ρ_5 are greater than 1, and so we reject this possible solution.

To complete the solution, we use the root

$$\rho_1 = (5/7)^{1/2}$$

and the relation

$$\rho_j = \rho_1/w_{1j}$$

to compute these parameters:

$$\rho_2 = (5/7)^{1/2}(7/10)^{1/2} = (1/2)^{1/2};$$
$$\rho_3 = (5/7)^{1/2}(7/15)^{1/2} = (1/3)^{1/2};$$
$$\rho_4 = (5/7)^{1/2}(1/5)^{1/2} = (1/7)^{1/2};$$
$$\rho_5 = (5/7)^{1/2}(7/55)^{1/2} = (1/11)^{1/2}.$$

Using the identity

$$1 + 2d_j = (1/\rho_j)^2,$$

the values of the d_j are found to be:

$$d_1 = 0.2; d_2 = 0.5; d_3 = 1.0; d_4 = 3.0; d_5 = 5.0.$$

Now the b's and a's can be calculated, using the formulas

$$(b_i)^2 = (1 + d_i)^2(1 + 2d_i)/q_{ii}(d_i)^2$$
$$a_i = p_i - b_i/(1 + d_i), \qquad \text{for all } i.$$

The reader can easily verify that the results agree with the original parameters, given in Table 1.

4.2 An Example of Measuring Social Rigidity[3]

We now turn to an actual example of the application of the latent content model. It is sometimes argued that, within the personality, there is some summarizing trait which we might call rigidity, which in its social expression involves aspects of intolerance of disobedience, prejudice against minority groups and intolerance of (what are perceived as) minority points of view.

_____

[3]This section was taken from Robert Somers, "Latent Content Model of Latent Structure," unpublished Ph.D. dissertation, Columbia U., 1961, with the permission of the author. The estimates of parameters were obtained by an approximation technique, not involving third-order data, which is outlined in Section 4.3.

185

In order to attempt to measure such an underlying trait, it seems reasonable to turn to attitudes that reflect those social expressions. For example, in September, 1947, a sample of 500 persons living in and around Cincinnati, Ohio, were asked (among other things) the following questions, in the form of statements with which they were asked to agree or disagree. In some cases a respondent was unable to decide what his feelings were toward the statement: because of the phrasing of the statements, and the resulting distribution of answers, any respondent who agreed with a statement, or was unable to decide, was considered as having a "positive" response. This was taken as an indicator of the presence, in some degree, of the underlying concept we have termed rigidity.

1. It would be best to keep Negroes from voting or they would get too much power in the south. (36.8% say "agree" or "can't decide")
2. Generally speaking, Negroes are lazy and ignorant. (71.6% say "agree" or "can't decide")
3. Negroes who have had higher education are more likely to be rude than other Negroes. (42.1% say "agree" or "can't decide")

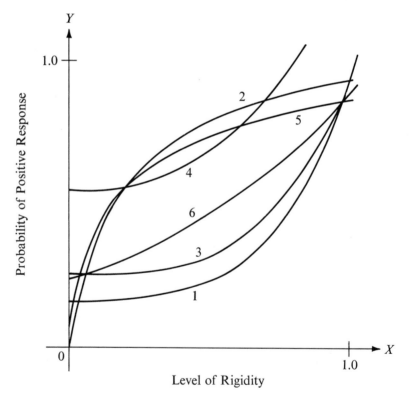

FIGURE 7

Tracelines of Items Measuring Social Rigidity (Item Numbers Shown Beside Curves)

4. The most important thing to teach children is absolute obedience to parents. (72.2% say "agree" or "can't decide")
5. Any good leader should be strict with people under him to gain their respect. (68.6% say "agree" or "can't decide")
6. Prison is too good for sex criminals; they should be publicly whipped or worse. (52.1% say "agree" or "can't decide")

As data with which to solve the model, the proportion of respondents answering positively each item, and each pair and triplet of items, were utilized in the accounting equations. The matrix Q is shown in Table 3. The resulting trace-lines are shown in Figure 7; the estimated latent parameters from which these curves were plotted are shown in Table 4.

TABLE 3

Matrix Q of Cross Product Reciprocals, for the Items Measuring Social Rigidity

	Item					
	1	2	3	4	5	6
1	—	18.2	16.2	13.4	29.4	18.2
2	18.2	—	21.6	29.2	26.4	28.7
3	16.2	21.6	—	19.3	32.3	18.2
4	13.4	29.2	19.3	—	21.8	20.2
5	29.4	26.4	32.3	21.8	—	21.6
6	18.2	28.7	18.2	20.2	21.6	—

TABLE 4

Latent Parameters Estimated from Data on Social Rigidity (Ordered in Terms of d_i)

Item	a_i	b_i	d_i
1	0.12	1.00	3.04
3	0.18	0.79	2.32
4	0.46	0.80	1.98
6	0.18	0.75	1.22
5	−0.15	1.07	0.27
2	−0.22	1.19	0.26

From these tracelines one can learn a great deal about the meaning of these several items in the measurement of that which they have in common, which we have designated by the term social rigidity. First, however, it should be noted that the model does not fit perfectly, since some of the probabilities are greater than 1.0, and some are less than 0. It may be assumed that this minor degree of error is present because the model postulates a situation somewhat simpler than actually obtains in nature. However, the situation shown here is not so bad that it precludes an interpretation of the results; the main source of difficulty is that the marginal of item 4 ($p_4 = 0.722$) is too high. It is conceivable that what we have observed in our sample is a poor estimate of this population parameter, from which the population values of the latent parameters are in turn estimated.

The interpretation of these items is most interesting. Notice, for one thing, that all the items except 4 start at a relatively low point on the left; there is little "cultural overlay" in these responses, which are instead a rather direct expression of social rigidity. The exception is item 4 ("the most important thing to teach children is obedience to parents"). As we have seen, this suggests that there is a culturally shared opinion about the teaching of obedience, more than about the other items. This is not unreasonable, since such teaching by parents is a visible act between parents and in many circumstances between neighbors, while the holding of other opinions is not necessarily so visible. Put differently, a respondent need not himself be rigid, but merely need to accept the rigidity of his spouse or neighbor in his matter, in order to give a positive response.

An interesting contrast with item 4 is item 5. These both have high marginals ($p_4 = 0.722$, $p_5 = 0.686$) but for very different reasons. A person who has little rigidity has almost no chance of agreeing with item 5 ("any good leader should be strict . . .") but it takes only a very little rigidity to greatly increase this probability. There is little cultural sharing of such an opinion, but at the same time the level of rigidity necessary to induce this sort of an opinion is relatively low.

This type of item, in turn, can be contrasted with item 1 ("it would be best to keep Negroes from voting . . ."). It is perhaps surprising that it takes a high level of rigidity in order to lead to a positive response to this item, but that is the case. Since this is true, the marginal for this item is relatively low ($p_1 = 0.368$). One might speculate that in this matter there is a cultural impact acting in the opposite way, to *prevent* this opinion from being expressed. Even 20 years ago when these questions were asked, there may have been a feeling that it was "un-American" to keep Negroes from voting. The cultural prescription of a right to vote for everyone conflicted with the personal disposition to be anti-Negro, and a high level of rigidity was required to overcome this conflict with the norm of equality in voting.

From this brief illustration it is clear that a great deal that is ordinarily hidden from view can be learned about the indicators of a concept by performing this kind of analysis. It can be anticipated that this type of analysis can add a great deal to our knowledge of such intuitively grasped but still vague concepts as, in this case, social rigidity.

188

As an illustration, one can conceive of a systematically planned survey that attempted to test out some of the speculations that have been cast as interpretations here. If, for example, it is true that feelings about teaching obedience to children are more socially shared than the other opinions, one might suppose that younger parents with children in the home would have a greater tendency to share in this culture, while older parents, or couples without children, might exhibit tracelines quite different from item 4, starting at a much lower point to the left. Again, if the cultural and personality responses conflict in item 1, it could be anticipated that the traceline in an unreconstructed southern town of the United States might be quite different from the traceline shown here, for respondents in Cincinnati.

4.3 The Analysis of Real Data

A systematic study of the problems that arise when sampling variation is present in the manifest probabilities has not been carried out. Part of such a study would involve generating random samples from a latent content model and seeing how the estimates of the latent parameters varied. This would be similar to the kind of work that has been done on latent class models.

It would also be valuable to be able to state rules for deciding whether certain data seem to satisfy the restrictions of this model. A computer program would be required, of course, but the writing of a useful program offers many challenges. An early program for the IBM 650, by Somers, considered the Q matrix, the condition that it be of rank two, and the estimation of the diagonal entries, (q_{ii}), but his work has not been followed up.

The model was applied to several different sets of data, and some results are reported in Somers (1961) and Lazarsfeld (1959b). The method of estimating the latent parameters did not follow the solution of the accounting equations given here, however. Generally, the estimation used as data the marginals (p_i) and the cross product reciprocals (q_{ij}), ignoring the third-order data. The procedure uses the same logic as does the estimation procedure for the latent class model developed by Gibson, which we mentioned in Chapter 4.

Briefly, the method is as follows. The sample Q matrix will not be exactly rank two, so the first step is to find a matrix that is of rank two, and is also as close as possible to the sample matrix. Then values of (r_i) and (s_i) are found so that the i, j entry of this "fitted" matrix equals

$$(r_i s_j + r_j s_i)/2.$$

Finally Theorem 3 is used to characterize the set of all possible r's and s's which satisfy the relation. This leaves one free parameter, which required third-order data, as we saw in Section 2. With real data, however, it may turn out that the conditions on the latent parameters, such as the requirement that

$$s_i - r_i > 2/p_i, \qquad \text{for all } i,$$

leave little freedom on acceptable values of r_i and s_i. Some "average" solution is thus offered as a final estimate.

189

In fact, it was usually the case that there was *no* estimate derived in this way from the marginal proportions and a "fitted" Q matrix that satisfied all the conditions on all the items. For instance, in the example of items dealing with social rigidity which was included above, the final estimates included "impossible" values for some of the latent parameters: negative values of a, and values of $a + b$ greater than 1. Thus the estimation problem became one of finding the least unacceptable parameters, rather than one of choosing arbitrarily among a set of equally acceptable estimates.

Some of these inconsistencies are surely due to the fact that the latent content model does not really apply to the actual situation being studied. It is difficult to say for certain, however, until we know how much sampling variability can be expected simply by chance if the model *did* apply.

Let us be a little more specific about some of the details of the estimating procedure just described. First, concerning the computation of a fitted Q matrix, which has rank 2, it is necessary to define some criterion of "closeness". A "least squares" criterion was used by Somers. That is, if

$$\bar{Q} = (\bar{q}_{ij})$$

is the sample matrix, the fitted matrix satisfies the condition that

$$\sum_{i \neq j} \sum (\bar{q}_{ij} - q_{ij})^2$$

is a minimum, subject to the condition that Q has rank two. More directly, we could estimate the (r_i) and (s_i) by those values which make

$$\sum_{i \neq j} \sum (\bar{q}_{ij} - r_i s_j/2 - r_j s_i/2)^2$$

a minimum. There is not a unique set of r's and s's, but a condition such as $r_1 = 1$ will permit us to obtain one such set.

A more sophisticated program might not require that the observed marginals, p_i, satisfy exactly the accounting equation $p_i = a_i + b_i/(1 + d_i)$, when doing so leads to unacceptable estimates of a_i or b_i. For instance, we might ask (a computer) for those values of a_i, b_i, and d_i, which minimized

$$\sum_i (\bar{p}_i - p_i)^2 + \sum_{i \neq j} \sum (\bar{p}_{ij} - p_{ij})^2$$

where
$$p_i = a_i + b_i/(1 + d_i)$$

and $p_{ij} = a_i a_j + a_i b_j/(1 + d_j) + a_j b_i/(1 + d_i) + b_i b_j/(1 + d_i + d_j)$

subject to the constraints that:

$$0 < a_i < 1$$
$$0 < b_i < 1$$
$$0 < a_i + b_i < 1$$

and
$$0 < d_i.$$

These are only two of the possible ways of manipulating the available data in order to get estimates of the latent content model. This is certainly an area where imagination is important, both in developing criteria of goodness-of-fit of an estimate and in finding ways of computing estimates that will be most accurate, with respect to those criteria.

5. Some Special Cases, and a Generalization

5.1 *Special Case: Equal Curvature*

Suppose that each of the tracelines has the same curvature, that is, the parameters d_j are all equal to the same value, d. Substitution shows that the accounting equations of first, second, and third order are:

$$p_i = a_i + b_i/(1 + d)$$
$$[ij] = b_i b_j d^2/(1 + d)^2(1 + 2d)$$
$$[ijk] = b_i b_j b_k d^3(8d^3 - 6d - 2)/(1 + d)^3(1 + 2d)^3(1 + 3d)$$

for any items i, j, and k. The third-order parameter simplifies to

$$[ijk] = 2b_i b_j b_k d^3(d - 1)/(1 + d)^3(1 + 2d)(1 + 3d). \qquad (58)$$

Notice that the cross product matrix and the Q matrix of cross product reciprocals will have rank one under these conditions. Any 2×2 determinant is equal to zero. For instance:

$$\begin{vmatrix} [12] & [14] \\ [23] & [34] \end{vmatrix} = (d^2/(1 + d)^2(1 + 2d))^2 \begin{vmatrix} b_1 b_2 & b_1 b_4 \\ b_2 b_3 & b_3 b_4 \end{vmatrix}$$
$$= 0.$$

The diagonal entries of the cross product matrix would be computed as follows: $[ii] = [ij][ik]/[jk] = b_i^2 d^2/(1 + d)^2(1 + 2d)$. Thus, if the parameter d is known, the b_i can be computed for any item i. The third-order parameter must be used to solve for d.

Eliminate the b's from Equation (58), and square to avoid square roots. This leads to the equation:

$$\frac{[ijk]^2}{4[ii][jj][kk]} = \frac{(d - 1)^2(1 + 2d)}{(1 + 3d)^2}. \qquad (59)$$

Although this cubic equation may have more than one positive root, it is always possible to determine the true d, because the sign of $d - 1$ is available to tell us whether d is less than or greater than 1. These results are summarized below.

(1) If $[ijk]$ is positive, we know that d is greater than 1. In that case Equation (59) has only one positive root, which must be the desired value of d.

(2) If $[ijk]$ is negative, d must lie between 0 and 1. In that case Equation (59) has two positive roots, but one of them is greater than 1 and so can be ignored.

To prove statement (1) we let $z = d - 1$ and

$$h^2 = [ijk]^2/4[ii][jj][kk].$$

In standard form the cubic equation becomes:

$$f(z) = 2z^3 - 3(3h^2 - 1)z^2 - (24h^2)z - 16h^2 = 0.$$

The value of $f(0)$ is negative $(-16h^2)$, and the slope of the function at $z = 0$ is also negative $(-24h^2)$. There will therefore be only one crossing of the positive z axis.

To prove statement (2) we let $y = 1 - d$, so that we are looking for a y that is between 0 and 1. Substituting, and simplifying, we obtain the cubic equation:

$$g(y) = 2y^3 - 3(1 - 3h^2)y^2 - (24h^2)y + 16h^2 = 0.$$

Here the slope of the function at $y = 0$ is negative, so that the curve is decreasing there, but the value $g(0) = 16h^2$ is greater than 0. There will be two positive roots, therefore. Consider now what the curve looks like at $y = 1$. The value

$$g(1) = 2 - 3(1 - 3h^2) - 24h^2 + 16h^2 = -1 + h^2.$$

The slope at $y = 1$ is

$$6 - 6(1 - 3h^2) - 24h^2 = -6h^2$$

and is negative. Therefore the curve is still decreasing; since it must eventually rise, there must be a positive crossing of the y-axis somewhere beyond $y = 1$. Only one root can fall between 0 and 1.

(In the above discussion we have referred to the properties of the graph of the cubic function used earlier in the chapter and illustrated in Figures 5 and 6.)

Because the Q matrix only has rank one, we cannot use the various derivations that we made in the general case. All of those earlier computations, e.g., the calculation of the terms q_{ii}, depended on the fact that the Q matrix had rank two. In practice, therefore, it would be a good idea to consider this hypothesis (of equal d_j) before proceeding with the general analysis, by checking the rank of the matrix Q.

5.2 Special Case: All a_i Equal Zero

Suppose that $a_i = 0$, for all i. This means that the traceline of each item starts at zero:

$$p_i(0) = 0 \qquad \text{for all } i.$$

In this special case the remaining parameters, the b_i and d_i, can be found without using third-order information. The accounting equations become:

$$p_i = b_i/(1 + d_i)$$
$$[ij] = b_i b_j d_i d_j/(1 + d_i)(1 + d_j)(1 + d_i + d_j).$$

The equation for the cross product is unchanged from the general situation, and there are no restrictions on the b_i and d_i. The matrix Q has the same rank two character as in the general case. In particular, we can calculate the diagonal entries of Q from the off-diagonal entries. Considering that q_{ii} is known, the accounting equation

$$q_{ii} = (1 + d_i)^2(1 + 2d_i)/(b_i d_i)^2$$

can be used, together with the marginal equation, to solve for d_i.

$$\frac{(p_i)^2}{q_{ii}} = \frac{(d_i)^2}{1 + 2d_i}.$$

Either algebraic argument can be used to show that there is only positive root to this equation. We leave as an exercise for the reader to complete, the demonstration that

$$d_i = (p_i)^2/q_{ii} + [(p_i^2/q_{ii})(1 + p_i^2/q_{ii})]^{1/2}.$$

A further simplification, which is just as logical as letting the a_i all equal zero, is to let $b_i = 1$ as well. Then the symmetrization of the traceline is complete: near the low end of the distribution there is almost a zero probability of a positive response, while near the high end a positive response is almost certain to occur. Of course the model is quite trivial in its implications. It is not even necessary to examine the second-order manifest probabilities in order to solve for the remaining parameters:

$$p_i = 1/(1 + d_i)$$
$$d_i = (1 - p_i)/p_i.$$

It is interesting to note that even though the cross products are determined by the marginal probabilities,

$$[ij] = (1 - p_i)(1 - p_j)p_i p_j/(p_i + p_j - p_i p_j)$$

the cross product matrix does not have a particularly simple form, as far as some kind of rank condition is concerned. (The Q matrix still has rank two.) We probably would never think to look at a cross product matrix with this particular structure in mind, until we had gone to the trouble of studying this special case of the latent content model. It is the d-parameters which express the non-linear relationship between the latent continuum and the response probabilities, and it is these parameters which cause the unusual structure of the relations between items as expressed by the cross products.

5.3 Special Case: Symmetric Traceline

By "symmetric traceline" we mean that the probability of a positive response at the lower end of the scale equals the probability of a negative response at the upper end:

$$p_i(0) = 1 - p_i(1) \qquad \text{for all } i.$$

This implies that

$$a_i = 1 - a_i - b_i,$$

or

$$2a_i = 1 - b_i.$$

The accounting equations of second and third order (for [ij] and [ijk], that is) have the same form as in the general case, since they involve only the b's and d's. The marginal equation becomes:

$$p_i = a_i + b_i/(1 + d_i)$$
$$= (1 - b_i)/2 + b_i/(1 + d_i).$$

Solving for b_i, we get:

$$b_i = (2p_i - 1)(1 + d_i)/(1 - d_i).$$

Q has rank two, as in the general model, and the diagonal entries can be computed from the off-diagonals. Considering that q_{ii} is known, we get the equation

$$q_{ii} = (1 + d_i)^2(1 + 2d_i)/b_i^2 d_i^2.$$

Substitute for b_i, leaving an equation in d_i alone.

$$q_{ii} = (1 + 2d_i)(1 - d_i)^2/d_i^2(2p_i - 1)^2.$$

In the usual form:

$$2d_i^3 - d_i^2(q_{ii}(2p_i - 1)^2 + 3) + 1 = 0. \tag{60}$$

Equation (60) has one root between 0 and 1, and one root larger than 1. We can tell whether d_i is larger than one or less than one by looking at the size of p_i:

$$d_i < 1 \text{ if } p_i > 1/2$$

and

$$d_i > 1 \text{ if } p_i < 1/2.$$

There is no problem in choosing the correct root of (60).

To show that there is one root between 0 and 1, and one root greater than 1, we notice that

$$f(0) = 1$$

and the slope of the curve at 0 is zero. Hence there are two positive roots. Next, we note that

$$f(1) = 2 - 3 - q_{ii}(2p_i - 1)^2 + 1$$
$$= -q_{ii}(2p_i - 1)^2$$

is less than zero. Therefore the curve must have crossed the d-axis somewhere between 0 and 1, and since it must eventually rise it will cross again somewhere above $d = 1$.

5.4 An Alternative Distribution of the Latent Variable

Requiring that the latent variable distributed uniformly on the unit interval seems to restrict the use of the latent content in many situations. A distribution which tended to cluster about some modal value and had small "tails" would probably be more appealing as a model of some particular social phenomena. In this section we shall show how the introduction of a distribution function that has one or two parameters complicates the general model.

Consider the Beta distribution, on the unit interval:

$$f(x) = Bx^\beta(1 - x)^\lambda, \qquad 0 \le x \le 1.$$

β and λ are positive parameters, and B is a function of β and λ, chosen so that the integral of $f(x)$, over the interval $[0, 1]$, equals 1.

$$1/B = \int_0^1 x^\beta(1 - x)^\lambda \, dx.$$

Using this distribution, we find that it is very hard to make any progress toward a solution of the latent content model. As a result, we try to analyze the one parameter distribution defined by setting $\lambda = 1$.

Under the condition $\lambda = 1$, we find that the coefficient B is

$$(\beta + 1)(\beta + 2).$$

the tth moment of the distribution, $M(t)$, is

$$M(t) = B \int x^t x^\beta(1 - x) \, dx$$
$$= (\beta + 1)(\beta + 2)/(\beta + t + 1)(\beta + t + 2).$$

The general accounting equations derived in Section 2.1 enable us to write the accounting equations for this particular distribution. At least one special case, that of the symmetric tracelines, can be analyzed fairly easily.

Suppose that for all items $a_i = 0$ and $b_i = 1$. The accounting equations become:

$$p_i = (\beta + 1)(\beta + 2)/(\beta + 1 + d_i)(\beta + 2 + d_i) \qquad (61)$$

and $$p_{ij} = (\beta + 1)(\beta + 2)/(\beta + 1 + d_i + d_j)(\beta + 2 + d_i + d_j). \qquad (62)$$

These equations can be solved for β, according to the following argument. First, verify the identity,

$$(\beta + 1 + d_i + d_j)(\beta + 2 + d_i + d_j) = (\beta + 1 + d_i)(\beta + 2 + d_i)$$
$$+ (\beta + 1 + d_j)(\beta + 2 + d_j)$$
$$- (\beta + 1)(\beta + 2) + 2d_i d_j.$$

195

Using this identity, we find that

$$1/p_{ij} - 1/p_i - 1/p_j + 1 = 2d_i d_j/(\beta + 1)(\beta + 2).$$

The last equation indicates that the manifest matrix G, defined by

$$g_{ij} = 1/p_{ij} - 1/p_i - 1/p_j + 1$$

has rank one. Define the diagonal element

$$g_{ii} = g_{ij} g_{ik}/g_{jk} = 2d_i^2/(\beta + 1)(\beta + 2). \tag{63}$$

From Equation (61) we find that

$$1/p_i = 1 + d_i(2\beta + 3)/(\beta + 2)(\beta + 1) + d_i^2/(\beta + 1)(\beta + 2)$$

and therefore we can solve for d_i:

$$d_i = [1/p_i - 1 - g_{ii}/2](\beta + 1)(\beta + 2)/(2\beta + 3). \tag{64}$$

Finally, when we substitute into Equation (63), we get

$$g_{ii} = 2[1/p_i - 1 - g_{ii}/2]^2(\beta + 1)(\beta + 2)/(2\beta + 3)^2,$$

leading to a quadratic equation in β. Once this has been solved, a substitution in (64) gives us the d_i.

We shall not discuss the implications of this choice of a distribution function any further. The reader might be interested in looking for solutions in some of the other special cases, or even in seeing whether some other choice for $f(x)$ leads to an interesting model.

In closing, we mention once again that it will often be necessary to use unusual methods of manipulating manifest data.

The latent content model permits different items to have different curvilinear relationships to the latent variable, measured by the different values of the d-parameter. As a result there are usually no particular conditions visible that the cross product matrix must satisfy. In the general model, with the uniform distribution, we found that the matrix of reciprocal cross products, $1/[ij]$, had to satisfy a rank condition. In the model discussed in the last section we found that a matrix whose entries were $(1/p_{ij} - 1/p_i - 1/p_j + 1)$ had rank one, an even more unusual condition.

There is no reason to examine a matrix such as the last mentioned if we do not believe that it might be possible to apply the particular form of the latent content model which gives rise to it in a natural way. Analogously, however, there is no reason to examine the rank of a matrix of correlation coefficients unless we believe that it might be possible to apply some model that gives rise to that condition in a natural way.

7

Latent Structure Models with
Continuous Latent Space: II

In this chapter we continue to assume the existence of a one-dimensional, continuous-valued latent variable. We first consider the polynomial traceline models, where all items are related to the latent variable by polynomial functions of a specified degree. Then we discuss three models which have been applied to psychological testing situations, where the tracelines vary monotonically from zero to one as the latent variable varies from minus infinity to plus infinity.

1. Polynomial Traceline Models

In Chapter 5, while discussing the concept of "located classes," we suggested the use of polynomial functions to describe the probability structure of the several items. That is, assume that the tracelines $p_i(x)$ which describe the probability of positive response to item i at a value x of the latent variable, are polynomials of a given degree in x.

$$p_i(x) = a_{0i} + a_{1i}x + a_{2i}x^2 + \cdots + a_{ri}x^r. \tag{1}$$

Notice that we have the first subscript of a coefficient such as a_{ti} indicate the degree of the term it modifies, while the second subscript indicates the item in question: a_{32} is the coefficient of x^3 in the polynomial $p_2(x)$. Of course, if $t > r$, $a_{ti} = 0$. We extend this notation in an obvious way in Section 1.1 in order to represent the coefficients of powers of x in the polynomial formed by multiplying two or more functions together.

Since the conditional probabilities $p_i(x)$ must always lie between 0 and 1, it is clear that x cannot be permitted to vary over the whole of the real line. At present, we shall not make specific assumptions about the distribution of values of x, however, assuming only that x has a probability density $f(x)$ on some closed interval $\alpha < x < \beta$, $\int_\alpha^\beta f(x)\, dx = 1$, and that all of the $p_i(x)$ are between 0 and 1 as long as x is between α and β.

Notice that in these models we treat r, the degree of the polynomial functions, just as we treated the number of classes in the latent class models. That is, in our discussions we suppose that it is a fixed known integer. These integers can be determined exactly by examination of the manifest probabilities, and it will always be possible to *test*, with sample data, an assumption that r takes on a particular value. This contrasts with the latent content model, where d_i, the power of x, is considered a variable parameter which can take on any positive real value. In what follows, we shall implicitly assume that the coefficients a_{ri} of x^r are not zero, for every i. This is not a necessary condition, but it makes our presentation a little simpler.

Polynomial tracelines permit a great deal of variety in the type of smooth curves that can be approximated. Furthermore, the manifest probabilities, as we shall see, depend on the distribution of X only through the integral moments of that distribution, i.e., on

$$E(X^t) = \int x^t f(x)\, dx = M_t, \qquad t = 0, 1, 2, \ldots .$$

When a particular function $f(x)$ is specified, it is usually easier to calculate these integral moments than is the case when t is not an integer.

1.1 Accounting Equations

Applying the assumption of local independence as in the case of the latent content model, we express the manifest probabilities of positive response to one, two, and three items by the following equations:

$$p_i = \int p_i(x) f(x)\, dx,$$

$$p_{ij} = \int p_i(x) p_j(x) f(x)\, dx, \qquad i \neq j, \tag{2}$$

$$p_{ijk} = \int p_i(x) p_j(x) p_k(x) f(x)\, dx, \qquad j \neq k \neq i.$$

The product of two polynomials of degree r is a polynomial of degree $2r$. For instance, if $r = 2$,

$$p_i(x) p_j(x) = \left(\sum_{t=0}^{2} a_{ti} x^t \right) \left(\sum_{t=0}^{2} a_{tj} x^t \right)$$

$$= a_{0i} a_{0j} + (a_{1i} a_{0j} + a_{0i} a_{1j}) x + (a_{2i} a_{0j} + a_{1i} a_{1j} + a_{2i} a_{0j}) x^2$$
$$+ (a_{1i} a_{2j} + a_{2i} a_{1j}) x^3 + a_{2i} a_{2j} x^4.$$

We define a_{tij} to be the coefficient of x^t in the polynomial formed by multiplying $p_i(x)$ and $p_j(x)$. Thus, for instance, when $r = 2$,

$$a_{1ij} = a_{1i} a_{0j} + a_{0i} a_{1j}.$$

The rule for writing a_{tij} in terms of the original item coefficients a_{ti} is quite simple:

$$a_{tij} = \sum_{\alpha+\beta=t} a_{\alpha i} a_{\beta j}. \tag{3}$$

That is, a_{tij} is the sum of products $a_{\alpha i} a_{\beta j}$ for which $\alpha + \beta = t$. By writing

$$p_i(x)p_j(x) = \sum_{t=0}^{2r} a_{tij} x^t,$$

we see that the accounting equations of second order will be

$$p_{ij} = \sum_{t=0}^{2r} a_{tij} M_t. \tag{4}$$

We shall define the coefficients involved in a product of three traceline functions to be a_{tijk}, and we can extend this notation to take in any number of items.

$$p_i(x)p_j(x)p_k(x) = \sum_{t=0}^{3r} a_{tijk} x^t$$

and, therefore,

$$p_{ijk} = \sum_{t=0}^{3r} a_{tijk} M_t, \tag{5}$$

where

$$a_{tijk} = \sum_{\alpha+\beta+\gamma=t} a_{\alpha i} a_{\beta j} a_{\gamma k}.$$

ASIDE: Because the product of three polynomials can be expressed as the product of the first two, times the third, we could have defined the third-order coefficients a_{tijk} in terms of the previously defined second-order coefficients. That is, by writing $a_{tijk} = \sum_{\alpha+\beta=t} a_{\alpha ij} a_{\beta k}$. (Of course, the items i, j, and k could be permuted in any way without altering this expression.) This type of recursive definition is very convenient for expressing the general definition, e.g.,

$$a_{t123\cdots n} = \sum_{\alpha+\beta=t} a_{\alpha 1} a_{\beta 23\cdots n}. \quad \blacksquare$$

The symmetric manifest parameters [ij] and [ijk] are obtained by replacing $p_i(x)$ by $p_i(x) - p_i$ in Equations (2), just as we did in the analysis of the latent content model.

$$[ij] = \int (p_i(x) - p_i)(p_j(x) - p_j) f(x)\, dx, \tag{6}$$

$$[ijk] = \int (p_i(x) - p_i)(p_j(x) - p_j)(p_k(x) - p_k) f(x)\, dx. \tag{7}$$

The deviation of the traceline $p_i(x)$ from its average value p_i is

$$p_i(x) - p_i = \sum_{t=0}^{r} a_{ti}x^t - \sum_{t=0}^{r} a_{ti}M_t$$

$$= \sum_{t=1}^{r} a_{ti}(x^t - M_t).$$

The product of two of these is

$$\left(\sum_t a_{ti}(x^t - M_t)\right)\left(\sum_s a_{sj}(x^s - M_s)\right)$$

$$= \sum_t \sum_s a_{ti}a_{sj}(x^{t+s} - x^t M_s - x^s M_t + M_s M_t).$$

Thus, when we integrate over all values of x, we find that

$$[ij] = \sum_{t,s=1}^{r} a_{ti}a_{sj}(M_{t+s} - M_t M_s).\tag{8}$$

Likewise, the third-order symmetric parameter is

$$[ijk] = \sum_{t,s,u=1}^{r} a_{ti}a_{sj}a_{uk}\sigma_{tsu},\tag{9}$$

where

$$\sigma_{tsu} = \int (x^t - M_t)(x^s - M_s)(x^u - M_u)f(x)\,dx$$

$$= M_{t+s+u} - M_t M_{s+u} - M_s M_{t+u} - M_u M_{t+s} + 2M_t M_s M_u.$$

1.2 Matrix Formulation

As is so often the case, the use of matrix notation enables us to express efficiently a number of different equations at one time. The *basic* matrices of manifest probabilities, whose use led to the solution of the latent class model, are just as important here in the polynomial traceline model. We shall see in the next section that their use leads us in the direction of a general solution, though such a solution has not been attained. In this section we show how the accounting equations can be expressed as matrix and vector products.

The polynomial $p_i(x)$ can be easily represented as the product of two vectors, one involving the coefficients (a_{ti}) of the polynomial, and the other involving the powers of x. Let A_i stand for the column vector of the $r+1$ coefficients for item i:

$$A_i' = (a_{0i}, a_{1i}, \ldots, a_{ri}).$$

Let X_r be the column vector which includes all the powers of x up to x^r (beginning with $x^0 = 1$):

$$X_r' = (1, x, \ldots, x^r).$$

Obviously,

$$p_i(x) = A_i' X_r = X_r' A_i.$$

The product of two of these polynomials can be expressed in more than one way. The most straightforward way is to take the equations

$$p_i(x) = A_i' X_r$$

and

$$p_j(x) = X_r' A_j$$

and multiply them. The result,

$$p_i(x)p_j(x) = A_i' X_r X_r' A_j,$$

neatly separates the item-specific coefficients (A_i, A_j) and the latent variable powers $(X_r X_r')$. The product $X_r X_r'$ is, of course, a square matrix of order $r + 1$. The entries of this matrix are powers of x, proceeding systematically from $x^0 = 1$ in the upper left corner to x^{2r} in the lower right corner. For instance, with $r = 2$,

$$X_2 X_2' = \begin{pmatrix} 1 & x & x^2 \\ x & x^2 & x^3 \\ x^2 & x^3 & x^4 \end{pmatrix}.$$

The manifest probability p_{ij} is equal to the expected value of $p_i(x)p_j(x)$. This involves replacing the powers of x by the corresponding moments M_t. The equation is:

$$p_{ij} = (a_{0i}, a_{1i}, \dots, a_{ri}) \begin{pmatrix} M_0 & M_1 & \cdots & M_r \\ M_1 & M_2 & \cdots & M_{r+1} \\ \vdots & \vdots & \vdots\vdots\vdots & \vdots \\ M_r & M_{r+1} & \vdots\vdots\vdots & M_{2r} \end{pmatrix} \begin{pmatrix} a_{0j} \\ a_{1j} \\ \vdots \\ a_{rj} \end{pmatrix}.$$

Let M stand for the matrix of moments, of order $r + 1$.

As in the latent class model, we can extend this equation to include the marginal probabilities p_i by defining the dummy item, "0," whose latent probability of positive response is always 1. That is, $p_0(x) = 1$, for all x, and so the coefficient vector A_0 consists of 1, followed by r zeros. The basic matrix, of first- and second-order probabilities, is

$$B_{hv} = A_h' M A_v. \tag{10}$$

The signatures h and v consist of two sets of items that do not overlap except in their leading item, item "0." For example, with $h = (0, 1, 2)$ and $v = (0, 3, 4)$,

$$B_{hv} = \begin{pmatrix} 1 & 0 & 0 \\ a_{01} & a_{11} & a_{21} \\ a_{02} & a_{12} & a_{22} \end{pmatrix} \begin{pmatrix} M_0 & M_1 & M_2 \\ M_1 & M_2 & M_3 \\ M_2 & M_3 & M_4 \end{pmatrix} \begin{pmatrix} 1 & a_{03} & a_{04} \\ 0 & a_{13} & a_{14} \\ 0 & a_{23} & a_{24} \end{pmatrix}.$$

In the latent class case the basic matrix was defined to be of order m, where m is the number of latent classes. The reader will notice that in the example just given, with $r = 2$, the basic matrix had order 3. A basic matrix for the polynomial traceline model of degree r will always have order $r + 1$. In the latent class model, where the size of the matrix V of latent class frequencies determined the maximum rank of this type of matrix, so here the degree of the polynomial, as indicated by the size of the matrix M, determines the maximum rank. B_{hv}, of order $r + 1$, is the largest such matrix that can have an inverse.

A different way of writing the product of two polynomials leads to the matrix expression for third- and fourth-order manifest probabilities. We have already introduced the notation a_{tij} to stand for the coefficient of x^t in the expansion of the product $p_i(x)p_j(x)$. That is, we wrote:

$$p_i(x)p_j(x) = \sum_{t=0}^{2r} a_{tij}x^t.$$

An equation for these $2r + 1$ coefficients was given above (3). In vector form, we can write this as the product of a coefficient vector with $2r + 1$ entries and a vector of powers of x that goes up to x^{2r}. The latter vector is X_{2r}, by an extension of the notation already used. We call the vector of coefficients $A_{(ij)}$. Thus,

$$p_i(x)p_j(x) = A'_{(ij)}X_{2r} = X'_{2r}A_{(ij)}.$$

Now it is quite simple to express the product of three polynomials, using this notation:

$$p_i(x)p_k(x)p_j(x) = p_i(x)(p_k(x)p_j(x))$$
$$= A'_i X_r X'_{2r} A_{(kj)}.$$

The product $X_r X'_{2r}$ is a matrix with $r + 1$ rows and $2r + 1$ columns, containing the powers of x running systematically from x^0 in the upper left, to x^{3r} in the lower right. As before, we obtain the manifest probabilities by replacing the powers of x by their expected values, the moments (M_t). Define M^* to be this moment matrix, of order $(r + 1, 2r + 1)$, exemplified by (for $r = 2$):

$$M^* = \begin{pmatrix} 1 & M_1 & M_2 & M_3 & M_4 \\ M_1 & M_2 & M_3 & M_4 & M_5 \\ M_2 & M_3 & M_4 & M_5 & M_6 \end{pmatrix}.$$

The manifest probability is:

$$p_{ikj} = A'_i M^* A_{(kj)}.$$

The problem now is to "untangle" the latent parameters of items k and j as they appear in the combination vector $A_{(kj)}$. This can be accomplished by means of the *semi-diagonal matrix*, D_k. In the case $r = 2$ the matrix is defined as follows:

$$D_k = \begin{pmatrix} a_{0k} & 0 & 0 \\ a_{1k} & a_{0k} & 0 \\ a_{2k} & a_{1k} & a_{0k} \\ 0 & a_{2k} & a_{1k} \\ 0 & 0 & a_{2k} \end{pmatrix}.$$

Notice the similarity between this matrix and an ordinary diagonal matrix: D_k appears to be a 3×3 diagonal matrix, but with the vector A_k inserted in the diagonal cells. The result is, of course, a matrix with 5 rows and 3 columns. The general definition is the natural extension, the resulting matrix having $2r + 1$ rows and $r + 1$ columns. In each column the $r + 1$ place vector A_k appears, but each time it is dropped down one place.

The vector $A_{(kj)}$ equals the product of D_k and the vector A_j, a very convenient result. The example, when $r = 2$,

$$D_k A_j = \begin{pmatrix} a_{0k} & 0 & 0 \\ a_{1k} & a_{0k} & 0 \\ a_{2k} & a_{1k} & a_{0k} \\ 0 & a_{2k} & a_{1k} \\ 0 & 0 & a_{2k} \end{pmatrix} \begin{pmatrix} a_{0j} \\ a_{1j} \\ a_{2j} \end{pmatrix} = A_{(kj)}$$

should be compared with Equation (3), which defined the elements of the vector $A_{(jk)}$.

Our formula for the third-order manifest probability is now:

$$p_{ikj} = A'_i M^* D_k A_j.$$

When we consider the two *signatures*, h and v, and the *stratified* basic matrix B_{hvk}, this equation for fixed k permits us to write:

$$B_{hvk} = A'_h M^* D_k A_v. \tag{11}$$

Comparing Equations (10) and (11), we see that the matrices of coefficients of items in the two signatures are common to both equations; but that in addition to the presence of the semi-diagonal matrix D_k of stratifier item coefficients, the moment matrices M and M^* differ. M is square, of order $r + 1$, while M^* has $r + 1$ rows and $2r + 1$ columns.

We mention also the equation for the fourth order probabilities. Using the above derivation, the reader should verify that:

$$p_i(x)p_n(x)p_k(x)p_j(x) = A'_i D'_n X_{2r} X'_{2r} D_k A_j.$$

Let M^{**} stand for the matrix of moments which are the expected values of the powers of x in the product $X_{2r} X'_{2r}$: this will be a square matrix, of order $2r + 1$. The manifest probability of fourth-order is therefore:

$$p_{inkj} = A'_i D'_n M^{**} D_k A_j.$$

1.3 Approaches to a General Solution

We can proceed with a straightforward analysis of Equations (10) and (11). If B_{hv} does have an inverse, we can eliminate the latent coefficients of the items in one signature by multiplying the stratified matrix by the inverse of the unstratified basic matrix:

$$B_{hv}^{-1}B_{hvk} = A_v^{-1}M^{-1}A_h'^{-1}A_h'M^*D_kA_v$$
$$= A_v^{-1}M^{-1}M^*D_kA_v. \tag{12}$$

The approach is the same as in the latent class models, but the result, at this stage, is not as simple. Recall that in the latent class model we find that

$$B_{hv}^{-1}B_{hvk} = L_v^{-1}D_kL_v,$$

where D_k is a *diagonal* matrix; we conclude that the entries of D_k, which are the latent probabilities of item k, are the characteristic roots of the manifest matrix $B_{hv}^{-1}B_{hvk}$. Here, since the matrix $M^{-1}M^*D_k$ is *not* diagonal, we do not have an immediate identification of some latent parameters with the characteristic roots of $B_{hv}^{-1}B_{hvk}$.

The following *intermediate* result can be used, however.

THEOREM 1: *The characteristic roots of $B_{hv}^{-1}B_{hvk}$ are identical with the characteristic roots of $M^{-1}M^*D_k$.*

PROOF: Suppose that λ is a characteristic root of G, and that $G = A^{-1}FA$. Then λ must satisfy the determinantal equation

$$|G - \lambda I| = 0.$$

But

$$|G - \lambda I| = |A^{-1}(F - \lambda I)A| = |A^{-1}|\,|F - \lambda I|\,|A| = |F - \lambda I|,$$

and, therefore, λ must be a characteristic root of F. ∎

Theorem 1 shows us how to obtain $r + 1$ equations which relate manifest information to a limited set of unknown latent parameters. On one side of these equations appear the $r + 1$ characteristic roots of $B_{hv}^{-1}B_{hvk}$. On the other side appear the $r + 1$ characteristic roots of $M^{-1}M^*D_k$, functions only of the stratifier item k and of the distribution of the latent variate X in the form of the moments up to M_{3r}. There appear $r + 1$ coefficients in these $r + 1$ equations (a_{tk}, $t = 0, 1, \ldots, r$). Therefore, we can proceed hoping that it is possible to solve for each of these unknowns *in terms of the moments*. If this is possible, the model would be solved for those situations in which the distribution of X is completely specified, and all the moments are known. As we shall show below, in discussing the special case $r = 2$, we cannot expect to be able to solve these equations uniquely for the a_{tk} in terms of the moments, since many of them are not linear in these unknowns. Nevertheless, it is of great value in the analysis of a model to be able to specify equations, such as these, which are simpler functions of the latent parameters than are the basic accounting equations.

It is possible to get more equations which contain, as unknowns, the item parameters of a single item and moments of the X distribution, by arranging manifest probabilities in the form of ascending matrices. Recall that an ascending matrix differs from a basic matrix in that its signatures may contain combinations of items. We prove in Section 3 below that, in a polynomial traceline model with degree r, it is possible to form an ascending matrix of order $2r + 1$ which will be of full rank. If we call this matrix P_{hv}, then

$$P_{hv} = A_h^{*\prime} M^{**} A_v^*,$$

where A_h^* and A_v^* are the coefficient matrices of the two signatures which contain pairs of items as elements, and are of order $2r + 1$, and M^{**} is the square moment matrix which is also of order $2r + 1$. The formation of this matrix is discussed below; here we simply assert that it can be done, and that it has the same type of matrix form as did the basic matrix.

This ascending matrix can be stratified, by item k, say, and the matrix form of the stratified matrix is familiar:

$$P_{hvk} = A_h^{*\prime} M^* D_k^* A_v^*.$$

We have asserted that P_{hv} will have an inverse, so that

$$P_{hv}^{-1} P_{hvk} = A_v^{*-1} M^{**-1} M^* D_k^* A_v$$

will exist, and a familiar argument equates the characteristic roots of $P_{hv}^{-1} P_{hv}$ with those of $M^{**-1} M^* D_k^*$. These equations will involve the $r + 1$ coefficients a_{tk}, and moments, but there will be $2r + 1$ of *these* equations, because the matrices are larger than the simple basic matrices.

Of course, in the ascending matrix formulation many more moments will enter into these equations: if M^{**} is of order $2r + 1$ it includes moments up to M_{4r}; and M^*, the nonsquare matrix will include moments up to M_{5r}. If we restrict ourselves to the characteristic roots of the matrix $P_{hv}^{-1} P_{hvk}$, as manifest information, therefore, we cannot hope to find a general solution. On the other hand, if all the information in that matrix is used, we cannot rule out the possibility of a solution.

That is, we note that the matrix $P_{hv}^{-1} P_{hvk}$ contains $(2r + 1)^2$ entries, each of which defines an equation in the unknown latent parameters. There are involved in these equations a total of $r^2 + 8r + 2$ latent parameters: the $5r$ moments $M_1, \ldots, M_{5r}$; the $r + 1$ coefficients of the stratifier traceline; and the $(r + 1)^2$ coefficients associated with the $r + 1$ items making up the signature v. Thus, when $r = 2$, this matrix equation would provide 25 equations, in 22 unknowns. The possibility of a unique solution cannot be ruled out. We leave this unsolved problem as a challenge, then: to either derive a solution from these equations, or to show that such a solution is impossible; either in general or in the special case of quadratic tracelines.

Falling between the extremes of assuming that the distribution of X is specified completely, the moments all known, and of taking every single moment as an unknown parameter, is the quite reasonable assumption that the distribution has some particular functional form involving a few parameters. For instance, if the distribution involved r or fewer parameters, it might be possible to work directly from the $2r + 1$ characteristic roots of the matrix $P_{hv}^{-1} P_{hvk}$, to find a solution.

One possible way of defining the moments would be to use the Pearson characterization of distribution functions. In the Pearson system, all higher moments can be written as functions of M_3 and M_4, assuming that $M_1 = 0$ and $M_2 = 1$, and distributions with many different shapes can be represented. (See, for instance, Rietz (1927), pp. 50–60.) The recursion formula for the moments is:

$$M_{t+1} = t(aM_t - bM_{t-1})/(1 + c(t + 2)), \qquad t = 1, 2, \ldots.$$

Here, a, b, and c are parameters which can be written in terms of M_3 and M_4. They can be obtained explicitly by setting t equal to 1, 2, and 3, in turn, and solving for them. We have not studied the implications of an assumption such as this on the analysis of the polynomial traceline model, and it seems to be an interesting idea for further study.

ASIDE: The Pearson system of distribution functions deserves a more complete discussion than we can provide here. The interested reader can turn to Chapter 4 of Elderton's book (Elderton, 1937). The basic idea is that the density function $f(x)$ should satisfy the differential equation

$$f'(x) = f(x)[(x + a)/(b - ax + cx^2)].$$

The formula for the moments given above is derived from this relation. One particularly simple form is the "Type III" curve, obtained by setting $c = 0$. We then find that $b = -1$ and $a = M_3/2$, while $M_4 = 3(M_3^2/2 + 1)$. With only one free parameter to describe the distribution, it might be possible to find a solution of the latent polynomial model using this density function. ∎

2. Special Cases of Polynomial Tracelines

2.1 Linear and Quadratic Traceline Functions

The linear traceline model

$$p_i(x) = a_{0i} + a_{1i}x$$

has already been discussed in Chapter 6 as a special case of the latent content model. We now include a brief reanalysis of the model in order to illustrate the method of deriving equations from the characteristic roots of $B_{hv}^{-1}B_{hvk}$.

The characteristic roots of $B_{hv}^{-1}B_{hvk}$ are the roots of the determinantal equation

$$|B_{hv}^{-1}B_{hvk} - \lambda I| = 0.$$

Let this equation be written, in general, as

$$\lambda^{r+1} - c_r\lambda^r + c_{r-1}\lambda^{r-1} + \cdots \pm c_0 = 0, \tag{13}$$

where we know what the coefficients c_i are (they are computed from the known matrix $B_{hv}^{-1}B_{hvk}$). We shall refer to Equation (13) as the *characteristic equation* of the matrix.

Now, in the special case $r = 1$, we have

$$M^{-1}M^*D_k = \begin{pmatrix} 1 & M_1 \\ M_1 & M_2 \end{pmatrix}^{-1} \begin{pmatrix} 1 & M_1 & M_2 \\ M_1 & M_2 & M_3 \end{pmatrix} \begin{pmatrix} a_{0k} & 0 \\ a_{1k} & a_{0k} \\ 0 & a_{1k} \end{pmatrix}.$$

We have substituted $M_0 = 1$ already, but we may make the arbitrary assignment of $M_1 = 0$ and $M_2 = 1$, fixing the location and scale of the variable X. Thus we obtain

$$M^{-1}M^*D_k = \begin{pmatrix} a_{0k} & a_{1k} \\ a_{1k} & a_{0k} + a_{1k}M_3 \end{pmatrix}.$$

The general rule for finding the coefficients of a characteristic equation is stated in Appendix A; that is, c_t is the sum of all the principal minors of order $r + 1 - t$ contained in the matrix. For a 2×2 matrix this simply means that c_0 is the determinant of the matrix and c_1 is the *trace*, or sum of diagonal elements. Here then, we find

$$c_1 = 2a_{0k} + a_{1k}M_3,$$
$$c_0 = a_{0k}^2 + a_{0k}a_{1k}M_3 - a_{1k}^2,$$

and the equation for p_k is

$$p_k = a_{0k} + a_{1k}M_1 = a_{0k}.$$

Three equations and three unknowns: the solution is

$$a_{0k} = p_k,$$
$$a_{1k}^2 = p_k^2 + p_k(c_1 - 2p_k) - c_0,$$
$$M_3 = (c_1 - 2p_k)/a_{1k}.$$

Notice that the sign of a_{1k} is arbitrary, as far as these equations are concerned, but that the sign of M_3 will depend on that choice. This arbitrariness is always present, and reflects our ability to think of our tracelines as increasing with x, or decreasing with x, as long as we are consistent, from item to item.

ASIDE: We have not calculated c_0 and c_1 in terms of the manifest probabilities. The reader should work out the identities

$$c_0 = (p_k p_{ijk} - p_{ik}p_{jk})/[ij]$$

and

$$c_1 - 2p_k = [ijk]/[ij],$$

where i and j are the items in the signatures h and v, respectively. ∎

When all items have linear tracelines, all the moments of X can be determined by examining fourth and higher-order manifest probabilities.

Next, let us suppose that all of the traceline functions are of second degree:

$$p_i(x) = a_{0i} + a_{1i}x + a_{2i}x^2.$$

We have

$$M^{-1}M^*D_k = \begin{pmatrix} 1 & 0 & 1 \\ 0 & 1 & M_3 \\ 1 & M_3 & M_4 \end{pmatrix}^{-1} \begin{pmatrix} 1 & 0 & 1 & M_3 & M_4 \\ 0 & 1 & M_3 & M_4 & M_5 \\ 1 & M_3 & M_4 & M_5 & M_6 \end{pmatrix} \begin{pmatrix} a_{0k} & 0 & 0 \\ a_{1k} & a_{0k} & 0 \\ a_{2k} & a_{1k} & a_{0k} \\ 0 & a_{2k} & a_{1k} \\ 0 & 0 & a_{2k} \end{pmatrix}.$$

This is a good point at which to note that the first $r + 1$ columns of M^* make up the M matrix, and that, therefore, the first $r + 1$ columns of the product $M^{-1}M^*$ will always be an identity matrix. It follows that the first column of $M^{-1}M^*D_k$ will be made up of the coefficients $(a_{0k}, a_{1k}, \ldots, a_{rk})$. For convenience, therefore, let the matrix $M^{-1}M^*$ be written

$$M^{-1}M^* = (I, Q),$$

where the elements of $Q(q_{ij}$, where $i = 0, 1, \ldots, r$ and $j = 1, 2, \ldots, r)$ can be related to the moments by the obvious matrix multiplication.

When $r = 2$, using this notation we find that

$$M^{-1}M^*D_k = (I, Q)D_k = \begin{pmatrix} a_{0k} & q_{01}a_{2k} & q_{01}a_{1k} + q_{02}a_{2k} \\ a_{1k} & a_{0k} + q_{11}a_{2k} & q_{11}a_{1k} + q_{12}a_{2k} \\ a_{2k} & a_{1k} + q_{12}a_{2k} & a_{0k} + q_{21}a_{1k} + q_{22}a_{2k} \end{pmatrix}.$$
(14)

As has already been pointed out, we have immediately four equations available: the three coefficients of the characteristic equation of $B_{hv}^{-1}B_{hvk}$ plus p_k. These four involve the coefficients a_{tk} and the moments up to M_6. If we specified a distribution function that depended on one parameter, we might be able to solve for that parameter. It is much too difficult to work with all moments up to M_6, however, and since we have no "nice" distributions in mind for our applications, we make a very arbitrary specification.

We shall suppose that $f(x)$ is a symmetrical distribution. Therefore, all odd moments will equal zero. In the quadratic case, this leaves us with M_4 and M_6 to deal with in the above equations.

$$Q = \begin{pmatrix} 1 & 0 & 1 \\ 0 & 1 & 0 \\ 1 & 0 & M_4 \end{pmatrix}^{-1} \begin{pmatrix} 0 & M_4 \\ M_4 & 0 \\ 0 & M_6 \end{pmatrix}$$

$$= \frac{1}{M_4 - 1} \begin{pmatrix} M_4 & 0 & -1 \\ 0 & M_4 - 1 & 0 \\ -1 & 0 & 1 \end{pmatrix} \begin{pmatrix} 0 & M_4 \\ M_4 & 0 \\ 0 & M_6 \end{pmatrix}$$

$$= \begin{pmatrix} 0 & (M_4^2 - M_6)/(M_4 - 1) \\ M_4 & 0 \\ 0 & (M_6 - M_4)/(M_4 - 1) \end{pmatrix}.$$

Let
$$M_4 = y,$$
and let
$$(M_6 - M_4)/(M_4 - 1) = z.$$
Then
$$q_{02} = (M_4^2 - M_4 + M_4 - M_6)/(M_4 - 1) = y - z.$$

Substituting in Equation (14) gives the following results:

$$M^{-1}M^*D_k = \begin{pmatrix} a_{0k} & 0 & (y-z)a_{2k} \\ a_{1k} & a_{0k} + ya_{2k} & ya_{1k} \\ a_{2k} & a_{1k} & a_{0k} + za_{2k} \end{pmatrix}.$$

The coefficients c_0, c_1, and c_2 equal

$$c_2 = a_{0k} + a_{0k} + ya_{2k} + a_{0k} + za_{2k},$$

$$c_1 = \begin{vmatrix} a_{0k} & 0 \\ a_{1k} & a_{0k} + ya_{2k} \end{vmatrix} + \begin{vmatrix} a_{0k} & (y-z)a_{2k} \\ a_{2k} & a_{0k} + za_{2k} \end{vmatrix} + \begin{vmatrix} a_{0k} + ya_{2k} & ya_{1k} \\ a_{1k} & a_{0k} + za_{2k} \end{vmatrix},$$

$$c_0 = |M^{-1}M^*D_k|.$$

These equations become, when simplified somewhat,

$$c_2 = 3a_{0k} + za_{2k} + ya_{2k}, \tag{15}$$

$$c_1 = 3a_{0k}^2 + 2a_{2k}a_{0k}(y+z) + a_{2k}^2(yz - y + z) - ya_{1k}^2, \tag{16}$$

$$c_0 = a_{0k}^3 + a_{0k}^2 a_{2k}(y+z) + a_{0k}a_{2k}^2(yz + z - y) - a_{2k}^3 y(y-z)$$
$$- ya_{0k}a_{1k}^2 + (y-z)a_{2k}a_{1k}^2. \tag{17}$$

The marginal probability is

$$p_k = a_{0k} + a_{2k}. \tag{18}$$

If the moments were known *a priori*, so that y and z in the above equations were given numbers, Equations (15) and (18) could be solved for a_{0k} and a_{2k}. Then, substituting in Equation (16), we could find a_{1k}^2. Equation (17) would then be an identity required if the model, with given parameters, is correct. On the other hand, if y and z were not known, we could proceed to find a_{0k}, a_{1k}^2, and a_{2k} in terms of y and z from Equations (15), (16), and (18), and substitute into Equation (17). This equation would involve only y and z, but not in a linear fashion, so it would be difficult to present a closed expression for, say, z in terms of y.

We point out that other equations are also available. Suppose that we varied the stratifier item k, using a second value k'. We would be able to express the coefficients of item k' in terms of y and z, also. Returning to Equation (8), we find that the cross product

$$[kk'] = a_{1k}a_{1k'} + a_{2k}a_{2k'}M_4. \tag{19}$$

(Remember $M_4 = y$.) By substituting for a_{1k}, $a_{1k'}$, a_{2k}, and $a_{2k'}$ in Equation (19), we would obtain another equation that involved only y and z as unknowns. Again, this is not a linear equation, so that the two equations in z and y may not have a unique solution. We can derive more such equations, however, by continuing to vary the stratifier item, and it may be possible to obtain a unique solution for y and z in this way.

2.2 Example: Linear Traceline Assumption

The example discussed in this section is taken from Lazarsfeld (1959). The six items, all dealing with job satisfaction, are shown in Table 1, along with the proportion of positive responses to each item. The matrix of cross products is shown in Table 2. Linear tracelines were assumed, and $M_1 = 0$ and $M_2 = 1$ were fixed. The item parameters a_{0i} and a_{1i} were estimated by using the equations for marginal proportions and cross products, namely,

$$p_i = a_{0i},$$

and

$$[ij] = a_{1i}a_{1j}.$$

TABLE 1

	Question	Positive Response	p_i
1.	"Are there any things about your job that you particularly like?	"A lot of things"	0.34
2.	"Are there any things about your job that you particularly dislike?"	"None" and "not many"	0.57
3.	"How often do you look forward with some pleasure to your day on the job?"	"Every day" and "almost every day"	0.62
4.	"If someone asked you about getting a job like yours, which of the following would you be inclined to do? Encourage her? Discourage her? Neither?"	"Encourage her"	0.48
5.	"Do you ever feel you would like to quit and get a job with some other company?"	"Never"	0.38
6.	"Do you feel that you would like to get a transfer from your present job to some other kind of work in your department?"	"Seldom" and "never"	0.58

Rather than determine the estimates of a_{1i} by using the equation

$$\bar{a}_{1i}^2 = [ij][ik]/[jk]$$

for an arbitrary choice of auxiliary items j and k, a fitting formula was used. This formula,

$$\bar{a}_{1i}^2 = \left(\left(\sum_{j \neq i}[ij]\right)^2 - \sum_{j \neq i}[ij]^2\right) \Big/ \left(\sum_{j \neq k}\sum[jk] - 2\sum_{j \neq i}[ij]\right),$$

210

TABLE 2

Cross Product Matrix

	1	2	3	4	5	6
1	—	0.041	0.062	0.069	0.057	0.029
2	0.041	—	0.080	0.088	0.077	0.050
3	0.062	0.080	—	0.107	0.088	0.054
4	0.069	0.088	0.107	—	0.103	0.061
5	0.057	0.077	0.088	0.103	—	0.058
6	0.029	0.050	0.054	0.061	0.058	—

yields estimates which minimize the total sum of squared error, i.e.,

$$\sum_i \sum_j ([ij] - a_{i1}a_{ij})^2.$$

The resulting estimates of the traceline coefficients are given in Table 3. Notice that $p_3(x)$ becomes greater than 1 in the vicinity of $x = 1.2$, and $p_5(x)$ becomes less than 0 near $x = -1.2$. The entire distribution of X must, therefore, be concentrated between these limits. We can estimate the higher moments of this distribution by looking at higher-order manifest probabilities. Although these higher-order data were not reported in the article cited, values of M_3, M_4, and M_5 were estimated and given as

$$M_3 = -0.011; \quad M_4 = 1.57; \quad M_5 = 5.47.$$

TABLE 3

The Traceline Coefficients

Item number i	1	2	3	4	5	6
a_{i0}	0.34	0.57	0.62	0.48	0.38	0.58
a_{i1}	0.185	0.254	0.309	0.348	0.300	0.181

3. Conditions of Reducibility

In the latent class model, the number of classes determines the upper bound on the rank of any basic matrix. Furthermore, as was shown in Chapter 3, this upper bound (equal to the number of classes) remains the same for any *ascending* matrix. (Recall that the elements of the signatures of an ascending matrix do not have to be single items.) The degree of a polynomial traceline also serves to define an upper bound for the rank of a basic matrix. The equation

$$B_{hv} = A'_h M A_v$$

which we derived in earlier sections of this chapter shows that the rank of a basic matrix B_{hv} cannot be greater than $r + 1$, the number of columns in A'_h

(and rows of A_v), no matter how many items are included in the signatures h and v.

In contrast to the situation when the latent class model applies, however, we shall show below that ascending matrices can be constructed which can have rank greater than $r + 1$ when the polynomial traceline model underlies the responses. This result enables us to distinguish, in theory, between a class model and a latent continuum model with polynomial tracelines. The practical problems of analyzing real data in terms of these models make it quite difficult to make such a precise identification in practice; the most important considera-tion in studying a problem remains the researcher's feeling as to how the latent variate ought to be defined: continuously or discretely.

Consider the basic matrix B_{hv} where, for convenience, we number the items so that $h = (0, 1, 2, \ldots, r)$ and $v = (0, r + 1, r + 2, \ldots, 2r)$. Suppose that we have added to the signature h the element consisting of the item-pair $1k$, where $k > 2r$. How will this affect the accounting equation, which originally was

$$B_{hv} = A'_h M A_v?$$

We have added a row to B_{hv}, made up of the probabilities

$$(p_{k1}, p_{k1r+1}, p_{k1r+2}, \ldots, p_{k,1,2r}).$$

We use the notation a_{tk1} to denote the coefficient of x^t in $p_k(x)p_1(x)$.

$$p_{k1j} = \sum_{t=0}^{3r} a_{tk1j} M_t$$

$$= \sum_{t=0}^{2r} \sum_{s=0}^{r} a_{tk1} a_{sj} M_{t+s}.$$

These follow from Equation (5), and the Aside which follows that equation.

The row

$$(p_{k1j}, j = 0, r + 1, r + 2, \ldots, 2r)$$

is, therefore, equal to

$$(a_{0k1}, a_{1k1}, \ldots, a_{2r,k,1}) M^* A_v,$$

where M^* is a moment matrix, formed in the same way as M, but with $2r + 1$ rows. These results lead us to define an ascending matrix $P_{hv,ij}$ whose hori-zontal signature includes all the items in h plus all pairs ki, where k belongs to h (except $k = 0$); and whose vertical signature includes all the items in v, plus all pairs mj, where m belongs to v (except $m = 0$). We know that i and j must be distinct, and must not equal any of the items in h and v. For instance, when $r = 2$ this matrix might be

$$\begin{pmatrix} 1 & p_3 & p_4 & p_{36} & p_{46} \\ p_1 & p_{13} & p_{14} & p_{136} & p_{146} \\ p_2 & p_{23} & p_{24} & p_{236} & p_{246} \\ p_{15} & p_{125} & p_{145} & p_{1356} & p_{1456} \\ p_{25} & p_{235} & p_{245} & p_{2356} & p_{2456} \end{pmatrix}.$$

This matrix can be written in terms of the latent parameters very easily:

$$P_{hv,ij} = A_{h,i}^{*\prime} M^{**} A_{v,j}^{*}. \tag{20}$$

M^{**} is a square moment matrix of order $2r + 1$, containing moments of order up to $4r$. The first $r + 1$ rows of $A_{h,i}^{*}$ are identical with A_h', followed by r columns of zeros. The last r rows contain the composite coefficients

$$a_{tki} = \sum_{\alpha+\beta=t} a_{\alpha k} a_{\beta i},$$

where t goes from 0 to $2r$, and k ranges over the elements of h. We may define $A_{v,j}$ similarly. All the matrices in Equation (20) are of order $2r + 1$, and we show below that the ascending matrix P can actually have full rank.

When $r = 2$, the matrix $A_h^{*\prime}$ is

$$\begin{pmatrix} 1 & 0 & 0 & 0 & 0 \\ a_{01} & a_{11} & a_{21} & 0 & 0 \\ a_{02} & a_{12} & a_{22} & 0 & 0 \\ a_{01}a_{05} & a_{01}a_{15} + a_{11}a_{05} & a_{01}a_{25} + a_{11}a_{15} + a_{21}a_{05} & a_{11}a_{25} + a_{21}a_{15} & a_{21}a_{25} \\ a_{02}a_{05} & a_{02}a_{15} + a_{12}a_{05} & a_{02}a_{25} + a_{12}a_{15} + a_{22}a_{05} & a_{12}a_{25} + a_{22}a_{15} & a_{22}a_{25} \end{pmatrix}.$$

When a matrix has a triangular form such as this, its determinant equals the product of the two determinants of the "main diagonal" matrices. That is, if

$$A_{h,i}^{*\prime} = \begin{pmatrix} A_h' & 0 \\ F & G \end{pmatrix},$$

we know that

$$|A_{h,i}^{*}| = |A_h| \, |G|.$$

In the $r = 2$ case illustrated above, $|G|$ is easy to compute. We find that

$$|G| = a_{25}^2(a_{22}a_{11} - a_{12}a_{21}) = a_{25}^2|A_h|.$$

Therefore, if A_h were a non-singular matrix, and if a_{25}, the coefficient of x^2 in the traceline of the item added, is not zero, $A_{h,5}^{*}$ must also be non-singular. The same argument also applies to $A_{v,6}^{*}$.

The 5×5 moment matrix can also be of full rank. That is, it may or may not, but there is no reason, a priori, to expect that it will be singular. For instance, in the case in which the first eight moments of X are equal to the moments of a standard normal distribution,

$$M^{**} = \begin{pmatrix} 1 & 0 & 1 & 0 & 3 \\ 0 & 1 & 0 & 3 & 0 \\ 1 & 0 & 3 & 0 & 15 \\ 0 & 3 & 0 & 15 & 0 \\ 3 & 0 & 15 & 0 & 105 \end{pmatrix},$$

we find that $|M^{**}| = 288$.

If there are polynomial tracelines of degree r, a basic matrix B_{hv} can have rank equal to $r + 1$ at most. If it is possible to find $2r$ items so that the matrices of coefficients A_h and A_v are non-singular, then the moments M_t, $t \leq 2r$, will determine whether the maximum rank will be achieved. If h and v can be found so that B_{hv} has rank $r + 1$, there will exist an ascending matrix which has rank $2r + 1$ if there are two additional items i and j for which the coefficients a_{ri} and a_{rj} are not zero, and if the moments M_t, $t \leq 2r + 4$ permit. This matrix $P_{hv,ij}$ is formed by adding to the signature h all pairs i, k, where k is in h, and adding to v all pairs j, n, where n is in v. The determinant of the extended coefficient matrices $A_{h,i}^*$ and $A_{v,j}^*$ will equal, respectively, $|A_h|^2(a_{ri})^r$ and $|A_v|^2(a_{rj})^r$.

The following theorem is the basis for the above statement.

THEOREM 2: *Let* $B = (b_{ij})$ *be a non-singular matrix of order* r ($i, j = 1, 2, \ldots, r$). *Let* $(c_1, c_2, c_3, \ldots, c_r)$ *be a vector, with* $c_r \neq 0$. *Let* B^* *be a matrix of order* $2r + 1$, *defined as:*

$$B^* = \begin{pmatrix} 1 & 0 & 0 \\ \alpha & B & 0 \\ \beta & F & G \end{pmatrix}$$

where α *and* β *are arbitrary column vectors;* F *is an arbitrary* $r \times r$ *matrix;* $G = (g_{ij})$ *is as follows:*

$$g_{ij} = \sum_{s+t=j} b_{is} c_t \qquad (i, j = 1, 2, \ldots, r).$$

Then B^* *is non-singular, and* $|B^*| = |B|^2(c_r)^r$.

PROOF: First of all,

$$|B^*| = \begin{vmatrix} 1 & 0 & 0 \\ \alpha & B & 0 \\ \beta & F & G \end{vmatrix}$$

$$= \begin{vmatrix} B & 0 \\ F & G \end{vmatrix}$$

$$= |B|\,|G|.$$

This can be proved in several ways. We note, for example, that

$$\begin{pmatrix} B & 0 \\ F & G \end{pmatrix} = \begin{pmatrix} B & 0 \\ 0 & I \end{pmatrix}\begin{pmatrix} I & 0 \\ F & I \end{pmatrix}\begin{pmatrix} I & 0 \\ 0 & G \end{pmatrix}.$$

Therefore,

$$\begin{vmatrix} B & 0 \\ F & G \end{vmatrix} = \begin{vmatrix} B & 0 \\ 0 & I \end{vmatrix}\begin{vmatrix} I & 0 \\ F & I \end{vmatrix}\begin{vmatrix} I & 0 \\ 0 & G \end{vmatrix},$$

and this product equals

$$|B|\,|G|.$$

We can write

$$G = BC,$$

where C is a triangular matrix, with zeros above the main diagonal, and c_r along the main diagonal. For instance, when $r = 3$,

$$C = \begin{pmatrix} c_3 & 0 & 0 \\ c_2 & c_3 & 0 \\ c_1 & c_2 & c_3 \end{pmatrix},$$

and the construction is analogous when r is larger.

The determinant of a triangular matrix equals the product of its diagonal entries; hence $|C| = (c_r)^r$, and

$$|G| = |B|\,|C| = |B|(c_r)^r. \ \blacksquare$$

It should be obvious how to apply Theorem 2 to our problem. We begin with a matrix of coefficients A_h', which corresponds to the section

$$\begin{pmatrix} 1 & 0 \\ \alpha & B \end{pmatrix}$$

of the matrix B^*. The augmented matrix $A_h^{*\prime}$ has, in its lower right hand corner, the coefficients of x^{r+1}, x^{r+2}, ..., x^{2r} in the expansion of the products $p_i(x)p_k(x)$, where k is an item from h and i is the auxiliary item. Since the coefficient of x^{r+j} is

$$\sum_{t+s=r+j} a_{ti}a_{sk},$$

we have the form of the matrix G, in the theorem, where the vector $(c_1, \ldots, c_r)$ in the theorem corresponds to the coefficients of the auxiliary item i

$$(a_{1i}, a_{2i}, a_{3i}, \ldots, a_{ri}).$$

Now, let us suppose that there are two more items, i' and j', whose tracelines include an x^r term, and augment the ascending matrix in the obvious way: add to the horizontal signature all triples of the form k, i, i', where k is in h, and add to the vertical signature all triples n, j, j', where n is in v. The manifest matrix will now include sixth-order probabilities $p_{knii'jj'}$; the coefficient matrices and the moment matrix will be of order $3r + 1$; the coefficient matrix $A_h^{**\prime}$ will have the form

$$\begin{pmatrix} 1 & 0 & 0 & 0 \\ \alpha & B & 0 & 0 \\ \beta & F & G & 0 \\ \gamma & H & J & K \end{pmatrix},$$

and its determinant equals $|B|\,|G|\,|K|$. The same argument which showed that

$$|G| = (a_{ri})^r |A'_h|$$

can be applied to show that

$$|K| = (a_{ri'})^r |G|,$$

and, therefore, we see that the determinant

$$|A^{**}_{h,i,i'}| = |A_h|^3 (a_{ri})^{2r} (a_{ri'})^r$$

will not vanish as long as the original determinant $|A_h|$ does not vanish. Obviously, this process could be repeated over and over again, as long as additional items were available, producing matrices of manifest probabilities of order $3r + 1$, $4r + 1$, $5r + 1$, etc., which will be non-singular as long as the corresponding *moment* matrices are non-singular.

To emphasize the importance of the above results, we shall compare three different models: three latent classes, with no restrictions; five located classes, with quadratic tracelines; and quadratic tracelines with X having a continuous density function whose first twelve moments equal those of the standard normal distribution.

In the first case, the ordinary latent class model, suppose that B_{hv} has its maximum rank 3 equal to its order. The ascending matrices $P_{hv,ij}$ and $P_{hv,ij'j'}$ of order 5 and 7, respectively, constructed as above, will also have rank 3.

In the second case, if B_{hv} has rank 3, we find that $P_{hv,ij}$ has rank 5 and $P_{hv,ij,i'j'}$ also has rank 5. This is so because the 7×7 matrix of moments M^{***} has rank equal to 5, just as the 5×5 moment matrix M^{**} does. When there is a discrete distribution of the latent variable along a single dimension, the moments are related to the locations x_α and the relative frequencies at each location v^α in the following way:

$$M_t = \sum_{\alpha=1}^{m} v^\alpha (x_\alpha)^t.$$

(In this case, $m = 5$.) Any matrix of moments is, therefore, equal to a product which involves the $m \times m$ diagonal matrix $V = (v^\alpha)$:

$$M = X'VX,$$
$$M^{**} = X^{*\prime}VX^{*},$$
$$M^{***} = X^{**\prime}VX^{**},$$

where, for instance,

$$X' = \begin{pmatrix} 1 & 1 & 1 & 1 & 1 \\ x_1 & x_2 & x_3 & x_4 & x_5 \\ x_1^2 & x_2^2 & x_3^2 & x_4^2 & x_5^2 \end{pmatrix}.$$

Here, $X^{*\prime}$ includes two more rows: the third and fourth powers of the location points; and $X^{**\prime}$ includes the fifth and sixth powers. The maximum rank of a moment matrix has been fixed by the number of locations, or latent classes.

216

In the third case P_{hv} also has rank 3, but both of the augmented, ascending matrices will have full rank, for when the moments of the normal distribution are substituted, we find that M^{**} and M^{***} have rank 5 and 7, respectively.

When we specify a general class model, the number of classes determines the maximum rank an ascending matrix can have. When we specify a polynomial model, with a continuous probability density function $f(x)$ over some interval of the real line, the degree of the polynomial will determine the maximum rank of a basic matrix P_{hv}, but non-singular ascending matrices of any size can be constructed as long as there are enough items available. The located class, polynomial traceline, model falls between these two: the rank of the basic matrix will be determined by the degree of the polynomial traceline[1] r, but there will be an upper bound of m, the number of classes, on the size of a non-singular ascending matrix.

4. Test Theory Models

The use of polynomial traceline models with degree that is higher than two or three is very difficult, due to the problems of estimating the item parameters. In addition, there is the important point that a polynomial function of x will always take on values outside the interval [0, 1] if x is sufficiently large or small. Thus, we can never really have a normally distributed variable, or any other distribution which gives positive probability to every interval on the real line.

The models which are discussed in this section were developed in the field of psychological testing, and were designed to apply to a latent variable that can vary over an infinite interval, either $(-\infty, +\infty)$ or $(0, \infty)$. The traceline functions specified here are all bounded, and cannot vary outside the interval [0, 1]. These models have the added advantage of having only a few item parameters; two in one case, and one in the other; and these can be easily interpreted, as well. In the polynomial model, it becomes difficult to explain what each of the parameters (a_{ti}) means, in terms of the substantive content of the items, when r becomes large.

4.1 *Ogive Tracelines*

We are referring in this section to the work of Tucker, Lord, and their associates at the Educational Testing Service. (Tucker, 1946, Lord, 1952, 1953a.) Lazarsfeld has contrasted latent structure analysis and test theory in a volume sponsored by ETS (Lazarsfeld, 1960).

Let $\Phi(x;\mu,\sigma^2)$ be the cumulative distribution function of the normal distribution with mean μ and variance σ^2. This function is sometimes called the normal *ogive*. Here, x varies between minus and plus infinity, and, because of its definition as a cumulative distribution function, ϕ always lies between 0 and 1. The

---

[1] When we speak of such a model, we always assume that $r + 1 \leq m$, for otherwise there is no chance of identifying the parameters, as we discussed in Chapter 5.

definition is

$$\Phi(x;\mu,\sigma^2) = \frac{1}{\sqrt{2\pi}} \int_{-\infty}^{x} e^{-(t-\mu)^2/2\sigma^2} \, dt. \tag{21}$$

The function also has these properties:

(i) Φ is a strictly increasing function of x;
(ii) $\Phi(-\infty;\mu,\sigma^2) = 0$; $\Phi(+\infty;\mu,\sigma^2) = 1$;
(iii) $\Phi(\mu;\mu,\sigma^2) = 1/2$.

A two-parameter family of tracelines is defined by

$$p_i(x) = \Phi(x;a_i,b_i). \tag{22}$$

It is very awkward to try to apply our ordinary methods of analysis under this assumption, since the accounting equations for the manifest probabilities involve a double integral:

$$p_i = \int p_i(x)f(x) \, dx = \int \Phi(x;a_i,b_i)f(x) \, dx. \tag{23}$$

Tucker showed that if X is assumed to have a normal distribution, with mean 0 and variance 1, then,

$$p_i = \Phi(h_i;0,1), \tag{24}$$

where $h_i = -a_i/(1 + b_i^2)^{1/2}$, so that the value of h_i could be computed, given p_i, by consulting a table of the standard normal distribution. Equation (23) can be derived by using the techniques of changing the variable of integration, and reversing the order of integration. Let $\phi(x;\mu,\sigma^2)$ be the density function of the normal distribution

$$\phi(x;\mu,\sigma^2) = \frac{1}{\sqrt{2\pi}} e^{-(x-\mu)^2/2\sigma^2}.$$

Then, supposing that $f(x) = \phi(x;0,1)$, Equation (22) becomes

$$p_i = \int_{-\infty}^{\infty} \int_{-\infty}^{x} \phi(t;a_i,b_i) \, dt \phi(x;0,1) \, dx.$$

First of all, let

$$t = y + x + a_i,$$

implying that

$$p_i = \int_{-\infty}^{\infty} \int_{y=-\infty}^{-a_i} \phi(y + x + a_i;a_i,b_i) \, dy \phi(x;0,1) \, dx. \tag{25}$$

The product

$$\phi(y + x + a_i;a_i,b_i)\phi(x;0,1) = (1/2\pi)e^{-(y+x)^2/2b_i^2 - x^2/2}$$

and the exponent is $-1/2$ times

$$(y^2 + 2yx + x^2(b_i^2 + 1))/b_i^2.$$

This, in turn, equals

$$(x + y/(b_i^2 + 1))^2(b_i^2 + 1)/b_i^2 + y^2/(b_i^2 + 1).$$

This identity can be expressed more usefully in terms of the density functions:

$$\phi(y + x + a_i; a_i, b_i)\phi(x; 0, 1) = \phi(x; y/(b_i^2 + 1), b_i^2/(b_i^2 + 1))\phi(y; 0, b_i^2 + 1).$$

Now, in Equation (25), reverse the order of integration:

$$p_i = \int_{y=-\infty}^{-a_i} \left[\int_{-\infty}^{\infty} \phi(x; \mu, \sigma^2) \, dx \right] \phi(y; 0, b_i^2 + 1) \, dy,$$

where $\mu = y/(b_i^2 + 1)$ and $\sigma^2 = b_i^2/(b_i^2 + 1)$. The term within brackets, being the integral of a probability density function over its entire range, equals one, and therefore,

$$p_i = \int_{-\infty}^{-a_i} \phi(y; 0, b_i^2 + 1) \, dy$$

$$= \int_{-\infty}^{h_i} \phi(y; 0, 1) \, dy$$

$$= \Phi(h_i; 0, 1),$$

where $h_i = -a_i/(b_i^2 + 1)^{1/2}$ as in Equation (24).

4.2 Use of Scores

While the above specification of the tracelines of the items is attractive, it is not desirable to require that the underlying distribution be normal, nor are accounting equations of higher order easy to analyze. Efforts were made, therefore, to devise techniques for estimating the item parameters (a_i, b_i) without making any assumptions about $f(x)$. The success of these efforts depended on one major difference between the usual "test" and the usual "set of items" which would arise in a survey analysis application, namely, that the test is much longer.

Define a respondent's *score* as the number of positive responses he gives, and let S_n stand for the score on a test consisting of n items.

The *expected* relative score of an individual located at x will be the average probability of a positive response:

$$\frac{1}{n} E(S_n|x) = \frac{1}{n} \sum_{i=1}^{n} p_i(x) = S_n^*(x).$$

If n is very large, S_n/n will probably be very close to this average value S_n^*. The exact formulation of this fact is a simple restatement of the weak law of large numbers.

Introducing the idea that there exists an *infinite* set of items, from which a sample of n has been chosen, we define

$$S^*(x) = \lim_{n \to \infty} S_n^*(x). \tag{26}$$

219

We call $S^*(x)$ the *true score* of an individual whose ability is x.

If the traceline is the normal ogive, it is strictly increasing:

$$\text{if } x < x',$$

then
$$p_i(x) < p_i(x').$$

It follows that the corresponding true scores will also have the order property:

if
$$p_i(x) < p_i(x'),$$

then
$$S_n^*(x) < S_n^*(x'),$$

and
$$S^*(x) \leq S^*(x').$$

Thus, if we had N respondents, whose *true scores* were known, that ordering would imply an ordering on the latent ability x:

if
$$S^*(x) < S^*(x'),$$

then
$$x < x'.$$

Then, since the true scores would be closely approximated by the actual score $S_n(x)/n$ on a very long test, we could obtain an empirical ranking of the respondents which ought to correspond closely to the true x-ordering. If we plotted the "proportion responding positively to item i, given score s" against the score s, we would have a curve which should approximate the actual traceline $p_i(x)$.

Notice that the "true score" and the "ability" are not the same concept: persons having the same true score may not necessarily have the same value of x; this depends on the effect of the passage to the limit (26). Obviously, persons with the same raw score S_n will have been recruited from different positions on the x-axis, but, as n gets large, the interval from which they *probably* were recruited gets very small.

Ways of estimating the item parameters (a_i, b_i) based on the above results, are described in Lord (1952), and Torgerson (1958), pp. 389–391. The idea is to take the empirical tracelines and find a transformation onto the entire real line of the score axis, which varies from 0 to 1. This transformation should be such as to make the transformed tracelines have, as closely as possible, the desired shape of normal ogives. The parameters a_i and b_i would be computed by a fitting procedure such as probit analysis (Finney, 1947).

A particularly useful tool has been the concept of a test consisting of equivalent items, i.e., items having identical tracelines. Obviously, if $p_i(x) = p(x)$ for all i, the "true score," given x, is exactly $p(x)$:

$$S^*(x) = \lim_{n \to \infty} S_n^*(x) = \lim_{n \to \infty} np(x)/n = p(x).$$

With only a single traceline to determine, the ordering and fitting procedure can be carried out fairly easily.

4.3 *Maximum Likelihood Estimation*

Lord has derived the equations necessary for maximum likelihood estimation of the parameters of the normal ogive model (Lord, 1953b). Although these equations are quite complicated in the general situation, we shall mention a few important special results. The first has to do with the problem of estimating an individual's position x on the latent continuum, when the test consists of equivalent items. Under this condition, the respondent's *raw score*, the number of correct answers, is a sufficient statistic for x. That is, for the purpose of estimating x_α, given the item parameters, the data may be reduced to S_α, the score of respondent α, without losing any information. We shall demonstrate this by showing that the maximum likelihood estimate of x_α depends on the data only through S_α, and that this does not depend on the choice of traceline function.

Let $p_i(x)$ be the traceline function, as usual. Let $z_{i\alpha}$ be 1 if α responds positively to item i, and 0 otherwise. Then the logarithm of the likelihood function is equal to

$$\sum_\alpha \sum_i z_{i\alpha} \log p_i(x_\alpha) + (1 - z_{i\alpha}) \log \left(1 - p_i(x_\alpha)\right). \tag{27}$$

If we differentiate with respect to x_α, and set the result equal to zero, we obtain

$$0 = \sum_i [z_{i\alpha}/p_i(x_\alpha) - (1 - z_{i\alpha})/(1 - p_i(x_\alpha))] \frac{\partial p_i(x_\alpha)}{\partial x_\alpha}. \tag{28}$$

Now, suppose that all the items are equivalent: $p_i(x) = p(x)$ for all i. Equation (28) becomes

$$\sum_i [z_{i\alpha}/p(x_\alpha) - (1 - z_{i\alpha})/(1 - p(x_\alpha))] = 0,$$

which further reduces to

$$\sum_i z_{i\alpha} = \sum_i p(x_\alpha).$$

Therefore,

$$\sum_i z_{i\alpha} = S_\alpha = np(x_\alpha). \tag{29}$$

When item parameters are known, or estimated, x_α will be estimated by solving Equation (29) for x_α, and, as long as the traceline is strictly monotone increasing, there will be a unique solution. This result gives support to the natural use of the test score as the basic statistic for ranking respondents. Remember the requirements: monotone tracelines; equivalent items; a one-dimensional latent continuum.

When the items are not equivalent, the score does not in general have this property, even if the concept of score is extended to include a *weighted* sum of the correct responses. Alan Birnbaum has shown that a weighted sum of positive responses is a sufficient statistic for x_α only when the traceline has a particular functional form, the logistic. (Birnbaum (1957), referred to by Solomon (1961).) We shall show how this result comes about.

221

Our aim is to obtain an equation, derived from Equation (28), that has the following form,

$$\sum_i z_{i\alpha} g_i(\theta) = h(x_\alpha, \theta), \tag{30}$$

where θ stands for the set of item parameters, g_i is some function of these parameters that does not depend on x_α, and h is a function of x_α and θ that is monotonic in x_α. For simplicity in what follows, let

$$p_i'(x_\alpha) = \frac{\partial p_i(x_\alpha)}{\partial x_\alpha}.$$

Equation (28) can be written as

$$\sum_i [(z_{i\alpha} - p_i(x_\alpha)] p_i'(x_\alpha)/p_i(x_\alpha)(1 - p_i(x_\alpha)) = 0,$$

$$\sum_i z_{i\alpha}[p_i'(x_\alpha)/p_i(x_\alpha)(1 - p_i(x_\alpha))] = \sum_i p_i'(x_\alpha)/(1 - p_i(x_\alpha)). \tag{31}$$

In order to achieve the form of Equation (30), the term in brackets on the left side of Equation (31) must be factorable, with one factor depending on x_α, but not on i, and the other factor depending on i, but not on x_α:

$$g_i f(x_\alpha) = p_i'(x_\alpha)/p_i(x_\alpha)(1 - p_i(x_\alpha)) \tag{32}$$

(g_i stands for $g_i(\theta)$).

Now, we can consider Equation (32) as a differential equation, to be solved for $p_i(x_\alpha)$. Since

$$\int \frac{dy}{y(1 - y)} = \int \left[\frac{dy}{y} + \frac{dy}{1 - y}\right] = \log y - \log (1 - y),$$

the solution is

$$\log [p_i(x)/(1 - p_i(x))] = g_i \int f(x)\, dx = g_i F(x) + \log C_i, \tag{33}$$

say (log C_i is a constant of integration). Taking the exponential of each side, and solving, we find that

$$p_i(x) = r_i(x)/(1 + r_i(x)), \tag{34}$$

where

$$r_i(x) = C_i \exp[g_i F(x)].$$

Substitution in the likelihood equation (31) gives

$$\sum_i z_{i\alpha} g_i f(x_\alpha) = \sum_i g_i f(x_\alpha) p_i(x_\alpha), \tag{35}$$

$$S_\alpha = \sum_i z_{i\alpha} g_i = \sum_i g_i p_i(x_\alpha) = \sum_i g_i r_i(x)/(1 + r_i(x_\alpha)). \tag{36}$$

Here, S_α is the *weighted* score, which, of course, depends on the item parameters θ, through the function $g_i = g_i(\theta)$.

Notice from Equation (34) that the function $F(x)$ should have the properties $F(\infty) = \infty$, and $F(-\infty) = -\infty$, as well as being monotonic in x, in order

222

that $p_i(x)$, the traceline, vary monotonically from 0 to 1. The simplest such function is, of course, $F(x) = x$. Thus, the simplest traceline function having the desired property is

$$p_i(x) = C_i e^{g_i x}/(1 + C_i e^{g_i x}). \tag{37}$$

This is the two-parameter logistic traceline, and Birnbaum has also noted that any normal ogive function can be approximated very accurately by a function of this type. Hence, one could retain the normal ogive assumption, and also use weighted scores to estimate individual x values, knowing that the amount of information being sacrificed is relatively small, since it depends on the small difference between the normal and the logistic tracelines.

It is very interesting to note that the traceline of Equation (37), which Birnbaum derived from certain statistical considerations, is almost identical to the function proposed independently by G. Rasch, which we discuss in the following section. Rasch's model is obtained as a special case of Equation (37) by letting $g_i = 1$, and letting $y = e^x$:

$$p_i(y) = c_i y/(1 + c_i y), \quad 0 < y < \infty.$$

With $g_i = 1$, the score appropriate for estimating x_α (or y_α) becomes an unweighted score. Rasch has noted that he chose this function simply because it was very convenient for his purposes; it turned out to be a very sound choice indeed.

4.4 Rasch's Model

Independently of the work of Tucker, Lord, and Birnbaum, Georg Rasch proposed and analyzed a model which is also intended to be applied to intelligence and achievement tests. His monograph (Rasch, 1960) includes the analysis of several sets of data, while his article (Rasch, 1966) is a briefer explanation of the essentials of the model.

In our terminology, Rasch assumes that the latent variable can assume values on the positive part of the real line, and that the traceline function is

$$p_i(x) = x\epsilon_i/(1 + x\epsilon_i), \quad 0 \le x < \infty. \tag{38}$$

This function is strictly increasing with x, as long as $\epsilon_i > 0$, achieving its extreme values, 0 and 1, at the extreme values of x. The single item parameter ϵ_i can be called the "easiness" of the item: if

$$\epsilon_i < \epsilon_j,$$

then

$$p_i(x) < p_j(x), \quad 0 < x < \infty.$$

Rasch chooses to make the model population free, i.e., not to assume any prior distribution for the latent variable x. When dealing with a sample of respondents, the x-values of these individuals are treated as parameters which have to be estimated. Because of the simple form of the tracelines, Rasch can show that the item parameters can be estimated independently of the "person" parameters, and vice versa. We shall outline the form of such an analysis, and refer the reader to Rasch's work for examples and complete documentation.

Suppose that x_α is the location of individual α. The probability that this person will respond positively to item i is

$$p_i(x_\alpha) = x_\alpha \epsilon_i/(1 + x_\alpha \epsilon_i), \tag{39}$$

and the probability of a negative (incorrect) response is one minus this,

$$p_{\bar{i}}(x_\alpha) = 1/(1 + x_\alpha \epsilon_i). \tag{40}$$

If we consider a pair of items i and j, there are four possible patterns of response, symbolized as usual by

$$ij, \ \bar{i}j, \ i\bar{j}, \ \bar{i}\bar{j}.$$

Let S be the number of positive responses. Considering only two items, S can be either 2, 1, or 0. The probabilities that our respondent at x_α will give each of the four possible response sequences are computed from Equations (39) and (40) by applying the assumption of local independence.

$$\begin{aligned} p_{ij}(x_\alpha) &= \epsilon_i\epsilon_j x_\alpha^2/(1 + x_\alpha\epsilon_i)(1 + x_\alpha\epsilon_j), \\ p_{\bar{i}j}(x_\alpha) &= \epsilon_j x_\alpha/(1 + x_\alpha\epsilon_i)(1 + x_\alpha\epsilon_j), \\ p_{i\bar{j}}(x_\alpha) &= \epsilon_i x_\alpha/(1 + x_\alpha\epsilon_i)(1 + x_\alpha\epsilon_j), \\ p_{\bar{i}\bar{j}}(x_\alpha) &= 1/(1 + x_\alpha\epsilon_i)(1 + x_\alpha\epsilon_j). \end{aligned}$$

Notice that the ratio of the second and third of these probabilities does not depend on x_α:

$$p_{\bar{i}j}(x_\alpha)/p_{i\bar{j}}(x_\alpha) = \epsilon_j/\epsilon_i. \tag{41}$$

Suppose that we know that person α has a score S_α, which equals 1. The probability of this occurring is simply the sum of the probabilities of $\bar{i}j$ and $i\bar{j}$,

$$\Pr[S_\alpha = 1] = p_{\bar{i}j}(x_\alpha) + p_{i\bar{j}}(x_\alpha).$$

The conditional probability that the response to item i was positive, given that the score was 1, is

$$\begin{aligned} p_i(x_\alpha | S_\alpha = 1) &= p_{i\bar{j}}(x_\alpha)/\Pr[S_\alpha = 1] \\ &= p_{i\bar{j}}(x_\alpha)/[p_{\bar{i}j}(x_\alpha) + p_{i\bar{j}}(x_\alpha)], \end{aligned}$$

or,

$$p_i(x_\alpha | S_\alpha = 1) = \epsilon_i/(\epsilon_i + \epsilon_j). \tag{42}$$

If we had a large number of individuals, all of whom had exactly the same location x_α, we could estimate the probabilities $p_{\bar{i}j}(x_\alpha)$ and $p_{i\bar{j}}(x_\alpha)$ by the appropriate proportions, and thus estimate the ratio of the two-item parameters by Equation (41). We can't tell whether respondents have the same x-value, however, so this point is of theoretical interest only. On the other hand, we can take all persons whose score on the two items equalled 1, and compute the proportion of those who gave the positive response to item i. We can use this proportion to estimate $\epsilon_i/(\epsilon_i + \epsilon_j)$, because Equation (42) tells us that this conditional probability does not depend on x_α, and, therefore, it is permissible to combine individuals with different x-values in order to estimate it.

Because the "easiness" of an item is a relative concept, Rasch chooses some item and arbitrarily sets its parameter equal to 1. Thus, in the above argument, if i had been this unit item $\epsilon_i = 1$, we can solve Equation (42) for ϵ_j. By varying j, all of the item parameters could be estimated by using as data the proportion responding positively to item i among those who have a score of 1 on the pair of items i and j.

The argument can be extended to a larger subset of the items, in the interests of getting better estimates of the parameters. For instance, if we considered three items, i, j, k; the scores can vary from 0 to 3; we find that the conditional probability of positive response to item i by person α, given that his score is 1, is

$$p_i(x_\alpha | S_\alpha = 1) = \epsilon_i/(\epsilon_i + \epsilon_j + \epsilon_k). \tag{43}$$

We could also find the conditional probability of responding positively to items i and j, given that the score was 2:

$$p_{ij}(x_\alpha | S_\alpha = 2) = \epsilon_i \epsilon_j/(\epsilon_i + \epsilon_j + \epsilon_k). \tag{44}$$

Equation (42) demonstrates a relationship between the parameters and an estimable quantity, and if a unit item is defined this relation is sufficient to determine all of the unknown parameters. On the other hand, there are many more such accounting equations, for instance (43) and (44), which could also be used to compute the latent parameters.

Rasch does not offer an exact procedure for estimating the x_α. He does show, however, that the total scores, the number of positive responses, are sufficient statistics for estimating these parameters when the item parameters ϵ_i are known. We have obtained this result as a special case of Birnbaum's analysis in Section 4.3. In Rasch (1960), Chapter 5, he describes an approximation based on the assumption that individuals who have similar scores will have very similar x-values.

By grouping the respondents in this way, and having previous estimates of the item parameters, he can use equations such as Equation (39) to estimate x_α. Having a sample of individuals who are assumed to have about the same value of x_α, the probability $p_i(x_\alpha)$ can be estimated, and then the value of x_α can be estimated. This is the same kind of assumption that was made by Tucker and Lord when they propose to estimate the tracelines by assuming that the ordering according to the actual score would be approximately the same as the true ordering, if the number of items was large.

8

More General Models

In the preceding chapters, we have shown how different models can be developed by altering the assumptions made about the *latent* space. Latent classes, ordered classes, a latent continuum, these assertions about the way in which the population is distributed combine with the axiom of local independence to define different models. Always, however, we retained the "classical" assumption about the manifest responses, i.e., that the various items be dichotomous.

It is very easy, conceptually, to extend this calculus to other manifest spaces, although many practical problems of analysis may arise in such an extension. In this chapter, we shall examine some models for non-dichotomous items: first the case of several discrete responses, and second, the case of a real-valued (or "continuous") manifest variable. In part, this chapter is meant to be suggestive, to propose to the reader that the logic of latent structure analysis may be of value in some situation of empirical data analysis, even if none of the models which we have discussed seems to apply to the data at hand. In addition, we believe that the latent profile model, which applies latent class analysis to real-valued manifest variables should be considered as an alternative to the factor analytic techniques which are often applied to such variables.

This latter model was first discussed by Gibson (1959). An even more general formulation has been given by Anderson (1959), and McDonald (1962a), including discussion of multidimensional continuous latent spaces. These general "non-linear factor analysis" models are beyond the scope of our book though we shall mention a simple special case later in this chapter.

1. Items With More than Two Discrete Responses

Making the simplest extension of the manifest data, we suppose that we have *n trichotomous* items. No ordering of the three responses is assumed, as we retain only the notion of discrete response. For example:

Religion: Catholic, Protestant, Jewish;

Politics: Republican, Democrat, Independent;

or the many cases where a third response of "don't know" is allowed as alternative to "yes" and "no" on a questionnaire.

Suppose that there exist m latent classes. Let p_i, q_i, and r_i denote the probability of giving each of the three possible responses to item i, and, similarly, let p_i^α, q_i^α, and r_i^α be the respective *latent* probabilities, within class α. If, as usual, v^α denotes the relative frequency of class α, we have accounting equations of first order:

$$\text{(a)} \quad p_i = \sum v^\alpha p_i^\alpha,$$
$$\text{(b)} \quad q_i = \sum v^\alpha q_i^\alpha, \qquad (1)$$
$$\text{(c)} \quad r_i = \sum v^\alpha r_i^\alpha.$$

Of course, given that some response must be shown for every item,

$$p_i + q_i + r_i = 1 \quad \text{and} \quad p_i^\alpha + q_i^\alpha + r_i^\alpha = 1.$$

The natural application of local independence would give second- and third-order accounting equations that look exactly like those of the models for dichotomous items, if we let p_{ij} be the probability of the first response on both i and j; q_{ij} and r_{ij} similarly:

$$\text{(aa)} \quad p_{ij} = \sum v^\alpha p_i^\alpha p_j^\alpha,$$
$$\text{(bb)} \quad q_{ij} = \sum v^\alpha q_i^\alpha q_j^\alpha, \qquad (2)$$
$$\text{(cc)} \quad r_{ij} = \sum v^\alpha r_i^\alpha r_j^\alpha.$$

$$\text{(aaa)} \quad p_{ijk} = \sum v^\alpha p_i^\alpha p_j^\alpha p_k^\alpha,$$
$$\text{(bbb)} \quad q_{ijk} = \sum v^\alpha q_i^\alpha q_j^\alpha q_k^\alpha, \qquad (3)$$
$$\text{(ccc)} \quad r_{ijk} = \sum v^\alpha r_i^\alpha r_j^\alpha r_k^\alpha.$$

Obviously, by considering first equations (1a), (2aa), and (3aaa) we could solve for all of the p_i^α and the v^α by the methods of Chapter 3. Notice that this would correspond to pooling responses (b) and (c) together as "not-(a)," and analyzing the resulting dichotomous variables. Of course, by using (1b), (2bb), and (3bbb) the parameters q_i^α could be found, and, of course, the v^α as well.

If the model were true, and the manifest probabilities were known the independent computations of the v^α would agree, as would the correspondence of $(1 - p_i^\alpha - q_i^\alpha)$ with the r_i^α obtained from the Equations (1c), (2cc), (3ccc), and the solutions of Chapter 3. The problems of parameter *estimation* from real data have increased greatly, however. For one thing, we have ignored in our

227

Equations (2) and (3) the manifest probabilities of "mixed" responses, i.e.,

$$
\begin{aligned}
\text{(ab)} \quad & \sum v^\alpha p_i^\alpha q_j^\alpha, \\
\text{(ac)} \quad & \sum v^\alpha p_i^\alpha r_j^\alpha, \\
\text{(ba)} \quad & \sum v^\alpha q_i^\alpha p_j^\alpha, \\
\text{(bc)} \quad & \sum v^\alpha q_i^\alpha r_j^\alpha, \\
\text{(ca)} \quad & \sum v^\alpha r_i^\alpha p_j^\alpha, \\
\text{(cb)} \quad & \sum v^\alpha r_i^\alpha q_j^\alpha,
\end{aligned}
\tag{4}
$$

and the twenty-four combinations of response for three items. It seems very difficult to discover any "reasonable" method of averaging solutions so all of these data have equal weights in the ultimate estimates, and even harder to practically compute a maximum likelihood estimate of the parameters. The extension to trichotomous items increases the number of latent parameters by a factor of n: from $m(n+1)$ to $m(2n+1)$; but the number of possible response patterns jumps from 2^n to 3^n.

In a recent article, Harper (1967) has worked out the notation for latent class analysis of items with any number of discrete response categories. Since such analysis is a relatively simple extension of the trichotomous case, we have chosen not to reproduce his results. The important characteristic is that if the assumptions of local independence do apply to all the response categories, then any dichotomization of these items will also satisfy these assumptions. Thus, by successively pooling different responses, one can, by ordinary class analysis, determine the latent parameters for each response category.

2. The Latent Profile Model

Suppose that we have a number of continuous manifest variables $X_1, X_2, \ldots, X_n$. We are thinking of such variables as age, income, score on an IQ test, and so on. Obviously, the use of the words "continuous" and "real-valued" to describe such quantities is misleading, for our measurements hardly ever have such fine gradations. Our use of these words is based on the undisputable fact that the variable takes on a value along a one-dimensional scale, i.e., the observations can be ordered; and on the more subjective fact that there are "enough" possible measure-points along the scale for our purposes.

The manifest distributions of such variables is best described by specifying the moments, or expected values of powers of the variables. The means of these variables,

$$\mu_i = E(X_i),$$

and the covariances,

$$\sigma_{ij} = E(X_i X_j) - E(X_i)E(X_j),$$

are the functions that are studied in factor analysis, regression analysis, and other statistical models which are often based on the assumption that the joint distribution of the manifest variables is multivariate normal. Here we explicitly recognize that the variables X_i are *not* normally distributed in the total population. This means that the complete specification of the distribution of the variables X_i will depend on higher-order moments such as the third-order covariances:[1]

$$\sigma_{ijk} = E[(X_i - EX_i)(X_j - EX_j)(X_k - EX_k)]$$
$$= E(X_i X_j X_k) - \mu_i \sigma_{jk} - \mu_j \sigma_{ik} - \mu_k \sigma_{ij} - \mu_i \mu_j \mu_k.$$

(We shall use the traditional notation σ_{ij}, σ_{ijk}, $\sigma_{12...m}$ for these "central moments," reserving the "symmetric parameter" notation $[ij]$, $[ijk]$, $[12 \cdots m]$ for the case of dichotomous items.)

The latent structure that we propose to study is one of discrete classes. As in the ordinary latent class model, we suppose that the population is divided among m classes, of size $v^1, v^2, \ldots, v^m$. With the continuous variables, X_i, however, it is not enough to specify a single within-class parameter: the distribution of responses within classes will depend on within-class means:

$$\mu_i^1, \mu_i^2, \mu_i^3, \ldots, \mu_i^m,$$

on within-class variances and covariances:

$$\sigma_{ii}^1, \sigma_{ii}^2, \ldots, \sigma_{ii}^m,$$
$$\sigma_{ij}^1, \sigma_{ij}^2, \ldots, \sigma_{ij}^m;$$

and, if the distributions are not normal, on higher-order moments, e.g., σ_{iii}^α.

Local independence, within-class independence, tells us to set *all* of the within-class covariances, and higher-order mixed central moments, equal to zero.

$$\sigma_{ij}^\alpha = 0, \qquad i \neq j;$$
$$\sigma_{ij...k}^\alpha = 0, \qquad \text{if at least two of the subscripts} \qquad (5)$$
$$i, j, \ldots, k, \text{ are distinct.}$$

If this is done, all variables are completely independent, within classes.

The accounting equations turn out to be entirely analogous to those of the model for dichotomous items (which, indeed, can be considered to be a special case). The overall mean,

$$EX_i = \mu_i,$$

is the weighted sum of the within class means:

$$EX_i = \mu_i = \sum_\alpha v^\alpha \mu_i^\alpha. \qquad (6)$$

The manifest covariances will not be equal to zero, of course, even though there is independence within the classes. As always, the mixture of different types of individuals causes the variables to appear correlated when the entire

---

[1]Recall how the moments of a univariate normal distribution are determined by the mean μ and the variance σ^2:

$$E(X - \mu)^k = \begin{cases} 0 \text{ is } k \text{ is odd,} \\ \sigma^k(1)(3)(5) \cdots (k-1) \text{ is } k \text{ is even.} \end{cases}$$

population is examined. The accounting equation:

$$\sigma_{ij} = \sum_\alpha v^\alpha(\mu_i^\alpha - \mu_i)(\mu_j^\alpha - \mu_j), \qquad i \neq j,$$

is derived as follows:

$$\sigma_{ij} = E(X_i - \mu_i)(X_j - \mu_j)$$
$$= \sum_\alpha v^\alpha E_\alpha[(X_i - \mu_i)(X_j - \mu_j)],$$

where "E_α" denotes the average value computed for the *members of class* α.
This is the conditional expectation, given the latent class, α. Local independence
implies the usual product rule:

$$E_\alpha[(X_i - \mu_i)(X_j - \mu_j)] = E_\alpha(X_i - \mu_i)E_\alpha(X_j - \mu_j).$$

But, by definition, $E_\alpha(X_i) = \mu_i^\alpha$ and $E_\alpha(X_j) = \mu_j^\alpha$, so

$$\sigma_{ij} = \sum_\alpha v^\alpha(\mu_i^\alpha - \mu_i)(\mu_j^\alpha - \mu_j), \qquad i \neq j. \tag{7}$$

ASIDE: If we did not use the product rule directly, but rather the fact that

$$\sigma_{ij}^\alpha = E_\alpha(X_i - \mu_i^\alpha)(X_j - \mu_j^\alpha) = 0,$$

Equation (7) could be derived by expanding the product:

$$\sigma_{ij} = \sum_\alpha v^\alpha E_\alpha[(X_i - \mu_i^\alpha + \mu_i^\alpha - \mu_i)(X_j - \mu_j^\alpha + \mu_j^\alpha - \mu_j)]$$
$$= \sum_\alpha v^\alpha E_\alpha[(X_i - \mu_i^\alpha)(X_j - \mu_j^\alpha) + (X_i - \mu_i^\alpha)(\mu_j^\alpha - \mu_j)$$
$$+ (\mu_i^\alpha - \mu_i)(X_j - \mu_j^\alpha) + (\mu_i^\alpha - \mu_i)(\mu_j^\alpha - \mu_j)]$$
$$= \sum_\alpha v^\alpha \sigma_{ij}^\alpha + \sum_\alpha v^\alpha(\mu_i^\alpha - \mu_i)(\mu_j^\alpha - \mu_j)$$
$$= \sum_\alpha v^\alpha(\mu_i^\alpha - \mu_i)(\mu_j^\alpha - \mu_j). \quad \blacksquare$$

When we multiply out the factors in (7), we find that:

$$\sigma_{ij} = \sum_\alpha v^\alpha \mu_i^\alpha \mu_j^\alpha - \mu_i\mu_j. \tag{7a}$$

An alternative development of the accounting equation would concentrate
on the non-central moments, e.g., on EX_iX_j. We would have, by the standard
analysis of a mixture:

$$EX_iX_j = \sum_\alpha v^\alpha E_\alpha X_i X_j,$$

and, the local independence would tell us that

$$E_\alpha X_i X_j = \mu_i^\alpha \mu_j^\alpha.$$

Thus

$$EX_iX_j = \sum_\alpha v^\alpha \mu_i^\alpha \mu_j^\alpha.$$

Since

$$\sigma_{ij} = EX_iX_j - \mu_i\mu_j,$$

Equation (7) could have been derived in this way. This approach, using non-central moments, is, of course, most analogous to our usual procedure in analyzing dichotomous items.

The third-order accounting equations follow at once, by the same reasoning:

$$E(X_i X_j X_k) = \sum_\alpha v^\alpha E_\alpha X_i X_j X_k$$
$$= \sum_\alpha v^\alpha \mu_i^\alpha \mu_j^\alpha \mu_k^\alpha, \qquad i \neq j \neq k, \tag{8}$$

and

$$\sigma_{ijk} = E(X_i - \mu_i)(X_j - \mu_j)(X_k - \mu_k)$$
$$= \sum_\alpha v^\alpha E_\alpha (X_i - \mu_i)(X_j - \mu_j)(X_k - \mu_k)$$
$$= \sum_\alpha v^\alpha (\mu_i^\alpha - \mu_i)(\mu_j^\alpha - \mu_j)(\mu_i^\alpha - \mu_k), \qquad i \neq j \neq k. \tag{9}$$

Furthermore, higher-order moments are written in a completely analogous way, *as long as no subscripts are repeated:*

$$E(X_i \cdots X_k) = \sum_\alpha v^\alpha \mu_i^\alpha \cdots \mu_k^\alpha.$$

Let's now introduce a new parameter, equal to the deviation of the within-class mean from the grand mean:

$$\delta_i^\alpha = \mu_i^\alpha - \mu_i.$$

Equations (6), (7), and (9) become:

$$\sum_\alpha v^\alpha \delta_i^\alpha = 0,$$

$$\sum_\alpha v^\alpha \delta_i^\alpha \delta_j^\alpha = \sigma_{ij},$$

$$\sum_\alpha v^\alpha \delta_i^\alpha \delta_j^\alpha \delta_k^\alpha = \sigma_{ijk},$$

etc., for i, j, k all distinct. These equations have the same structure as the accounting equations of the ordinary latent class model, with 0, σ_{ij}, σ_{ijk} replacing the manifest probabilities p_i, p_{ij}, p_{ijk}. The solution of the accounting equations that was derived in Chapter 3 can, therefore, be applied here. That is, unstratified and stratified basic matrices of manifest quantities are formed by selecting certain variables, and the same algebra is then carried out to determine the δ_i^α and v^α.

For example, if there are three classes, we let

$$B = \begin{pmatrix} 1 & 0 & 0 \\ 0 & \sigma_{24} & \sigma_{25} \\ 0 & \sigma_{34} & \sigma_{35} \end{pmatrix},$$

$$B_1 = \begin{pmatrix} 0 & \sigma_{14} & \sigma_{15} \\ \sigma_{12} & \sigma_{124} & \sigma_{125} \\ \sigma_{13} & \sigma_{134} & \sigma_{135} \end{pmatrix},$$

231

and compute $B_1 B^{-1}$. The three characteristic values of $B_1 B^{-1}$ will be the latent parameters δ_1^1, δ_1^2, and δ_1^3. The associated characteristic column vectors will provide the parameters of variables 2 and 3, the horizontal signature of B, and the parameters δ_4^α, δ_5^α, and v^α are then computed by going back to B.

ASIDE: We have chosen to use the manifest central moments, σ_{ij}, σ_{ijk}, etc., rather than the non-central moments for two reasons. First of all, it is usual in the analysis of continuous variables to compute and report covariances. Second, the computations required subsequently are somewhat simplified by the fact that the basic matrices B and B_1 contain zero entries. ∎

The matrix form of these equations is, of course,

$$B = L_h V L_v',$$
$$B_1 = L_h V D_1 L_v'$$

where δ_i^α replaces the p_i^α of Chapter 3:

$$L_{23} = \begin{pmatrix} 1 & 1 & 1 \\ \delta_2^1 & \delta_2^2 & \delta_2^3 \\ \delta_3^1 & \delta_3^2 & \delta_3^3 \end{pmatrix},$$

$$D_1 = \begin{pmatrix} \delta_1^1 & 0 & 0 \\ 0 & \delta_1^2 & 0 \\ 0 & 0 & \delta_1^3 \end{pmatrix}.$$

Once the δ_i^α have been calculated, the μ_i^α can be obtained by adding on the grand means, μ_i.

Every theorem dealing with the solution of the accounting equations and with identification of the p_i^α, and v^α in Chapter 3 can be carried over into a theorem involving identification of the μ_i^α and v^α for the latent profile model.

It is important to point out that either covariances or correlations may be used to determine the within-class means: the results will not be changed if the variables are standardized. The standardization involves the following familiar changes:

$$\rho_{ij} = \sigma_{ij}/(\sigma_{ii}\sigma_{jj})^{1/2},$$
$$\rho_{ijk} = \sigma_{ijk}/(\sigma_{ii}\sigma_{jj}\sigma_{kk})^{1/2}.$$

ρ_{ij} is the ordinary correlation coefficient, and we shall refer to ρ_{ijk} as a "third-order correlation." If we replaced the σ_{ij} and σ_{ijk} in the basic matrixes B and B_k by the corresponding ρ_{ij} and ρ_{ijk}, and solved, the resulting latent means would be equal to

$$\mu_i^\alpha/(\sigma_{ii})^{1/2};$$

that is, they would be standardized by the same factor: the manifest standard deviation of X_i. For instance, the equation

$$\sigma_{ij} = \sum_\alpha v^\alpha \delta_i^\alpha \delta_j^\alpha$$

is replaced by

$$\rho_{ij} = \sum_\alpha v^\alpha \lambda_i^\alpha \lambda_j^\alpha,$$

where the λ's are the standardized δ's: $\lambda_i^\alpha = \delta_i^\alpha/(\sigma_{ii})^{1/2}$. If the covariances were used, the resulting means are in the same units as the raw variables; if correlations were used, the resulting means must be multiplied by the manifest standard deviations in order to regain the original units.

3. An Empirical Example of Latent Profile Analysis

Gibson has published several articles in which he has applied the latent profile model to psychological data (Gibson, 1959). The example we include in this section is from our earlier article (Lazarsfeld and Henry, 1965). The data were taken from a study of community characteristics by C. T. Jonassen (1959). The units under analysis were the eighty-eight counties of Ohio, and the variables were based on census figures and other similar sources. We chose five variables and hypothesized a three-class model. These five, along with their means and standard deviations, are given in Table 1.

TABLE 1

*Means and Standard Deviations of Five Variables
for 88 Ohio Counties*

		Mean	Standard Deviation
1	(9)* Weekly per capita local newspaper circulation, 1950	1.445	0.99
2	(34) Percent of population 25 years of age or over who had completed high school, 1950	33.4	6.55
3	(1) Local educational expenditures per pupil, 1953	111.50	39.7
4	(62) Socio-economic status, 1950†	178	76.6
5	(77) Retail sales (in dollars) per capita, 1954	990	260.6

*The numbers in parentheses are Jonassen's numberings.
†SES index was derived from the rank of the county on family income, home value, the proportion of professional workers, and the proportion of unskilled workers. A high value of the index indicates a high socio-economic status.

The data used in the analysis were the standardized coefficients, ρ_{ij} and ρ_{ijk}, as defined in the previous section. Variable 5 was taken to be the stratifier, and the basic matrices were those given in Table 2.

TABLE 2

Data Used in Analysis

	Correlations B			Stratified B_5		
Variable	0	1	2	0	1	2
0	1	0	0	0	0.402	0.405
3	0	0.547	0.616	0.459	0.1089	−0.1995
4	0	0.545	0.835	0.505	0.0511	−0.2573

Direct application of the basic solution gives the numbers presented in Table 3. These are the standardized means: $(\mu_i^\alpha - \mu_i)/(\sigma_{ii})^{1/2}$. When these are transformed back into the original units, we obtain the numbers of Table 4.

TABLE 3

Latent Profile Solution in Standard Units

		Classes		
Item		1	2	3
1	Newspaper	1.19	−0.26	−0.64
2	High School	0.32	1.16	−1.23
3	Education	1.03	0.22	−0.95
4	SES	0.95	0.56	−1.17
5	Retail Sales	0.76	0.10	−0.63
Relative Class Sizes		0.273	0.343	0.384

TABLE 4

Latent Class Means in Original Units

		Classes			
Item		1	2	3	Units
1	Newspaper	2.62	1.19	0.81	Weekly circulation per capita
2	High School	36	41	25	Per cent of adult population
3	Education	153	120	74	Dollars per pupil
4	SES	250	220	89	SES index
5	Retail sales	1188	1016	826	Dollars per capita
	Class Sizes	0.273	0.343	0.384	

The interesting result of this analysis was that the three classes were not strictly ordered "high-middle-low" on all of the variables. The mean percentage of high school graduates was highest in Class 2, although otherwise, this class was intermediate on the other four variables. We tried to understand this result by looking for some "typical" counties, i.e., counties which exhibited the mean pattern of Class 1, 2, or 3. Then, we could use other facts about these counties to understand the latent classification.

For example, there is no doubt that the highly urbanized counties all belong to Class 1. High newspaper circulation, retail sales, and SES characterize those counties containing the principal cities of the state. On the other hand, many of the counties which contained smaller and less industrialized cities had higher proportions of high school graduates than the urban centers. Despite this fact, they were not spending as much money on education, per pupil, as were the big city centers at the time (*circa* 1950).

4. Further Analysis of the Latent Profile Model

There is more to the analysis of continuous variables within the framework of the latent class structure than is indicated by the accounting equations used by Gibson. When variables are dichotomous the "means" (p_i^α) tell us everything there is to know about the within-class distributions. For instance, if the mean of a dichotomous variable is p_i^α, its variance is $p_i^\alpha(1 - p_i^\alpha)$. Continuous variables have more complicated distributions. Unless there are specific statements to the contrary, one should not suppose that the means do describe the sub-population completely.

The methods of the previous section enable us to find the latent means (the means of the within-class distributions), as well as the relative sizes of the classes. But they do not tell us how to find within-class variances or any other higher moments of these distributions. Indeed, we *can* determine many of the within-class moments of the variables, even without making any assumptions about the functional form of the within-class distributions. And, further, if we suppose that each variable has a normal distribution *within* each latent class, then it becomes possible to make a number of probability statements about what class a respondent comes from, given his scores on the variables.

Consider the manifest variance of X_i:

$$\sigma_{ii} = E(X_i - \mu_i)^2$$
$$= \sum_\alpha v^\alpha E_\alpha (X_i - \mu_i^\alpha + \mu_i^\alpha - \mu_i)^2$$
$$= \sum_\alpha v^\alpha E_\alpha (X_i - \mu_i^\alpha)^2 + \sum_\alpha v^\alpha (\mu_i^\alpha - \mu_i)^2$$
$$\sigma_{ii} = \sum_\alpha v^\alpha \sigma_{ii}^\alpha + \sum v^\alpha (\mu_i^\alpha - \mu_i)^2, \tag{10}$$

σ_{ii}^α denotes the within-class variance of X_i. (Equation (10) simply indicates the familiar partition of variance into "within-class" variance, and "between-class" variance.)

If we suppose that the μ_i^α and v^α have already been calculated, then we have a linear equation in the unknowns σ_{ii}^α:

$$\sum_\alpha v^\alpha \sigma_{ii}^\alpha = \sigma_{ii} - \sum_\alpha v^\alpha (\mu_i^\alpha - \mu_i)^2 = h_{ii},$$

say, and h_{ii} is known.

If the (sometimes plausible) assumption is made that the variation about the mean is the same within all classes, then σ_{ii}^α does not depend on α and (since $\sum v^\alpha = 1$),

$$\sigma_{ii}^\alpha = h_{ii}$$

for all α.

It is possible to evaluate the σ_{ii}^α individually, however, if we are willing to look at higher-order moments of the X_i. Specifically, we shall be using manifest central moments such as σ_{iij}, σ_{iijj}, σ_{iii}, and so on.

ASIDE: It should not be hard to see how these are computed from the actual data. For instance,

$$\sigma_{iij} = E(X_i - \mu_i)^2 (X_j - \mu_j)$$

would be equal to

$$\left(\frac{1}{N}\right) \sum_n (X_{in} - \mu_i)^2 (X_{jn} - \mu_i)$$

if n ranges over all members of a finite population of size N. ∎

Consider what the accounting equation for σ_{iij} is, when $j \neq i$.

$$\begin{aligned}\sigma_{iij} &= E(X_i - \mu_i)^2 (X_j - \mu_j) \\ &= \sum_\alpha v^\alpha E_\alpha (X_i - \mu_i)^2 E_\alpha (X_j - \mu_j),\end{aligned}$$

since within the class α, variables i and j are independent. Therefore, using our previous knowledge, namely,

$$E_\alpha X_j = \mu_j^\alpha,$$

and

$$E_\alpha (X_i - \mu_i)^2 = \sigma_{ii}^\alpha + (\mu_i^\alpha - \mu_i)^2,$$

we have:

$$\sigma_{iij} = \sum_\alpha v^\alpha \sigma_{ii}^\alpha (\mu_j^\alpha - \mu_j) + \sum_\alpha v^\alpha (\mu_i^\alpha - \mu_i)^2 (\mu_j^\alpha - \mu_j) \qquad (11)$$

for any $j \neq i$.

If the v^α and μ_i^α are known, then Equation (11) is also a linear equation involving the σ_{ii}:

$$\sum_\alpha v^\alpha (\mu_j^\alpha - \mu_j) \sigma_{ii}^\alpha = \sigma_{iij} - \sum_\alpha v^\alpha (\delta_i^\alpha)^2 \delta_j^\alpha = h_{iij}, \qquad (12)$$

say, and h_{iij} is known. Now, if there are enough variables X_j, we can solve for all the σ_{ii}^α since there will be a new Equation (12) for any choice of $j \neq i$. For example, if there are only three classes, and if $i = 1$, then we would only have to take $j = 2$ and $j = 3$ in order to have three equations, enabling us to solve for these within-class variances.

We would then have:

$$\begin{pmatrix} v^1 & v^2 & v^3 \\ v^1\delta_2^1 & v^2\delta_2^2 & v^3\delta_2^3 \\ v^1\delta_3^1 & v^2\delta_3^2 & v^3\delta_3^3 \end{pmatrix} \begin{pmatrix} \sigma_{11}^1 \\ \sigma_{11}^2 \\ \sigma_{11}^3 \end{pmatrix} = \begin{pmatrix} h_{11} \\ h_{112} \\ h_{113} \end{pmatrix}.$$

As long as the coefficient matrix had an inverse, there would be a unique solution for the within-class variances. But we see immediately that this matrix equals $L_{23}V$, where L_{23} is the latent matrix of δ_i^α which we are quite familiar with. Therefore, the condition which permits us to solve for the within-class variances is no more restrictive than the condition required by the basic solution for the within-class means.

We now summarize this condition:

(i) In order to determine the within-class variances for X_i, it is sufficient that the within-class means and the class frequencies be known, and that there exist a signature s not including i having the property that the matrix L_s has an inverse. s must include m distinct subscripts, including the "null item" (which specifies the initial row of ones).

(ii) The "basic solution" for determining the latent means and the class frequencies requires that two sets of $m - 1$ variables each exist, making up two signatures h and v, so that both matrices L_h and L_v have inverses.

If (ii) is satisfied, then (i) must follow, for, if i is contained in the set of items h, we choose $s = v$; if i is in the set v, we choose $s = h$; and if i is some other item, we may choose either basic signature.

When there are no prior assumptions about the distribution of the variables within the latent classes, it would be possible to estimate as many of the within-class moments as we wish and thus to obtain an approximate idea of what these distributions look like. On the other hand, when some particular distribution is proposed for these variables, the higher-order moments would enable us to test that hypothesis.

For example, if we proposed the hypothesis that all of the variables have normal distributions within the classes, we could use the estimated values of σ_{iii}^α and σ_{iiii}^α to test the hypothesis, since, according to the hypothesis,

$$\sigma_{iii}^\alpha = 0,$$

and

$$\sigma_{iiii}^\alpha = 3(\sigma_{ii}^\alpha)^2.$$

Of course, even if these conditions appeared to be satisfied, we would not know for sure that the distributions were normal (for that, an infinite number of moments would have to be examined), but if they are clearly not satisfied, we would recognize that the distribution was not normal.

We have not considered the statistical problems involved in testing such hypotheses when the initial data are a random sample of the population. The fact that rather complicated estimation procedures are necessary to estimate

237

the latent parameters v^α, μ_i^α, and σ_{ii}^α (given the estimates of the manifest parameters) before parameters σ_{iii}^α and σ_{iiii}^α can be estimated, means that the sampling
distributions of these latter estimates are very complicated.

A more reasonable approach to testing a hypothesis such as "all within-class
distributions are normal" is to compute maximum likelihood estimates of the
parameters under the hypothesis of normality, and then examine the likelihood
of the observations in the sample, given these estimates, just as we did in the
case of dichotomous items. The size of the likelihood function would then serve
as a test of the normality hypotheses. Those who recall the complexity of the
task of obtaining maximum likelihood estimates in the case of dichotomous
items, described in Chapter 4, will understand the difficulties involved here.
There now are *two* parameters for each variable within each class, rather than
one. It is by no means impossible to write a computer program to carry out
such an estimation procedure, merely highly impractical at this time.

5. Recruitment Probabilities in the Latent Profile Model

The latent profile model permits us to construct a typology of respondents.
In many cases, this theoretical partitioning of the population into classes is
preferable to the results of a factor analysis, which tells us more about the
variables being analyzed than about the individuals who respond to those
variables.

In order to take advantage of this typology, i.e., to classify individuals on the
basis of their manifest responses, we have to have specified the within-class
distributions of the variables. For instance, if we know that $\mu_1^1 = 0.5$ and
$\mu_1^2 = 3$, and a respondent has the value $X_1 = 2$, it is not clear to which class
he "probably" belongs. His response is closer to Class 2, in an absolute sense.
If, however, $\sigma_{11}^1 = 1$ and $\sigma_{11}^2 = 0.09$, and the within-class distributions are
approximately normal, he is "probably" from Class 1:

$$(2 - \mu_1^1)/\sqrt{\sigma_{11}^1} = 1.5,$$
$$(\mu_1^2 - 1)/\sqrt{\sigma_{11}^2} = 1/0.3 = 3.3.$$

Thus, the within-class variances have to be considered if normal distributions
are assumed, while other moments would be involved if more complicated
distributions were hypothesized.

Suppose that $f_i^\alpha(x)$ is the probability density function of X_i within class α.
That is,

$$\int_{-\infty}^{Y} f_i^\alpha(x)\,dx$$

is the probability that $X_i < Y$, for those who belong to class α.

The manifest density function of a response $(X_1, X_2, \ldots, X_n) = X$ would
be:

$$f(X) = \sum_\alpha v^\alpha f_1^\alpha(X_1) f_2^\alpha(X_2) \cdots f_n^\alpha(X_n) = \sum_\alpha v^\alpha f^\alpha(X).$$

For classification, we want to know what is the probability that a respondent belongs to Class 1, 2, 3, . . . , or m, given a response vector $X = (X_1, \ldots, X_n)$. By Bayes Theorem this is:

$$\Pr(\alpha|X) = v^\alpha f^\alpha(X)/f(X) \qquad \text{for each } \alpha.$$

The most likely class is, therefore, the class α for which

$$v^\alpha f^\alpha(X) = v^\alpha f_1^\alpha(X_1)f_2^\alpha(X_2) \cdots f_n^\alpha(X_n)$$

is a maximum. Equivalently, we require that the logarithm of this:

$$h_\alpha(X) = \log v^\alpha + \sum_{i=1}^{n} \log f_i^\alpha(X_i)$$

be a maximum.

If each within-class distribution is assumed to be normal, with unspecified mean and variance, the density functions are:

$$f_i^\alpha(X_i) = (1/2\pi\sigma_{ii}^\alpha)^{1/2} \exp[-(1/2)(X_i - \mu_i^\alpha)^2/\sigma_{ii}^\alpha].$$

Of course,

$$\log f_i^\alpha(X_i) = -1/2[(X - \mu_i^\alpha)^2/\sigma_{ii}^\alpha + \log 2\pi\sigma_{ii}^\alpha]$$

and, therefore,

$$h_\alpha(X) = \log v^\alpha - 1/2 \sum_{i=1}^{n} (X_i - \mu_i^\alpha)^2/\sigma_{ii}^\alpha - 1/2 \sum_{i=1}^{n} \log 2\pi\sigma_{ii}^\alpha.$$

Notice that some of these terms do not depend on the response vector, X:

$$h_\alpha(X) = g_\alpha - 1/2 \sum_{i=1}^{n} (X_i - \mu_i^\alpha)^2/\sigma_{ii}^\alpha, \tag{13}$$

where

$$g_\alpha = \log v^\alpha + (-1/2) \sum_{i=1}^{n} \log 2\pi\sigma_{ii}^\alpha$$

does not depend on X.

If the means μ_i^α and variances σ_{ii}^α were known exactly, it would be a relatively simple problem to assign response vectors to the most likely class, using Equation (13). Such an assignment would minimize the amount of mis-classification, and this probability of error can be calculated, assuming normality, just as in the model for dichotomous items. When the parameters have been estimated from a random sample, however, it is difficult to evaluate this probability of error. In fact, the whole question of evaluating the probabilities of correct classification when latent parameters are only estimated is still unsolved, even in the dichotomous item situation.

6. Models Having Continuous Latent Spaces

In this section, we note briefly the existence of models wherein both manifest variables and latent variables are continuous, real-valued, variables.

$X_1, X_2, \ldots, X_n$ are real-valued manifest variables, and the moments of these variables are given by:

$$\mu_i = E(X_i),$$
$$\sigma_{ij} = E(X_i - \mu_i)(X_j - \mu_j),$$
$$\sigma_{ijk} = E(X_i - \mu_i)(X_j - \mu_j)(X_k - \mu_k), \quad \text{etc.}$$

Now, instead of assuming the existence of latent classes, we suppose that there is a single real-valued latent variable, Y. The location and scale of this variable may be set arbitrarily, by letting:

$$E(Y) = 0,$$

and
$$\text{Var}(Y) = 1,$$

and we further suppose that the distribution of Y is such that all of its moments exist.

The axiom of local independence in this model says that the manifest variables must be independent if a particular value of Y has been given. The conditional expectation of a product of X_i's will, therefore, always factor. For instance,

$$E(X_i X_j | Y = y) = E(X_i|y)E(X_j|y).$$

To complete the specification of the model, therefore, we need a set of functions giving the mean values of the various manifest variables for a particular value of $Y = y$:

$$E(X_i|y) = m_i(y).$$

As the simplest example of all, suppose that these functions are linear in y:

$$m_i(y) = a_i + b_i y.$$

Accounting equations can then be derived relating the parameters a_i, b_i, and the moments of Y to the manifest moments of the X_i.

$$\mu_i = E(m_i(Y)) = a_i + b_i E(Y) = a_i,$$
$$\sigma_{ij} = E(m_i(Y) - \mu_i)(m_j(Y) - \mu_j)$$
$$= b_i b_j E(Y^2)$$
$$= b_i b_j \quad \text{for } i \neq j.$$

The situation is just as it was in the case of dichotomous items with a model of linear tracelines: the item parameters a_i and b_i can be determined by examination of the means and the covariances of the manifest variables. This is also exactly the single-factor model of ordinary factor analysis, without any assumption concerning the actual distribution of Y. We can proceed to examine other aspects of the distribution of Y and of the conditional distributions of the X_i, given Y, just as we did in the case of the latent profile model.

For example, the variance of X_i will be a function of the conditional variance of X_i, given Y. Letting this conditional variance be

$$\sigma_{ii}(y) = E_y(X_i - m_i(y))^2 = E_y(X_i)^2 - (m_i(y))^2,$$

where E_y stands for the conditional expected value, given that $Y = y$, the equations follow:

$$
\begin{aligned}
\sigma_{ii} &= E(X_i - \mu_i)^2 = E(X_i)^2 - (\mu_i)^2 \\
&= E\big(\sigma_{ii}(Y) + (m_i(Y))^2\big) - (\mu_i)^2 \\
&= E\big(\sigma_{ii}(Y)\big) + (a_i)^2 + 2a_ib_iE(Y) + (b_i)^2E(Y^2) - (a_i)^2 \\
\sigma_{ii} &= E\big(\sigma_{ii}(Y)\big) + (b_i)^2.
\end{aligned}
$$

It is often assumed that the conditional variance $\sigma_{ii}(y)$ is constant over all values of y. If this is so,

$$
\sigma_{ii}(y) = c_i,
$$
$$
E\big(\sigma_{ii}(y)\big) = c_i,
$$

and then we find that

$$
c_i = \sigma_{ii} - (b_i)^2.
$$

This assumption is made in the factor-analysis model, the c_i being that part of the variance of X_i which is not explained by the function $m_i(y)$.

In the latent profile model there were only a finite number of these conditional variances (one for each class) for each variable X_i, and we were able to solve for them by examining the third-order manifest moments, σ_{iij}. Here, as alternatives to the assumption that they are constant, we might suppose (i) that they take on only a finite number of values, thus reducing the problem to that of the latent profile case; or (ii) suppose that $\sigma_{ii}(y)$ is some continuous function of y, with a few undetermined parameters which we could try to find by using those higher-order moments. Little work has been done in this area; we do not even have ideas as to what sort of functions $\sigma_{ii}(y)$ might be most useful.

Let us now consider more complicated functions $m_i(y)$. For example, the general quadratic function:

$$
m_i(y) = a_i + b_iy + d_iy^2.
$$

Evidently, the means and the covariances of the manifest variables are:

$$
\begin{aligned}
\mu_i &= a_i + b_iE(Y) + d_iE(Y^2) \\
&= a_i + d_i, \\
\sigma_{ij} &= E(a_i + b_iY + d_iY^2 - \mu_i)(a_j + b_jY + d_jY^2 - \mu_j) \\
&= E(b_iY + d_iY^2 - d_i)(b_jY + d_jY^2 - d_j) \\
&= b_ib_j + d_id_j - 2d_id_j + (b_id_j + b_jd_i)E(Y^3) + d_id_jE(Y^4).
\end{aligned}
$$

In order to evaluate the covariances, we have to specify what the third- and fourth-order moments of the latent variable Y are. Let's suppose that Y is normally distributed; then $E(Y^3) = 0$ and $E(Y^4) = 3$, and the above expressions become:

$$
\sigma_{ij} = b_ib_j - d_id_j + 3d_id_j = b_ib_j + 2d_id_j.
$$

The covariance matrix would, therefore, have rank two (disregarding the diagonal entries) and the b_i and d_i could be determined by the usual matrix factorization methods, except for an orthogonal rotation. This rotation, in two dimensions, would involve a single parameter, and thus we must ask whether that single parameter can be determined uniquely by considering third-order moments σ_{ijk}.

A third-order covariance σ_{ijk}, where i, j, and k are distinct, is

$$\sigma_{ijk} = E(m_i(Y) - \mu_i)(m_j(Y) - \mu_j)(m_k(Y) - \mu_k)$$
$$= E(b_iY + d_i(Y^2 - 1))(b_jY + d_j(Y^2 - 1))(b_k + d_k(Y^2 - 1)).$$

Normality implies that $E(Y^5) = 0$ and $E(Y^6) = 15$. Expanding, and making these substitutions, we find that:

$$\sigma_{ijk} = 8d_id_jd_k + 2(b_ib_jd_k + b_id_jb_k + d_ib_jb_k).$$

We notice the following way of expressing these results:

$$\sigma_{ij} = (b_i, d_i)\begin{pmatrix} 1 & 0 \\ 0 & 2 \end{pmatrix}\begin{pmatrix} b_j \\ d_j \end{pmatrix},$$

$$\sigma_{ijk} = (b_i, d_i)\begin{pmatrix} 2d_k & 2b_k \\ 2b_k & 8d_k \end{pmatrix}\begin{pmatrix} b_j \\ d_j \end{pmatrix}.$$

The form is suggestive of the unstratified and stratified basic matrices which were used to solve the equations of the latent class model, and so we define

$$A_{12} = \begin{pmatrix} b_1 & d_1 \\ b_2 & d_2 \end{pmatrix} \quad \text{and} \quad A_{34} = \begin{pmatrix} b_3 & d_3 \\ b_4 & d_4 \end{pmatrix},$$

and let

$$C = \begin{pmatrix} \sigma_{13} & \sigma_{14} \\ \sigma_{23} & \sigma_{24} \end{pmatrix} \quad \text{and} \quad C_k = \begin{pmatrix} \sigma_{13k} & \sigma_{14k} \\ \sigma_{23k} & \sigma_{24k} \end{pmatrix}.$$

Obviously,

$$C = A_{12}\begin{pmatrix} 1 & 0 \\ 0 & 2 \end{pmatrix}A'_{34},$$

and

$$C_k = A_{12}\begin{pmatrix} 2d_k & 2b_k \\ 2b_k & 8d_k \end{pmatrix}A'_{34},$$

and

$$C_kC^{-1} = A_{12}\begin{pmatrix} 2d_k & 2b_k \\ 2b_k & 8d_k \end{pmatrix}\begin{pmatrix} 1 & 0 \\ 0 & 1/2 \end{pmatrix}A_{12}^{-1}$$
$$= A_{12}\begin{pmatrix} 2d_k & b_k \\ 2b_k & 4d_k \end{pmatrix}A_{12}^{-1}.$$

The latent class solution does not work here, unless $b_k = 0$, for it required a diagonal matrix between A and A^{-1}. However, a solution is immediate, for it is easy to show that the sum of the diagonal elements of $C_k C^{-1}$ is equal to $6d_k$, thus determining d_k.

The result follows from an easily proved matrix identity. The sum of the diagonal elements of a matrix is called its *trace*, written

$$\operatorname{tr}(G) = \sum_i g_{ii}.$$

The general theorem states that if

$$G = ABC,$$

where A, B, and C are all square, then

$$\operatorname{tr}(G) = \operatorname{tr}(ABC) = \operatorname{tr}(CAB).$$

In particular, if $C = A^{-1}$, we find that

$$\operatorname{tr}(ABA^{-1}) = \operatorname{tr}(A^{-1}AB) = \operatorname{tr}(B),$$

from which we see that

$$\operatorname{tr}(C_k C^{-1}) = 2d_k + 4d_k = 6d_k.$$

Now, all the d's can be found by varying the stratifier k, and repeating the computation. Alternatively, we note that knowledge of only one d_k is enough to fix the rotation mentioned above, after the covariance matrix has been factored. Either method could be used, and the second would undoubtedly be the most efficient method if we were analyzing many variables.

Given the d's, we can find the a's:

$$a_i = p_i - d_i.$$

However, the b's cannot be determined uniquely: it will always be possible to change the sign of *all* of the b's without altering the manifest distributions: the manifest moments $(\mu_i, \sigma_{ij}, \ldots, \sigma_{123\ldots n})$ generated by a given set of parameters (a_i, b_i, d_i) would also be generated by the parameters $(a_i, -b_i, d_i)$. This follows from the fact that an even number of b's always occurs in every manifest moment, for whenever an odd number of b's occurs, there will be an odd power of Y, and the expected value of any odd power of Y is zero. The two sets of b's can be found by the factorization-rotation method, or, given the d's, from relations such as:

$$b_i b_j = \sigma_{ij} - 2d_i d_j,$$

which imply that

$$(b_k)^2 = (\sigma_{ik} - 2d_i d_k)(\sigma_{jk} - 2d_j d_k)/(\sigma_{ij} - 2d_i d_j).$$

The crucial assumption about the distribution of Y is that it is symmetric around 0, so that all of the odd moments of Y vanish. If we had other values than 3 and 15 for $E(Y^4)$ and $E(Y^6)$, it would still turn out that d_k is equal to a constant times the trace of $C_k C^{-1}$; the constant would depend on $E(Y^4)$ and

243

$E(Y^6)$, but if these were not known, a solution would be more difficult to work out.

In general, if $m_i(y)$ were a polynomial of degree r, we would find that the covariance matrix (σ_{ij}) would have rank r. This model, which postulates the existence of a single latent variable Y, has a complicated relation to the average values of the manifest variables, X_i. Contrast this with the linear model of factor analysis, which postulates the existence of r independent latent variables, which have a particularly simple relationship to the manifest variables. The differences are most instructive. In data analysis, we are always faced with the task of balancing simplicity in one aspect of our explanation, at the cost of complexity in some other aspect of the explanation. While in theory at least, the two models could be distinguished, e.g., by using higher-order moments σ_{ijk}, in practice the analysis of the pairwise covariances is often all that can be carried out, and the choice (between, say, one quadratic factor and two linear factors) must be made on nonstatistical grounds. The work begun by McDonald a few years ago (McDonald, 1962) may prove fruitful in developing practical alternatives to routine linear factor analysis.

Latent Class Models for
Repeated Behavior

1. Markov Chains

In this chapter, we shall study some models which can be applied to the analysis of behavior that is repeated over time, sometimes referred to as panel analysis. The general model, the *latent Markov chain*, which is discussed beginning in Section 3, was proposed originally by Lee Wiggins (Wiggins, 1955) and many of the results which we present can be found in his dissertation.

In this section, we shall only mention a few of the important descriptive properties of Markov chains. The reader should be acquainted with the more complete introductions (Kemeny, *et al.*, 1959, Parzen, 1962, Kemeny and Snell, 1961), but we shall try to make this chapter as self-contained as possible.

Suppose that we are concerned with a single characteristic of an individual, and how it changes over time. Further, suppose that there are only a finite number of manifestations of this characteristic: the individual is said to be in one of a finite number of *states* at any particular time. For example, a worker is employed in a certain industry; a respondent asserts that he prefers a certain candidate. In the former case, we have some coding scheme for classifying all possible industrial employers; in the latter there may be two, three, or more possible responses, depending on the number of candidates. These make up the finite list of states of the process. In dealing with most social science applications, we suppose that our processes can be observed only at discrete points in time: $t = 1, 2, 3, \ldots$.

Let the states be numbered from 1 to n. Let $p_i(t)$ be the probability that state i is observed at time t. The Markov chain model permits some dependence between the state observed (which we shall call the "response"), and previous responses, or states. This dependence is incorporated in a set of transition probabilities, $R = (r_{ij})$; r_{ij} is the conditional probability of being in state j at time $t + 1$, given state i at time t. Thus, being in a certain state i at time t

determines the probability distribution of the possible states at the next time, $t + 1$.

The *Markovian assumption* restricts the time dependence of this process by requiring that these transition probabilities not be affected by additional knowledge about the past states through which the process has passed. That is, the probability of being in state j at time $t + 1$, given that the process was in state i at time t and in state k at time s, where $s < t$, is still equal to r_{ij}.

Now, if $p_j(t)$ is the marginal probability of being in state j at time t, the usual probability law tells us that:

$$p_j(t) = \sum_i p_i(t - 1)r_{ij}, \tag{1}$$

the sum being over all the states. In matrix notation, letting $p(t)$ be the row vector $\left(p_1(t), p_2(t), \ldots, p_n(t)\right)$, we have:

$$p(t) = p(t - 1)R. \tag{2}$$

By repeated substitutions, we find that:

$$p(t) = p(0)R^t. \tag{3}$$

The entries of a power of R, say R^t, are the transition probabilities across an interval of length t.

A joint probability, $p_{ij}(1,2)$ (the probability of response i at time 1 and response j at $t = 2$), is equal to $p_i(1)r_{ij}$. Define $P(t)$ to be a diagonal matrix whose diagonal elements are the entries of the vector $p(t)$ for any t. The equality is represented by the matrix equation:

$$P(1,2) = P(1)R. \tag{4}$$

It is easy to see that Equation (4) generalizes to take care of joint probabilities at *any* pair of time points:

$$P(s, s + t) = P(s)R^t. \tag{5}$$

Quite clearly, the transition matrix R can be determined from any joint frequency matrix $P(t, t + 1)$:

$$R = P(t)^{-1}P(t, t + 1).$$

A hypothesis that R does not change over time can be tested if more than two time points are examined. If this is satisfied, the Markov chain assumption can be further tested by examining a pair of time points more than a unit apart.

For example, suppose that we have three time points, $t = 1, 2, 3$. There are three joint probability matrices, $P(1,2)$, $P(2,3)$, and $P(1,3)$. According to the Markov chain model, these equations must hold:

$$P(1,2) = P(1)R,$$
$$P(1,3) = P(1)R^2,$$
$$P(2,3) = P(2)R.$$

Thus, the manifest probability matrices must satisfy these conditions:

$$P(1)^{-1}P(1,2) = P(2)^{-1}P(2,3),$$

and   (6)

$$P(1,3) = P(1,2)P(1)^{-1}P(1,2).$$

When estimating R from data, we would expect these equations to be approximately true if the model fits: tests of significance can be developed accordingly. The work of Anderson (1954); Blumen, Kogan, McCarthy (1955); and Anderson and Goodman (1957), is particularly cited in this regard.

We are not concerned in this chapter with Markov chain models, *per se*, but in some alternative models for repeated behavior. It will be instructive, however, to be able to refer to these basic equations for the simple Markov chain in order to compare the implications of these models. Thus, in closing this section, we note what the Markov model implies about third-order probabilities, e.g., $p_{ijk}(1,2,3)$, the joint probability of response i at time 1, j at time 2, and k at time 3:

$$p_{ijk}(1,2,3) = p_i(1)r_{ij}r_{jk}$$
$$= p_{ij}(1,2)r_{jk}. \qquad (7)$$

Thus, the identity

$$r_{jk} = p_{ijk}(1,2,3)/p_{ij}(1,2)$$

is implied, in addition to the earlier ones:

$$r_{jk} = p_{jk}(1,2)/p_j(1) = p_{jk}(2,3)/p_j(2).$$

The models we discuss in the next sections involve more unknown parameters than does the Markov chain model, and we shall see that it is necessary for us to use third-order probabilities if we are to determine all of those parameters.

2. Latent Classes: A Mixture of Independent Processes

Vital to application of a Markov chain model is the assumption that an observed change from one state to another on the part of an individual is a "real" change. For instance, if the process consists of the responses to a question about political preference, with states "Republican," "Democrat," and "Other," the Markov chain requires that everyone who responds "Republican" have the same probability of changing his response at the next interview, regardless of his previous responses. The model is not consistent with our knowledge that, though such a thing as party identification may exist, the response to a particular question at a particular time may not exactly reflect this characteristic.

A latent class model is, then, one alternative to the Markov chain model. Suppose that the population is divided into m latent classes; suppose that the probability of giving response i at a particular time depends only on the class one belongs to; and suppose that responses are independent of one another, over time. The last assumption, local independence, as always, rests on a theory of response behavior that states that, at any particular time, extraneous causes act randomly to influence response: the only *systematically* present cause of response is supposed to be class membership. The assumption may or may not be reasonable in any particular application, but let us see what the implications of the model are.

Let the relative size of the classes be

$$v_1, v_2, \ldots, v_m.$$

We are going to assume that there is no movement from one class to another over time. Let v be the row vector of these probabilities and let V be the corresponding diagonal matrix.

Let $q_{\alpha j}$ be the probability of giving response j, given that the respondent belongs to class α.[1] $Q = (q_{\alpha j})$ is the matrix of these probabilities.

Some obvious results are immediate. The manifest probability of response j at time i will be the same for all t: there can be no change over time in the overall distribution of responses, except, of course, for that due to the random sampling. Letting $p_j(t)$ represent this probability, we see that

$$p_j(t) = \sum_\alpha v_\alpha q_{\alpha j}, \qquad (8)$$

or

$$p(t) = p = vQ. \qquad (9)$$

For example, suppose that there are two response categories, "Republican" and "Democrat," possible replies to a question about intended voting behavior. If we assume that there are actually two latent classes, consisting of "true Republicans" and "true Democrats," the latent parameters might look like this:

$$
Q : \quad
\begin{array}{c}
\text{True Rep.} \\[1.2em]
\text{True Dem.}
\end{array}
\begin{array}{cc}
\text{Response} \\
\text{Rep.} \quad \text{Dem.} \\
\left(
\begin{array}{cc}
0.8 & 0.2 \\[1em]
0.3 & 0.7
\end{array}
\right)
\end{array}
$$

$$v : \quad (0.4, 0.6).$$

Although there are more true Democrats than Republicans, the latter appear to be more loyal to the party. As a result, the following manifest response distribution would be expected:

$$p = vQ = (0.32 + 0.18, 0.08 + 0.42) = (0.5, 0.5).$$

Although this model requires that the marginal proportions be stable over time, it obviously permits individuals to change their responses from time to

---

[1] Notice that we have chosen to modify the notation which we have used throughout this book: a superscript to represent the class index is not used. In part, our reason is to take advantage of ordinary matrix notation; but, also, we want to emphasize the difference between the response probabilities and the parameters p_i^α. p_i^α was the conditional probability of a *positive* response to a dichotomous item, i. $q_{\alpha j}$, on the other hand, is the conditional probability of response j to some particular question that need not be restricted to dichotomous response.

time. In other words, we should observe *turnover* from one time to another, due to the probabilistic relationship between latent class and manifest response. If s and t are two points in time, then the probability of giving response i at time s and response j at time t is equal to:

$$p_{ij}(s, t) = \sum_{\alpha} v_{\alpha} q_{\alpha j} q_{\alpha i},$$ (10)

assuming that local independence holds.

In matrix form, since these probabilities are the same way for any s and t, we can write

$$P(s, t) = P = Q'VQ.$$ (11)

P is, of course, the joint response matrix. Notice that t and s do not affect this matrix: since all variation in individual response is supposed to be due to latent class membership, and this is not permitted to change, it does not matter what two points are specified.

If we continue our example, we find that:

$$
\begin{aligned}
P = Q'VQ &= \begin{pmatrix} 0.8 & 0.3 \\ 0.2 & 0.7 \end{pmatrix} \begin{pmatrix} 0.4 & 0 \\ 0 & 0.6 \end{pmatrix} \begin{pmatrix} 0.8 & 0.2 \\ 0.3 & 0.7 \end{pmatrix} \\
&= \begin{pmatrix} 0.32 & 0.18 \\ 0.08 & 0.42 \end{pmatrix} \begin{pmatrix} 0.8 & 0.2 \\ 0.3 & 0.7 \end{pmatrix} \\
&= \begin{pmatrix} 0.31 & 0.19 \\ 0.19 & 0.31 \end{pmatrix}.
\end{aligned}
$$

Thus, between *any* two time points, we expect 38% of the respondents to change their opinion: half of these in one direction, the rest in the opposite direction.

Third-order response probabilities are easily calculated.

$$p_{ijk}(s,t,u) = p_{ijk} = \sum_{\alpha} v_{\alpha} q_{\alpha i} q_{\alpha j} q_{\alpha k}.$$ (12)

The notation indicates response i at time s, j at time t, and k at time u. The usual way of displaying such information is in a stratified turnover table, as shown below for the data of our example:

Manifest Response Probabilities

| Time t | | Time u | | | | | |
| | | Republican | | | | Democrat | |
		Rep	Dem			Rep	Dem
Time s	Rep	0.221	0.089		Rep	0.089	0.101
	Dem	0.089	0.101		Dem	0.101	0.209

(These figures should be verified by the reader, using Equation (12).)

249

In matrix terms, we shall define X_k to be the diagonal matrix whose entries are q_{1k}, q_{2k}, etc., the kth column of the response matrix Q, and let $P_k(s,t;u)$ be the matrix of response probabilities at times s and t, stratified by response k at time u. In the example, these matrices have already been computed:

$$P_{\mathrm{Rep}}(s,t;u) = \begin{pmatrix} 0.221 & 0.089 \\ 0.089 & 0.101 \end{pmatrix} \quad \text{and} \quad P_{\mathrm{Dem}}(s,t;u) = \begin{pmatrix} 0.089 & 0.101 \\ 0.101 & 0.209 \end{pmatrix}.$$

It is not hard to see that the proper matrix equation, derived from (12), is

$$P_k(s,t;u) = Q'VX_kQ. \tag{13}$$

The resemblance between these equations, especially Equations (11) and (13), and the accounting equations of the general class model should be apparent. The solution for the latent parameters is obtained by exactly the same manipulations of these matrices as of the basic matrices. We merely need to be sure that certain inverses exist in order to carry out the specified operations. We mention only a few of the special cases.

(i) *The number of classes equals the number of response categories.* If Q^{-1} exists, and no class is empty, then P^{-1} exists and equals $Q^{-1}V^{-1}Q'^{-1}$. Then we see that:

$$P^{-1}P_k = Q^{-1}X_kQ. \tag{14}$$

Therefore, the entries of X_k (the kth column of Q) are the characteristic roots of $P^{-1}P_k$, and if they are all distinct, Q can be uniquely determined. Even if they are not all distinct, it may be possible to obtain Q uniquely by varying k.
(ii) *The number of classes is less than the number of response categories.* The matrix Q has m rows and n columns, and the manifest matrices P and P_k are n by n. If $m < n$, Equations (11) and (13) still apply, but P and P_k will not have inverses, since their rank cannot be greater than m. Let Q^* be a square matrix of order m formed by specifying m of the columns of Q, and suppose that Q^{*-1} exists. (We must assume that there exists at least one such submatrix which has an inverse.) Let P^* and P_k^* be the $m \times m$ submatrices obtained by specifying only those m response categories. It is clear that

$$P^* = (Q^*)'VQ^*$$

and

$$P_k^* = (Q^*)'VX_kQ^*.$$

Therefore, as in (i),

$$P^{*-1}P_k^* = Q^{*-1}X_kQ^*$$

serves to determine X_k and Q^*, and, consequently, V. The remaining columns of Q can be determined by considering the asymmetric section of P, consisting of all p_{ij}, with i belonging to the set of m columns specified above and j belonging to the set of remaining columns. If P^a stands for this submatrix and Q^{**} for the remaining columns of Q, then $P^a = Q^{*'}VQ^{**}$, so that

$$Q^{**} = V^{-1}(Q^{*-1})'P^a.$$

(iii) *The number of response categories is two.* If the observations are of a dichotomous item, but we suppose that there are $m > 2$ latent classes, we have the situation already discussed in Chapter 3, of *equivalent* dichotomous items. The latent parameters can be found if the number of observations at different times is sufficiently large.

The simplest possible situation, with two latent classes and two response categories, was discussed in Appendix 2 of *Conflict and Mood* (Kendall, 1954).

The assumption of local independence does not seem as plausible in the hypothetical example of voting intention suggested in this section as it does in some other applications. For instance, there may be little association between the items on a very long intelligence test, except for the fact that a smart student will tend to get many of them right, while a less smart student will tend to get many of them wrong. On the other hand, if an individual is presented with the same question over and over, we know that he will eventually recall previous replies and will modify his response accordingly.

The assumption does seem to be realistic in at least one area, however, that of purchase behavior. The model has been successful in analyzing newsstand purchases of magazines, for instance. The classes consist of "regular readers" and "non-readers," the former characterized by a higher probability of purchase than the latter. Over the short term, several weeks or months, the overall circulation of the magazines is relatively stable. The local independence assumption attributes the variation in individual purchases to random causes: the regular reader is travelling, and forgets to buy; the non-reader is attracted by the cover and does buy. Local independence rules out decision rules such as "I've bought two weeks in a row, so I won't buy this week"; even though some people may behave this way, they probably do not dominate the market behavior.

Table 1 below contains the results of an analysis of magazine purchasing, comparing four national magazines.

TABLE 1

*Latent Readership and Probabilities of Reading Four Magazines**

Magazine	Latent Classes		Latent Probability of Reading for	
	Regular Readers	Non-Readers	"Regulars"	"Non-Regulars"
A	0.16	0.84	0.57	0.05
B	0.20	0.80	0.68	0.10
C	0.11	0.89	0.62	0.05
D	0.06	0.94	0.78	0.07

*Taken from an unpublished report by Peter Rossi, "A Simple Model for Attitude Testing," *B.A.S.R.* (1950).

It is interesting to note that magazine "D," with the smallest percentage of regular readers, benefits from their more regular reading habits.

3. The Latent Markov Chain Model

For long term processes the latent class model is not acceptable because no real change is allowed to occur. Likewise, the Markov chain model often does not agree with the observations because of the overemphasis it places on changes in response which could be due to accidental factors. Therefore, we shall combine these two models in the hope of obtaining a model that will reflect actual behavior.

3.1 *The Model and a Solution*

We suppose that at any particular time the population is divided into latent classes, and that the probabilities of the various responses are determined solely by these classes. In addition, however, we assume that individuals can move from one class to another according to a simple Markov chain process. Coleman (1964b) has analyzed a very similar model and the dichotomous case has been discussed by Lazarsfeld (1965).

Suppose that there are m response categories, and m latent classes. As in Section 2, let Q be the matrix of response probabilities, given class membership, and let M be the transition matrix of the latent Markov chain. That is,

$q_{\alpha i} =$ probability of response i, given class α;

$m_{\alpha\beta} =$ probability of being in class β at time $t + 1$, given membership in class α at time t, for any t.

The only other parameters that need to be defined are initial class sizes, v_α. Let $v_\alpha(t) =$ probability of being in class α at time t; and $v_\alpha = v_\alpha(1)$. Since these vary according to the latent Markov chain, we have

$$v_\alpha(t) = \sum_\beta v_\beta(t - 1)m_{\beta\alpha},$$

or

$$v(t) = v(1)M^{t-1}. \qquad (15)$$

A manifest probability, such as $p_i(t)$, depends on the latent distribution at time t and on the response probabilities, Q.

$$p_i(t) = \sum_\alpha v_\alpha(t)q_{\alpha i}. \qquad (16)$$

In matrix terms,

$$p(t) = v(t)Q = v(1)M^{t-1}Q = vM^{t-1}Q. \qquad (17)$$

Notice how this sequence develops:

$$p(1) = vQ,$$
$$p(2) = vMQ = vQQ^{-1}MQ = p(1)Q^{-1}MQ,$$
$$p(3) = vM^2Q = p(2)Q^{-1}MQ,$$
etc.

We define $R = Q^{-1}MQ$, and summarize these equations as:

$$p(t) = p(t - 1)R = p(1)R^{t-1}. \tag{18}$$

The marginal proportions thus obey a law which is exactly that of an ordinary Markov chain: the marginal vector at any time is equal to the product of the previous marginal vector multiplied by a certain matrix (here R) which does not change with time. The difference, however, is that here R is *not* the transition matrix of a Markov chain process!

To understand how this model differs from the simple Markov chain, we have to examine the joint probability matrices, $P(s,t)$. For instance, the value of $p_{ij}(1,2)$ will depend on the relative frequencies of the classes at time 1 and 2.

$$p_{ij}(1,2) = \sum_\alpha \sum_\beta v_{\alpha\beta}(1,2)q_{\alpha i}q_{\beta j}, \tag{19}$$

where $v_{\alpha\beta}(1,2)$ is the probability of being in class α at $t = 1$ *and* in β at $t = 2$. But, because of the Markovian assumption, we know that

$$v_{\alpha\beta}(1,2) = v_\alpha(1)m_{\alpha\beta},$$

and so we can insert this into Equation (19),

$$p_{ij}(1,2) = \sum_\alpha \sum_\beta q_{\alpha i}v_\alpha m_{\alpha\beta}q_{\beta j}.$$

This equation is equivalent to the matrix equation:

$$P(1,2) = Q'VMQ. \tag{20}$$

Now, to obtain $P(1,t)$, we only need to replace M by M^{t-1}, the transition matrix of the latent process over an interval of length $t - 1$:

$$P(1,t) = Q'VM^{t-1}Q. \tag{21}$$

If the initial time is other than 1, we have to replace V by the appropriate diagonal matrix describing the latent distribution at that time:

$$P(s,t) = Q'V(s)M^{t-s}Q. \tag{22}$$

Although we can calculate $V(s)$, given V and M, by means of Equation (15), it is not possible to make a substitution directly into Equation (22).

It is clear, however, that this particular form of the accounting equations provides an interesting contrast to the ordinary Markov chain. That is, we compare:

$$P(s,t) = Q'V(s)QR^{t-s} \tag{23}$$

with the equation for a Markov chain with transition matrix R, Equation (5):

$$P(s,t) = P(s)R^{t-s}.$$

As we noted in the section on Markov model, $P(s)$ stands for the diagonal matrix giving the response distribution at time s, and as such is directly observable.

253

On the other hand, in the latent Markov chain, the corresponding matrix, $Q'V(s)Q$, will *not* be a diagonal matrix unless Q is the identity matrix. It is possible to give a meaning to the entries of this matrix: the i, jth entry represents "the probability of giving response i and response j if the question were asked twice, *simultaneously*, at time s" under the assumption of local independence.

Consider what the i, jth entry of $Q'V(s)Q$ looks like:

$$\sum_\alpha v_\alpha(s) q_{\alpha i} q_{\alpha j}.$$

If i and j represented two different dichotomous items, we would find the interpretation straightforward: a joint probability for the two items at time s, given a latent class model and within class independence. Since there is only one question, however, the entries of $Q'V(s)Q$ do not represent real responses, and cannot be measured directly. Nonetheless, the interpretation is valid, and useful, for the magnitude of the off-diagonal entries tells us something about the overall *uncertainty of response* at time s. Coleman (1964b) used the notation $P(s,s)$ to express the limit of $P(s,t)$ as the interval between repetitions of the question approaches zero. (Coleman, however, begins with different assumptions, and his model is not identical with this one.) The notation $Q'V(s)Q = P(s,s)$ is suggestive, and we shall use it where appropriate.

Obviously, we can solve for the particular combinations of latent parameters which we have denoted by R and $P(s,s)$. Taking observations at three time points, $t = 1$, 2, and 3, the turnover matrices are:

$$P(1,2) = Q'V(1)MQ = P(1,1)R,$$
$$P(1,3) = Q'V(1)M^2Q = P(1,1)R^2.$$

Therefore

$$R = P(1,2)^{-1}P(1,3), \tag{24}$$

and

$$P(1,1) = P(1,2)R^{-1} = P(1,2)P(1,3)^{-1}P(1,2). \tag{25}$$

While these two matrices tell us something about the latent process, we need more manifest information in order to determine M and Q.

Let us look at the third turnover table available, namely $P(2,3)$:

$$\begin{aligned}
P(2,3) &= Q'V(2)MQ \\
&= Q'V(2)V(1)^{-1}V(1)MQ \\
&= Q'V(2)V(1)^{-1}(Q')^{-1}Q'V(1)MQ \\
&= Q'V(2)V(1)^{-1}Q'^{-1}P(1,2).
\end{aligned}$$

Let $W = V(2)V(1)^{-1}$. W, of course, is a diagonal matrix.

$$Q'W(Q')^{-1} = P(2,3)P(1,2)^{-1}. \tag{26}$$

If the entries of W are all distinct, then Q' as well as W can be uniquely determined by analysis of the product $P(2,3)P(1,2)^{-1}$. The diagonal terms of W are the characteristic roots of that manifest matrix, and the corresponding characteristic column vectors, normalized to have sum 1, will be the appropriate columns of Q' (rows of Q). We can then ignore W, if we wish, for knowledge of Q is enough to determine M and V: since

$$R = Q^{-1}MQ = P(1,2)^{-1}P(1,3),$$
$$M = QP(1,2)^{-1}P(1,3)Q^{-1}; \tag{27}$$

and since

$$P(1,1) = Q'V(1)Q = P(1,2)P(1,3)^{-1}P(1,2),$$
$$V(1) = Q'^{-1}P(1,2)P(1,3)^{-1}P(1,2)Q'. \tag{28}$$

The solution of the latent Markov chain described above depends on a number of conditions, which we summarize here:

(i) The number of latent classes equals the number of response categories, i.e., Q is square.

(ii) Q and M are non-singular matrices.

(iii) $V(1)^{-1}V(2)$ has distinct diagonal entries. That is,

$$v_\alpha(2)/v_\alpha(1) \neq v_\beta(2)/v_\beta(1) \qquad \text{if } \alpha \neq \beta.$$

We might expect condition (iii) not to hold in many applications, for instance, when the latent process seems to be in equilibrium. Equilibrium means that the latent marginals are constant over time: $V(t) = V(1)$. Notice that when the latent process is in equilibrium the manifest process also will appear to be in marginal equilibrium:

$$p(s) = P(s,t)e = P(s,s)R^{t-s}e = P(s,s)e$$

(e being a column of ones), but if $V(s) = V(1)$, for any s, $P(s,s) = P(1,1)$ as well, so that $p(s) = p(1)$. If we observe equilibrium of the manifest marginal probabilities, we must use another method of finding the latent parameters. Such an alternative is described in Section 3.2 below: it requires analysis of stratified turnover tables, just as the simple latent class model of Section 2 did.

When there are more response categories than latent classes ($n > m$), but M and Q both have rank m, a modification of the above solution can be used. If we consider only an $m \times m$ section of the manifest matrices, the inverse of the reduced $P(1,2)$ would exist. Since this would affect the latent representation only by specifying those m rows of Q' and columns of Q, the unknown parameters follow from Equation (26).

When the number of latent classes is greater than the number of response categories, however, there is no simple generalization of the solutions we are discussing. It will usually be necessary to examine third-, fourth-, and higher-order joint manifest probabilities in such cases, depending on the number of classes. This is true because the size of the manifest turnover matrices depends on the number of response categories: increasing the number of classes means that the number of latent parameters is larger, but the amount of information in the turnover tables remains constant and will not serve to determine the parameters.

3.2 *Third-Order Manifest Probabilities*

In this section, we shall briefly set forth a solution which can be more generally applied than that of Section 3.1. It does require the use of third-order probabilities, in the form of a stratified turnover matrix. Let $P_k(1,3;2)$ stand for the turnover probabilities from time 1 to time 3, for those whose response at time 2 is "k." That is, the i, j entry of this matrix is p_{ikj}: response i at time 1, and k at time 2, and j at time 3.

We obtain the accounting equation for p_{ikj} in a straightforward manner:

$$p_{ikj} = \sum_\alpha \sum_\beta \sum_\delta v_\alpha q_{\alpha i} m_{\alpha\beta} q_{\beta k} m_{\beta\delta} q_{\delta j}. \tag{29}$$

Over three time points a given individual's latent states are specified by the vector (α,β,δ): if we know that someone was in state α at time 1, state β at time 2, and state δ at time 3, then his probability of *responding* (i,k,j) is simply $q_{\alpha i} q_{\beta k} q_{\delta j}$. On the other hand, the probability of the latent pattern (α,β,δ) is equal to $v_\alpha m_{\alpha\beta} m_{\beta\delta}$. Summing over all the α, β, and δ, gives us Equation (29).

In matrix form, Equation (29) becomes:

$$P_k = Q'VMX_kMQ. \tag{30}$$

X_k, as in Section 1, is defined to be the diagonal matrix whose diagonal terms are the kth column of Q: $(q_{1k}, q_{2k}, \ldots, q_{mk})$. Equations (29) and (30) are very similar to the basic equations of the ordinary latent class model, and the solution parallels that which we derived in Chapter 3. We consider:

$$P_k = Q'VMQ(Q^{-1}X_kQ)Q^{-1}MQ. \tag{31}$$

But we already know, from Equations (20) and (24), that:

$$Q'VMQ = P(1,2)$$

and

$$Q^{-1}MQ = P(1,2)^{-1}P(1,3).$$

Some of the unknown matrices can be eliminated from Equation (31):

$$P_k = P(1,2)Q^{-1}X_kQP(1,2)^{-1}P(1,3). \tag{32}$$

Therefore,

$$Q^{-1}X_kQ = P(1,2)^{-1}P_k(1,3;2)P(1,3)^{-1}P(1,2). \tag{33}$$

The entries of the diagonal matrix X_k can, therefore, be found as the characteristic roots of the manifest matrix on the right of Equation (33). The other columns of Q can be found as the corresponding column characteristic vectors, with no difficulties as long as the characteristic roots are all distinct.

Notice that this solution can be applied even if the process is observed to be in equilibrium: the only conditions on the latent parameters are the ones requiring that Q^{-1}, V^{-1}, and M^{-1} exist (so that $P(1,2)$ has an inverse), and that at least one column ("k") of Q have distinct entries.

Of course, once Q has been found, V and M follow easily:

$$v = p(1)Q^{-1} \qquad \text{(from Equation 17)},$$

and

$$M = QP(1,2)^{-1}P(1,3)Q^{-1} \qquad \text{(from Equation 24)}.$$

3.3 A Special Case

When there are only two classes and two response categories it is possible to see more easily how the latent parameters are actually obtained. A turnover table is then simply a fourfold table: if it is unstratified, its sum is equal to 1. Furthermore, the determinant of this matrix is nothing more than the cross product of the responses at the two times. For example, let's denote the two response categories by "+" and "−"; then:

$$|P(1,2)| = \begin{vmatrix} p_{++}(1,2) & p_{+-}(1,2) \\ p_{-+}(1,2) & p_{--}(1,2) \end{vmatrix} = p_{++}(1,2) - p_{+}(1)p_{+}(2) = [12].$$

In this context the notation $[ij]$ will denote the cross product between time i and time j, the determinant of $P(i,j)$.

Furthermore, it is entirely consistent to use the notation $[i,j;k]$, the conditional cross product, to indicate the determinant of the stratified matrix:

$$[13;2] = |P_{+}(1,3;2)|,$$

and

$$[13;\bar{2}] = |P_{-}(1,3;2)|.$$

In general, of course, $[ij;k] = |P_{+}(i,j;k)|$.

Now let us go back to the basic matrix equations, of our model (Equations 22, 30).

$$P(1,2) = Q'VMQ,$$
$$P(1,3) = Q'VM^2Q,$$
$$P_{+}(1,3;2) = Q'VMX_{+}MQ,$$
$$P_{-}(1,3;2) = Q'VMX_{-}MQ, \qquad (V = V(1)).$$

Take the determinant of each of these equations in turn:

$$[12] = |Q|^2|V|\,|M|,$$
$$[13] = |Q|^2|V|\,|M|^2,$$
$$[13;2] = |Q|^2|V|\,|M|^2|X_{+}|,$$
$$[13;\bar{2}] = |Q|^2|V|\,|M|^2|X_{-}|.$$

Thus,

$$[13;2]/[13] = |X_{+}| \quad \text{and} \quad [13;\bar{2}]/[13] = |X_{-}| \quad \text{and} \quad |M| = [13]/[12].$$

Let

$$Q = \begin{pmatrix} x & 1-x \\ y & 1-y \end{pmatrix};$$

257

then $|X_+| = xy$ and $|X_-| = (1 - x)(1 - y)$. Therefore,

$$x + y = 1 - |X_-| + |X_+| = 1 + ([13;2] - [13;\bar{2}])/[13],$$

while

$$xy = [13;2]/[13].$$

The two entries in the first column of Q are, therefore, the two roots of the quadratic equation:

$$x^2 - x([13] + [13;2] - [13;\bar{2}])/[13] + [13;2]/[13] = 0.$$

We can specify that $x > y$, since this is an arbitrary choice.

Once Q has been determined, we can solve for V and M quite easily. For instance,

$$p_+(1) = p_1 = vx + (1 - v)y = v(x - y) + y$$

and, therefore,

$$v = (p_1 - y)/(x - y).$$

Finally, we have noted that $|M| = [13]/[12]$. If

$$M = \begin{pmatrix} m_1 & 1 - m_1 \\ m_2 & 1 - m_2 \end{pmatrix}, \qquad |M| = m_1 - m_2.$$

The probability of a positive response at time 2 is:

$$p_+(2) = (v, 1 - v)M\begin{pmatrix} x \\ y \end{pmatrix} = (v, 1 - v)\begin{pmatrix} m_1(x - y) + y \\ m_2(x - y) + y \end{pmatrix}$$

$$= v(x - y)(m_1 - m_2) + m_2(x - y) + y.$$

Thus we can solve for m_2:

$$m_2 = (p_+(2) - y)/(x - y) - v(m_1 - m_2)$$
$$= (p_+(2) - y)/(x - y) - v[13]/[12].$$

In the next section, we shall use these equations in working out an example. There is no mathematical difference between this approach and that of Section 3.2, but, with the equations in this form, it is perhaps easier to see the relation between the solution and that of the two class model discussed back in Chapter 2.

3.4 An Application to Sociometric Choice

Katz and Proctor (1959) have reported a study of changes over time in the configuration of interpersonal relationships in a group of school children. At various points during the school year, the children were asked to name the person with whom they would like to sit. Generally, three choices were made by each child.

Katz and Proctor analyzed the data by considering each *pair* of children at each point in time: there could be mutual choice, one-way choice, or no relation (indifference). They then proposed the Markov chain model for this process.

We have pooled the first two states, so that each pair is either in contact (C) or indifferent (I). The data for three waves, September, November, and January are shown in Table 2 below.

TABLE 2

Sociometric Choice Analysis
Frequencies of Types of Pairs*

C: Contact		I: Indifference	
Time 1 (Sept.)	2 (Nov.)	3 (Jan.)	Frequency
C	C	C	24
C	C	I	12
C	I	C	6
C	I	I	18
I	C	C	11
I	C	I	12
I	I	C	20
I	I	I	197
		Total	300

*These data have been taken from Table 2, page 321, of the article by Katz and Proctor (1959).

TABLE 3

Sociometric Choice Analysis
Turnover Tables

Unstratified

$t = 2$

	C	I
$t = 1$ C	36	24
I	23	217

$t = 3$

	C	I
$t = 2$ C	35	24
I	26	215

Stratified
$t = 2$

C

$t = 3$

	C	I
$t = 1$ C	24	12
I	11	12

I

$t = 3$

	C	I
$t = 1$ C	6	18
I	20	196

In Table 3 the data is given in the usual turnover table form. It is obvious that the process is in marginal equilibrium, with the marginal vectors all very nearly equal to proportions (0.2, 0.8). We are going to apply the latent Markov chain to these data. As noted above, marginal equilibrium exists only if the latent process is also in equilibrium. We thus expect that $P(1,2) = P(2,3)$, and we see that this is very nearly the case. This matrix, $P(t, t + 1)$, is probably best approximated by:

$$\begin{pmatrix} 36/300 & 24/300 \\ 24/300 & 216/300 \end{pmatrix}$$

and this is shown in Table 4 as our estimate of $P(1,2) = Q'VMQ$.

TABLE 4

Sociometric Choice Analysis
Estimates of $P(1,2)$, $P(1,3)$, $P_C(1,3;2)$ and $P_I(1,3;2)$

$P(1,2) = \begin{pmatrix} 0.12 & 0.08 \\ 0.08 & 0.72 \end{pmatrix}$	$P(1,3) = \begin{pmatrix} 0.10 & 0.10 \\ 0.10 & 0.70 \end{pmatrix}$
$P_C(1,3;2) = \begin{pmatrix} 0.08 & 0.04 \\ 0.04 & 0.04 \end{pmatrix}$	$P_I(1,3;2) = \begin{pmatrix} 0.02 & 0.06 \\ 0.06 & 0.66 \end{pmatrix}$

We have manipulated the data so that the marginal equilibrium assumptions are exactly satisfied by the estimates of $P(1,2)$, $P(1,3)$, $P_C(1,3;2)$, and $P_I(1,3;2)$.

The model requires that:

$$P(1,2) = Q'VMQ,$$
$$P(1,3) = Q'VM^2Q,$$
$$P_C(1,3;2) = Q'VMXMQ,$$
$$P_I(1,3;2) = Q'VM(I - X)MQ,$$

where $X = \begin{pmatrix} x & 0 \\ 0 & y \end{pmatrix}$ is constructed from the first column of $Q = \begin{pmatrix} x & 1 - x \\ y & 1 - y \end{pmatrix}$.

The ratios of the determinants of the stratified matrices to the determinant of $P(1,3)$ will equal the determinants of X and $I - X$, respectively:

$$|X| = xy = \begin{vmatrix} 0.08 & 0.04 \\ 0.04 & 0.04 \end{vmatrix} \bigg/ \begin{vmatrix} 0.10 & 0.10 \\ 0.10 & 0.70 \end{vmatrix} = 16/600 = 8/300,$$

$$|I - X| = (1 - x)(1 - y) = \begin{vmatrix} 0.02 & 0.06 \\ 0.06 & 0.66 \end{vmatrix} \bigg/ \begin{vmatrix} 0.10 & 0.10 \\ 0.10 & 0.70 \end{vmatrix}$$
$$= 96/600 = 16/100.$$

Since
$$(1 - x)(1 - y) = 1 - x - y + xy,$$
we have
$$x + y = 1 + 8/300 - 16/100 = 260/300.$$

Thus x and y are the two roots of the quadratic equation:
$$x^2 - (26/30)x + 8/300 = 0.$$
These are:
$$13/30 \pm \tfrac{1}{2}\sqrt{26 \cdot 26/900 - 32/300},$$
$$13/30 \pm (\sqrt{145})/30.$$

Taking x to be the larger root, we therefore find that:
$$x = 0.835, \qquad y = 0.032,$$
so that
$$Q = \begin{pmatrix} 0.835 & 0.165 \\ 0.032 & 0.968 \end{pmatrix}.$$

Since the manifest marginal,
$$0.2 = vx + (1 - v)y = v(x - y) + y,$$
we can solve for v:
$$v = 0.168/0.803 = 0.21.$$

M can be determined in several ways, given the information we already have. Let $M = \begin{pmatrix} a & 1 - a \\ b & 1 - b \end{pmatrix}$. Since the latent process is in equilibrium,
$$(v, 1 - v)M = (v, 1 - v).$$
This tells us that
$$va + (1 - v)b = v,$$
or
$$b = v - v(a - b).$$

We already know what v is. Also, the ratio of the determinants of $P(1,3)$ and $P(1,2)$ equals the determinant of M, and this equals $(a - b)$:
$$\begin{vmatrix} 0.10 & 0.10 \\ 0.10 & 0.70 \end{vmatrix} \Bigg/ \begin{vmatrix} 0.12 & 0.08 \\ 0.08 & 0.72 \end{vmatrix} = |M| = a(1 - b) - b(1 - a) = (a - b);$$

$$\therefore \quad (a - b) = 600/800 = 3/4.$$

Thus,
$$b = 0.21 - 0.21(3/4) = 0.052,$$
and
$$a = 0.75 + 0.052 = 0.802.$$

The analysis is summarized in Table 5. It is valuable to compare the transition

TABLE 5

Latent Parameters for the Sociometric Choice Analysis

		Class 1	Class 2
Initial Latent Distribution v		0.21	0.79

		Class 1	Class 2
Transition matrix M of the latent process:	Class 1	0.802	0.198
	Class 2	0.052	0.948

		Type of Pair C	Type of Pair I
Response Probability Matrix Q:	Class 1	0.835	0.165
	Class 2	0.032	0.968

matrix, M, of the latent process and the comparable matrix for the manifest process, that is, $P(1,2)$ divided through by its row sums:

Latent Transition Matrix

$$\text{time } t \begin{array}{c} t+1 \\ \begin{pmatrix} 0.802 & 0.198 \\ 0.052 & 0.948 \end{pmatrix} \end{array}$$

Manifest Transition Matrix

$$\text{time } t \begin{array}{c} t+1 \\ \begin{pmatrix} 0.60 & 0.40 \\ 0.10 & 0.90 \end{pmatrix} \end{array}$$

Because some of the turnover has been "explained" by the uncertainty of response implied by the matrix Q, the diagonal entries of the latent matrix are larger than those of the manifest matrix.

In order to test whether this model adequately describes the process, it is necessary to examine some data not used to compute parameters. For instance, the turnover tables from January to May, from November to May, and from September to May, shown in Table 6 can be compared with those predicted

TABLE 6

Auxiliary Data*

		May C	May I			May C	May I			May C	May I
January	C	35	26	November	C	33	26	September	C	25	36
$(t=3)$	I	24	215	$(t=2)$	I	26	215	$(t=1)$	I	35	205

*From Table 1, Katz and Proctor (1959).

by the model. There is an added difficulty, however, namely that of specifying the time scale, for the interval January–May is twice as long as the other intervals between observations. Nevertheless, as we can see, the January–May data are very nearly exactly the same as the other unit-interval matrices, i.e., September–November and November–January (Table 3). Furthermore, the observed September–May matrix is almost exactly equal to $Q'VM^3Q$, which would be predicted by the model if those eight months were three of our "unit intervals."

The November–May data are not consistent with the model. They resemble the turnover matrices over a single time interval, rather than the $(t, t + 2)$ matrix that is exemplified by the September–January matrix in Table 3. Further analysis of the data, perhaps going back to the classification into three states of mutual choice, one-way choice, and indifference used in the original article, would be necessary before definitely accepting or rejecting the model.

Appendix A: Matrix Algebra

We have included this appendix in order to indicate the aspects of matrix algebra which are most important to latent structure analysis, and to provide an easy reference for definitions and a few theorems. Readers who have not had experience with matrix notation will probably want to turn to a text such as Kemeny, *et al.* (1959), Chapter 4, for examples and discussion. Hohn (1964), is recommended for a better understanding of the problem of reducing a matrix to its characteristic roots and vectors.

1. Definitions

A *matrix* is a rectangular array of numbers, which is usually denoted by an upper-case letter, e.g., A. If the matrix has m rows and n columns, we say that it has order (m,n); if it is square, it is possible to simply say that the order is n. The number in the ith row and jth column of a matrix A is denoted by a_{ij}, and the equation $A = (a_{ij})$ symbolizes this identity.

Two matrices are equal if and only if their corresponding elements are equal. Thus, $A = B$ means that $a_{ij} = b_{ij}$ for every pair i, j, and A and B must have the same order. Matrices of the same order can be added by adding term by term. Here, $A = B + C$ means that $a_{ij} = b_{ij} + c_{ij}$ for all i, j. Multiplication of a matrix by a number (scalar) is effected by multiplying each element of the matrix by the number. For instance,

$$\begin{pmatrix} 1 & 3 & 2 \\ -1 & 0 & 0 \end{pmatrix} + 3\begin{pmatrix} 4 & 0 & -1 \\ 7 & 2 & 1 \end{pmatrix} = \begin{pmatrix} 13 & 3 & -1 \\ 20 & 6 & 3 \end{pmatrix}.$$

A matrix of order $(m,1)$ is called a *column vector;* a matrix of order $(1,m)$ is called a *row vector.*

The *transpose* of a given matrix is formed by interchanging its rows and columns. For instance, the transpose of

$$\begin{pmatrix} 1 & 3 & 2 \\ -1 & 0 & 0 \end{pmatrix}$$

is

$$\begin{matrix} 1 & -1 \\ 3 & 0 \\ 2 & 0 \end{matrix} \ .$$

The transpose of A is denoted by A', and we note that if $B = A'$, then $b_{ij} = a_{ji}$. A square matrix is *symmetric* if $S = S'$, i.e., if $s_{ij} = s_{ji}$ for every pair i,j. The symmetry is with respect to the *main diagonal* of the matrix.

The product of two matrices, written AB, is defined only when the number of columns of A equals the number of rows of B. If the order of A is (n,m) and the order of B is (m,p), then the order of AB is (n,p). The definition is:

$$C = AB$$

if and only if

$$c_{ij} = \sum_{k=1}^{m} a_{ik} b_{kj},$$

where i varies over all the rows of A, j over all columns of B, and the sum is from 1 to m, the common dimension.

Matrix multiplication is generally not commutative, that is, $AB \neq BA$ except in special cases. Indeed, the two products AB and BA are both defined only if the order of A is (n,m) and the order of B is (m,n), and the question of equality can only arise if both matrices are square: $n = m$. An example demonstrates the non-commutativity. Let

$$A = \begin{pmatrix} 1 & 3 \\ 0 & 1 \end{pmatrix}, \qquad B = \begin{pmatrix} 1 & -1 \\ 2 & 1 \end{pmatrix};$$

then

$$AB = \begin{pmatrix} 7 & 2 \\ 2 & 1 \end{pmatrix}, \qquad BA = \begin{pmatrix} 1 & 2 \\ 2 & 7 \end{pmatrix}.$$

Whenever we indicate a matrix product, we assume that the matrices are of the proper order, so that the product is defined.

Although matrix multiplication is not commutative, it is associative. That is, a product of several matrices, e.g., ABC, is well-defined, as long as the products of adjacent matrices are defined. The equation $(AB)C = A(BC)$ indicates that the product of A and B may be multiplied by C, or A multiplied by the product of B and C. In terms of the elements of these matrices, the identity

$$\sum_{k} \left(\sum_{j} a_{ij} b_{jk} \right) (c_{km}) = \sum_{j} (a_{ij}) \left(\sum_{k} b_{jk} c_{km} \right)$$

is obvious. In general, note the correspondence between the matrix product

$$ABC \cdots XYZ$$

265

and the formula for a typical element of the product,

$$\sum_{j} \sum_{k} \sum_{g} \cdots \sum_{h} \sum_{p} \sum_{m} a_{ij} b_{jk} c_{kg} \cdots x_{hp} y_{pm} z_{mn}.$$

Recognition of this correspondence permits us to construct easily the matrix representations of accounting equations.

Some important types of square matrices are the *diagonal* matrices, and the *triangular* matrices. A triangular matrix T has zeros above the main diagonal ($t_{ij} = 0$ if $i < j$), or below the main diagonal ($t_{ij} = 0$ if $i > j$); if both conditions hold at the same time, then T is diagonal. The sum or the product of any two diagonal matrices is also diagonal, and furthermore, diagonal matrices commute: if D and E are diagonal then $DE = ED$.

An *identity matrix* is a square, diagonal matrix, whose diagonal elements are all ones. We let I stand for an identity matrix of any order, relying on the context in which the symbol is used to indicate what the order of I is. For any matrix A, the identity

$$AI = A = IA$$

holds.

The *inverse* of a square matrix A is a matrix X which satisfies the equations

$$AX = I,$$

and

$$XA = I.$$

Here, X must have the same order as A, and it is unique if these equations are satisfied. We write $X = A^{-1}$, to stand for the inverse of A. The inverse of A^{-1} is equal to A. If a matrix has an inverse, we say that it is *non-singular;* otherwise it is a *singular* matrix. Examples of each are:

$$\text{if} \quad A = \begin{pmatrix} 1 & 3 \\ 0 & 1 \end{pmatrix}, \quad A^{-1} = \begin{pmatrix} 1 & -3 \\ 0 & 1 \end{pmatrix};$$

$$\text{if} \quad B = \begin{pmatrix} 2 & 1 \\ 4 & 2 \end{pmatrix}, \quad \text{there is no inverse matrix.}$$

The case of 2×2 matrices yields a simple result:

$$\text{if} \quad A = \begin{pmatrix} a & b \\ c & d \end{pmatrix}, \quad A^{-1} = \begin{pmatrix} d/t & -b/t \\ -c/t & a/t \end{pmatrix},$$

as long as $t = ad - bc \neq 0$; if $t = 0$, A does not have an inverse.

We say that a matrix is *orthogonal*, if its inverse exists, and equals its transpose: $\theta\theta' = I = \theta'\theta$. For example,

$$\begin{pmatrix} 0.6 & 0.8 \\ -0.8 & 0.6 \end{pmatrix}$$

is orthogonal.

An equation such as $ax = 0$, where a and x are real numbers, implies that either $a = 0$ or $x = 0$. A similar result for matrices requires that one of the matrices be non-singular: if $AX = 0$, and if A^{-1} exists, then $X = 0$; if X^{-1} exists, then $A = 0$. The product of two non-zero matrices can equal 0, however, as shown below:

$$\begin{pmatrix} 2 & 1 \\ 4 & 2 \end{pmatrix} \begin{pmatrix} 1 & 1 \\ -2 & -2 \end{pmatrix} = \begin{pmatrix} 0 & 0 \\ 0 & 0 \end{pmatrix}.$$

Notice that *neither* of the matrices on the left has an inverse.

Two widely applied, and easy to prove, results are:

(i) $(AB)' = B'A'$;
(ii) $(AB)^{-1} = B^{-1}A^{-1}$, if these inverses exist.

Both extend to products of any number of matrices.

The *trace* of a square matrix is the sum of its diagonal elements. It is symbolized by

$$\text{tr}(A) = \sum_i a_{ii}.$$

The most useful property of this function is its commutativity:

$$\text{tr}(AB) = \text{tr}(BA),$$

assuming that the indicated products exist. The proof is simple:

$$\text{tr}(AB) = \sum_i \left(\sum_j a_{ij} b_{ji} \right) = \sum_j \left(\sum_i b_{ji} a_{ij} \right) = \text{tr}(BA).$$

The result can be generalized. For instance, $\text{tr}(ABC) = \text{tr}(BCA)$, and the following result is particularly important:

$$\text{tr}(ABA^{-1}) = \text{tr}(BA^{-1}A) = \text{tr}(B).$$

2. Determinants, and the Rank of a Matrix

The determinant of a square matrix is a number computed from the elements of the equation. Symbolized by placing vertical lines outside the matrix, the determinant is defined as follows.

$$|A| = \sum_J a_{1j_1} a_{2j_2} a_{3j_3} \cdots a_{nj_n} (-1)^{s(J)},$$

where

n is the order of A;
$J = (j_1, j_2, \ldots, j_n)$ is a permutation of the integers from 1 to n;
$s(J) = 1$ if J is an odd permutation, and $s(J) = 0$ if J is an even permutation;
$\sum_J$ indicates that the summation is over all $n!$ possible permutations.

J is an even permutation if it can be obtained from the sequence $(1,2, \ldots, n)$ by interchanging an even number of adjacent integers; otherwise it is said to be odd. For example, in the case $n = 3$, the six permutations are

$$(1,2,3), \quad (1,3,2)^*, \quad (3,1,2), \quad (3,2,1)^*, \quad (2,3,1), \quad (2,1,3)^*.$$

The asterisk indicates the odd permutations, so that the definition gives

$$|A| = a_{11}a_{22}a_{33} - a_{11}a_{23}a_{32} + a_{13}a_{21}a_{32} - a_{13}a_{22}a_{31}$$
$$+ a_{12}a_{23}a_{31} - a_{12}a_{21}a_{33}.$$

We state without proof several of the basic properties of determinants (see Hohn (1964), Ch. 2).

(1) The determinant of the product of two square matrices equals the product of the determinants: $|AB| = |A|\,|B|$.
(2) If T is a triangular matrix, $|T| = t_{11}t_{22} \cdots t_{nn}$, the product of the diagonal elements of T. Since a diagonal matrix is a special case of a triangular matrix, the determinant of a diagonal matrix is the product of the elements on its main diagonal.
   In particular, then, $|I| = 1$, and $|0| = 0$, and $|A^{-1}| = 1/|A|$, for any matrix such that $|A| \neq 0$. This last identity follows from $AA^{-1} = I$, $|AA^{-1}| = 1$, $|A|\,|A^{-1}| = 1$. It is necessary, therefore, that the determinant of a non-singular matrix be different from zero.
(3) $|A'| = |A|$.
This fact implies that the determinant of an orthogonal matrix equals 1, since if θ is orthogonal, $\theta' = \theta^{-1}$.
(4) If a matrix has a row of zeros, or a column of zeros, its determinant equals zero.
(5) If a matrix contains two identical columns or two identical rows, its determinant equals zero.

The *rank* of a matrix A is an integer which is equal to the order of the largest square submatrix of A which has a non-zero determinant. Any matrix has a rank, therefore, which cannot be greater than its smaller dimension. If A is square, and if A^{-1} exists, then the rank of A equals the order of A, since $|A| \neq 0$. An equivalent definition is: a matrix A, of order (m,n), has rank p if and only if there exist matrices B and C of order (m,p) and (p,n), respectively, such that $A = BC$, and A cannot be written as the product of matrices whose minimum dimension is less than p. The fact that A can be shown to equal the product BC implies that the rank of A is less than or equal to p.

(6) If A has rank m, and B has rank p, and if the product AB is defined, the rank of AB cannot exceed the lesser of m and p.

The following theorem is used in Chapters 4 and 6, and is important in latent structure and factor analysis, where it is necessary to find "factors" of a given matrix.

THEOREM 1: *Let Q be a symmetric matrix of order n, with rank $m \leq n$. Suppose that A and B are matrices of order (n,m) satisfying: $Q = AA'$ and $Q = BB'$. There exists an orthogonal matrix, θ, of order m, such that $B = A\theta$.*

PROOF: The theorem is proved by constructing such a matrix, given any A and B, and showing that $\theta\theta' = \theta'\theta = I$. From

$$AA' = BB',$$

we get

$$AA'B = BB'B,$$

where $B'B$ has order m, and also has rank m. Therefore $(B'B)^{-1}$ exists, and we obtain

$$AA'B(B'B)^{-1} = B.$$

Defining $\theta = A'B(B'B)^{-1}$, we have $A\theta = B$. Furthermore,

$$\theta'\theta = (B'B)^{-1}B'AA'B(B'B)^{-1} = (B'B)^{-1}B'BB'B(B'B)^{-1} = I,$$
$$\theta\theta' = A'B(B'B)^{-2}B'A.$$

Since $A'B = (A'A)^{-1}A'AA'B = (A'A)^{-1}A'BB'B,$

$$\theta\theta' = (A'A)^{-1}A'BB'B(B'B)^{-1}B'BB'A(A'A)^{-1}$$
$$= (A'A)^{-1}A'BB'A(A'A)^{-1} = (A'A)^{-1}A'AA'A(A'A)^{-1} = I.$$

Thus θ is an orthogonal matrix, since $\theta'\theta = \theta\theta' = I$.

The last property we shall mention is important for the computation of determinants, for it shows how the problem of finding the determinant of an $m \times m$ matrix can be reduced to a problem involving determinants of matrices of order $m - 1$. Let A be a square matrix, with elements a_{ij}. Let A_{ij} be the determinant of the submatrix formed by deleting the ith row and jth column of A, multiplied by $(-1)^{i+j}$.

(7) $|A| = a_{i1}A_{i1} + a_{i2}A_{i2} + \cdots + a_{im}A_{im},$ for any i.
(8) $|A| = a_{1j}A_{1j} + a_{2j}A_{2j} + \cdots + a_{mj}A_{mj},$ for any j.

(7) is called the *row expansion* of the determinant, by row i; and (8) is the *column expansion*, by column j. The following example, for a 3×3 matrix, expands around the elements of the first column:

$$\begin{vmatrix} a_{11} & a_{12} & a_{13} \\ a_{21} & a_{22} & a_{23} \\ a_{31} & a_{32} & a_{33} \end{vmatrix} = a_{11}\begin{vmatrix} a_{22} & a_{23} \\ a_{32} & a_{33} \end{vmatrix} - a_{21}\begin{vmatrix} a_{12} & a_{13} \\ a_{32} & a_{33} \end{vmatrix} + a_{31}\begin{vmatrix} a_{12} & a_{13} \\ a_{22} & a_{23} \end{vmatrix}.$$

Several of the properties of determinants which have been cited above can be derived quite easily from properties (7) and (8): particularly (2), (3), and (4).

The quantities A_{ij} are called cofactors of A. Properly, A_{ij} is the cofactor of the i, j element of A. These cofactors are related to the inverse of the matrix A: *The entry in row i and column j of A^{-1} is $A_{ji}/|A|$.* The proof of this statement is sketched. Suppose that $B = (b_{ij})$, and that $b_{ij} = A_{ji}/|A|$. The product AB has as entry in row i and column j

$$\sum_{k=1}^{m} a_{ik}b_{kj} = \sum_{k=1}^{m} a_{ik}A_{jk}/|A|.$$

Therefore, using (7), we see that the diagonal entries of AB equal one:

$$\sum_k a_{ik}A_{ik}/|A| = |A|/|A| = 1.$$

Now suppose that $i \neq j$. Looking at (7), we see that

$$\sum_k a_{ik}A_{jk}$$

equals the determinant of the matrix formed by replacing row j of A by row i of A, and otherwise leaving A unchanged. But this new matrix now has two identical rows, and therefore must have determinant zero, by property (5). Therefore the off-diagonal entries of AB will be zero, and we conclude that $AB = I$. This result shows explicitly that A^{-1} will exist if and only if $|A|$ is not zero.

At several points in the text the product of one matrix with the inverse of another appears. It is interesting to see how the elements of such a product, say $S^{-1}T$, are related to the elements of S and T. Suppose that $S^{-1}T = U$. The i,j element of U is

$$u_{ij} = \sum_k (S_{ki}/|S|)t_{kj}.$$

We have made use of the fact that $S_{ki}/|S|$ is the i,k element of S^{-1}. Now we compare this summation with that in (8), and see that

$$\sum_k t_{kj}S_{ki}$$

can be understood to be the determinant of a certain matrix. That is, $\sum t_{kj}S_{ki}$ is the determinant of the matrix formed by replacing *column i* of S by *column j* of T. The reader will notice that the argument used here is precisely that used above in showing that the matrix of cofactors (divided by $|S|$) was the inverse of S; but here we are speaking of two different matrices, S and T. We call this determinant a *hybrid*, since it is constructed by replacing a particular column of S by a particular column of T.

An analogous result holds when we reverse the order of multiplication, i.e., when the inverted matrix is on the right. The element in row i and column j of the product TS^{-1} is

$$\sum_k t_{ik}(S_{jk}/|S|).$$

The sum

$$\sum_k t_{ik}S_{jk}$$

is equal to the determinant of the matrix formed by substituting the *ith row* of T in place of the *jth row* of S. Thus, in considering the elements of a matrix product of this kind we need to keep in mind two rules. First, we substitute from the non-inverted matrix into the inverted matrix; and second, we substitute a *row* if the inverted matrix is on the right, and a *column* if the inverted matrix is on the left of the product. The desired elements are then the ratios of the appropriate hybrid determinant and the determinant of the matrix whose inversion is indicated.

270

3. Characteristic Roots and Vectors of a Matrix

Suppose that A is a square matrix of order n, and consider the equation

$$Ax = \lambda x, \tag{1}$$

where x is a column vector and λ is a number. We think of A as being given and x and λ as unknowns. Equation (1) can be written

$$(A - \lambda I)x = 0. \tag{2}$$

In this form, it is obvious that $x = 0$ is a trivial solution. On the other hand, if $x \neq 0$, the matrix $A - \lambda I$ must be singular. This implies that the determinant

$$|A - \lambda I| = 0. \tag{3}$$

If λ were known, we could find x by solving the linear Equations (2). Clearly some standardization will be necessary, since if x is one solution of (2), cx will also be a solution (c being any number). This can be done in several ways, for instance, by specifying the value of some non-zero element of x; or by requiring that the elements of x sum to one; or that the sum of squares of the elements sum to one, etc. (In Chapter 3, and elsewhere, we have the condition imposed that the first element of x equals 1.)

Equation (3), on the other hand, only involves λ, not x, so that the obvious solution scheme is to solve Equation (3) for λ; then substitute in (2) and solve for x. The *determinantal equation*, Equation (3), is actually a polynomial of degree n in λ, however, and as such it will have exactly n roots (some of which may be equal, some of which may be complex). For example, in the case $n = 2$,

$$|A - \lambda I| = \begin{vmatrix} a_{11} - \lambda & a_{12} \\ a_{21} & a_{22} - \lambda \end{vmatrix} = (a_{11} - \lambda)(a_{22} - \lambda) - a_{12}a_{21}$$

$$= \lambda^2 - \lambda(a_{11} + a_{22}) + a_{11}a_{22} - a_{12}a_{21} = 0.$$

The two roots, λ_1 and λ_2, say, thus have the properties that

$$\lambda_1 + \lambda_2 = a_{11} + a_{22} = \text{tr}(A),$$

and

$$\lambda_1 \lambda_2 = a_{11}a_{22} - a_{12}a_{21} = |A|.$$

In general, each of the coefficients of the determinantal equation can be expressed as sums of determinants of submatrices of A: the coefficient of $(-\lambda)^k$, in Equation (3), equals the sum of all the *principal minors* of order $n - k$ of A. A principal minor of A is the determinant of a submatrix of A whose main diagonal belongs to the main diagonal of A. Thus, when $n = 3$, the coefficient of $(-\lambda)$ is the sum:

$$\begin{vmatrix} a_{11} & a_{12} \\ a_{21} & a_{22} \end{vmatrix} + \begin{vmatrix} a_{11} & a_{13} \\ a_{31} & a_{33} \end{vmatrix} + \begin{vmatrix} a_{22} & a_{23} \\ a_{32} & a_{33} \end{vmatrix}.$$

The coefficient of $(-\lambda)^{n-1}$, according to this result, is the sum of the diagonal elements of A, while the constant term is always the determinant of A.

If the rank of A equals $m < n$, then, by definition, the determinants of sub-matrices of order larger than m will vanish. Hence the coefficients of powers of λ less than $n - m$ will be zero. Equation (3) will have the form

$$\lambda^n + c_{n-1}\lambda^{n-1} + \cdots + c_{n-m}\lambda^{n-m} = 0,$$

which implies that $n - m$ of the roots λ_i will equal zero.

The numbers $\lambda_1, \lambda_2, \ldots, \lambda_n$ are called the *characteristic roots* of A. In this book, we are primarily interested in matrices whose characteristic roots are distinct, for in that case each Equation (2) has a solution for x that is unique up to multiplication by a constant.

We call the vector x_i, corresponding to the root λ_i, a characteristic column vector of A. Equation (1) has an analogue for row vectors, y', namely,

$$y'A = \lambda y'.$$

These are the row characteristic vectors of A.

Next, suppose that a given matrix A can be factored in the following way,

$$A = BDC', \tag{4}$$

where D is a diagonal matrix of order m, with distinct diagonal entries; B has order (n,m), as does C; and $C'B = I$. Multiply both sides of A by B, on the right,

$$AB = BDC'B = BD. \tag{5}$$

If B_i stands for column i of B, we have

$$AB_i = B_i d_{ii}. \tag{6}$$

Thus each element of the diagonal matrix D is a characteristic root of A, and each column of B is a corresponding characteristic column vector of A. On the other hand, each row of C' is a row characteristic vector of A,

$$C'A = C'BDC' = DC',$$
$$(C_i)'A = (C_i)'d_{ii}.$$

If $n = m$, then $C'B = I$ implies that $C' = B^{-1}$. This form occurs most often throughout the text: $A = B^{-1}DB$ implies that the elements of D are the characteristic roots of A and the columns of B are characteristic vectors of A.

There are several ways of computing the characteristic roots and vectors of a given matrix, and details may be found in Faddeeva, 1959. If n is large, it turns out that it is inefficient to set up the determinantal equation (3) and solve for all the λ's. Iterative methods which find one characteristic vector at a time are preferable. There exist many computer programs which will carry out the necessary computations.

Appendix B: Large Sample Distribution Theory for Estimates of the Parameters of a Latent Class Model

T. W. Anderson

1. Introduction

In Chapters 2–4 of this book, the latent class model has been discussed extensively, and a method of estimating the parameter has been proposed. In this paper we give the large sample distribution theory for these estimates. We show that the estimates are consistent and are asymptotically normally distributed, and we find the asymptotic variances and covariances. That is, for sufficiently large samples, the estimates will be close to the parameters (with high probability) and the discrepancies are approximately normally distributed.

Because of the need to distinguish between parameters and estimates, the notation used in this Appendix differs from that used throughout the rest of the book. Here Greek letters will stand for the parameters, and the corresponding Roman letters for the estimates. Thus, for instance, π_{gik} is the manifest probability of positive response to items g, i, and k, and p_{gik} is the proportion of positive responses to that triple of items in the sample. The sample size is n.

2. The Asymptotic Normal Distribution of Sample Response Proportions

For convenience of notation, we introduce an artificial item, numbered 0, that always has a positive response ($\lambda_0^\alpha = 1$). Then $\pi_{00k} = \pi_k$ is the probability of a positive response on item k, etc., and the first column of Λ refers to this dummy item. Let $\Pi = (\pi_{gik})$ and $\bar{\Pi} = (\pi_{gi\bar{k}})$, where $g = 0, 1, \ldots, m - 1$ (the vertical signature) and $i = 0, m, m + 1, \ldots, 2m - 2$ (the horizontal signature) be two matrices of manifest probabilities. The matrix Λ_V consists of the latent probabilities of the items in the vertical signature and Λ_H, in the horizontal signature. V is a diagonal matrix with diagonal elements the class

273

proportions, ν^α, and Δ is a diagonal matrix with diagonal elements λ_k^α (for $k > 2m - 2$). The estimates of Λ_V, Λ_H, V, and Δ are denoted by L_V, L_H, N, and D. Finally, we remind the reader that $P = (p_{gik})$ and $\overline{P} = (p_{gi\bar{k}})$ consist of the sample relative frequencies of response patterns.

To demonstrate that the estimates are asymptotically normally distributed, we need to know that the sample relative frequencies have an asymptotic normal distribution.

THEOREM 1. *Let*

$$\sqrt{n}\,(P - \Pi) = X = (x_{gi}) \text{ and } \sqrt{n}\,(\overline{P} - \overline{\Pi}) = \overline{X} = (\overline{x}_{gi}),$$

where n is the number of individuals sampled. Then X and $\overline{X}$ have a limiting normal distribution with means EX = 0 and $E\overline{X}$ = 0 and variances and covariances:

$$Ex_{gi}x_{hj} = \pi_{gihjk} - \pi_{gik}\pi_{hjk},$$
$$E\overline{x}_{gi}x_{hj} = \pi_{gihj\bar{k}} - \pi_{gi\bar{k}}\pi_{hj\bar{k}}, \tag{1}$$
$$Ex_{gi}\overline{x}_{hj} = -\pi_{gik}\pi_{hj\bar{k}}.$$

PROOF: As before, any indices 0 are suppressed (and duplications of indices can be suppressed). The set of 2^K p's with K subscripts are the relative observed frequencies of the 2^K mutually exclusive events (complete patterns of responses); in other words, these are a set of multinomial variables. Hence, $\sqrt{n}$ times the deviations of these p's and the corresponding π's have, asymptotically, a joint normal distribution with zero means. Since the elements of $(P - \Pi)$ and $(\overline{P} - \overline{\Pi})$ are linear combinations of these deviations, it follows that $\sqrt{n}\,(P - \Pi)$ and $\sqrt{n}\,(\overline{P} - \overline{\Pi})$ are asymptotically normally distributed with zero means. It remains to find the variances and covariances. We note that

$$Ep_{gik} = \pi_{gik} \quad \text{and} \quad Ep_{gi\bar{k}} = \pi_{gi\bar{k}}.$$

Consider for a moment a sample of size 1. Then a p is 0 or 1 and $p_{gik}p_{hjk} = p_{gihjk}$ (= 0 or 1) and thus

$$Ep_{gik}p_{hjk} = Ep_{gihjk} = \pi_{gihjk}.$$

Also, if the sample size is 1, $p_{gik}p_{hj\bar{k}} = 0$, since the two events are mutually exclusive, and $Ep_{gik}p_{hj\bar{k}} = 0$. Thus, for a sample of size 1,

$$E(p_{gik} - \pi_{gik})(p_{hjk} - \pi_{hjk}) = Ep_{gik}p_{hjk} - \pi_{gik}\pi_{hjk} = \pi_{gihjk} - \pi_{gik}\pi_{hjk}$$

and

$$E(p_{gik} - \pi_{gik})(p_{hj\bar{k}} - \pi_{hj\bar{k}}) = -\pi_{gik}\pi_{hj\bar{k}}.$$

Now, let us return to a sample of size n. The second-order moments of the frequencies (not *relative* frequencies) are n times those given above, and the second-order moments of the relative frequencies (the p's for samples of n) are $1/n$ times those above (i.e., $1/n^2$ times those of the frequencies). The second-order moments of the x's are n times those of the p's. Thus Equation (1) follows.

3. The Asymptotic Theory of the Estimates

The main result of this paper is the following theorem:

THEOREM 2. *Let*

$$L_V^* = \sqrt{n}\,(L_V - \Lambda_V),\; L_H^* = \sqrt{n}\,(L_H - \Lambda_H),\; N^* = \sqrt{n}\,(N - V),$$

and

$$D^* = \sqrt{n}\,(D - \Delta).$$

Assume

$$|\Lambda_V| \neq 0,\; |\Lambda_H| \neq 0,\; |V| \neq 0,$$

and that the diagonal elements of Δ are different and ordered in descending order of magnitude. Then L_V, L_H, N, and D are consistent estimates of Λ_V, Λ_H, V, and Δ, respectively. L_V^*, L_H^*, N^*, and D^* are asymptotically normally distributed with means 0 and with variances and covariances given in Equations (23), (27), (30), (33)–(39), where $\theta^{\alpha\beta\gamma\delta}$ and $\bar{\theta}^{\alpha\beta\gamma\delta}$ are defined in Equations (21) and (22) and $B' = \Lambda_H^{-1}$ and $C' = \Lambda_H^{-1}$.

PROOF: The consistency of the estimates follows from the fact that P and $\overline{P}$ are consistent estimates of Π and $\overline{\Pi}$ (i.e., $\underset{n\to\infty}{\mathrm{plim}}\, P = \Pi$ and $\underset{n\to\infty}{\mathrm{plim}}\, \overline{P} = \overline{\Pi}$) and that L_V, L_H, N, and D are the same continuous functions[1] of P and $\overline{P}$ that Λ_V, Λ_H, V, and Δ are of Π and $\overline{\Pi}$.

To prove the second part of the theorem, we shall use the following well-known result:[2]

LEMMA. *Let Z_n be a random vector with a distribution depending on n. Let $w = f(z)$ be a vector-valued function of the nonrandom vector z, and let $W_n = f(Z_n)$. Suppose that $\mathrm{plim}\, Z_n = \mu$ and that $\sqrt{n}\,(Z_n - \mu)$ has a limiting normal distribution with mean 0 and covariance matrix Σ. Let the matrix of partial derivatives of w with respect to z be $\left(\dfrac{\partial f(z)}{\partial z}\right)$. If the elements of this matrix are continuous in a neighborhood of $z = \mu$, then $\sqrt{n}\,(W_n - f(\mu))$ has a limiting normal distribution with mean 0 and covariance matrix $\left(\dfrac{\partial f(\mu)}{\partial z}\right)\Sigma\left(\dfrac{\partial f(\mu)}{\partial z}\right)'$.*

The import of this lemma is that we can expand $f(z)$ into a Taylor's series and neglect all terms except the linear ones. Then, since linear combinations of normally distributed variables are again normally distributed, we obtain the lemma.[3]

In our case, the elements of Z_n are the elements of P and $\overline{P}$ (which were discussed in Section 2). The elements of W_n are the elements of L_V, L_H, N, and D. First, we show how $\sqrt{n}\,(P - \Pi) = X$ and $\sqrt{n}\,(\overline{P} - \overline{\Pi}) = \overline{X}$ can be expressed linearly in terms of

$$L_V^* = \sqrt{n}\,(L_V - \Lambda_V),\; L_H^* = \sqrt{n}\,(L_H - \Lambda_H),\; N^* = \sqrt{n}\,(N - V),$$

and

$$D^* = \sqrt{n}\,(D - \Delta).$$

---

[1]The notes to which the superscripts refer are found at the end of the Appendix.

From this, we express the latter set linearly in terms of the former.[4] The lemma justifies the assertion of asymptotic normality. Finally, we compute the variances and covariances of the limiting normal distribution.

From the definitions, we have

$$\Pi + \frac{1}{\sqrt{n}} X = P = L'_H N D L_V$$

$$= \left(\Lambda'_V + \frac{1}{\sqrt{n}} L_V^{*\prime}\right)\left(V + \frac{1}{\sqrt{n}} N^*\right)\left(\Delta + \frac{1}{\sqrt{n}} D^*\right)\left(\Lambda_H + \frac{1}{\sqrt{n}} L_H^*\right), \quad (2)$$

$$P = \Lambda'_V V \Delta \Lambda_H + \frac{1}{\sqrt{n}} (L_V^{*\prime} V \Delta \Lambda_H + \Lambda'_V N^* \Delta \Lambda_H + \Lambda'_V V D^* \Lambda_H + \Lambda_V V \Delta L_H^*)$$

$$+ \frac{1}{n}\left\{ \qquad \right\},$$

where $\{ \qquad \}$ contains the other terms in the expansion; each of these terms involves at least two of L_V^*, L_H^*, N^*, and D^*. Subtracting $\Pi = \Lambda'_V V \Delta \Lambda_H$ from both sides and multiplying by $\sqrt{n}$, we obtain

$$X = L_V^{*\prime} V \Delta \Lambda_H + \Lambda'_V N^* \Delta \Lambda_H + \Lambda'_V V D^* \Lambda_H + \Lambda'_V V \Delta L_H^* + \frac{1}{\sqrt{n}}\left\{ \qquad \right\}.$$

$$(3)$$

Multiplying (3) on the left by $(\Lambda'_V)^{-1}$ and on the right by Λ_H^{-1}, letting

$$(\Lambda'_V)^{-1} X \Lambda_H^{-1} = H, \qquad L_V^* \Lambda_V^{-1} = F, \qquad \text{and} \qquad L_H^* \Lambda_H^{-1} = G,$$

we obtain

$$H = F'V\Delta + N^*\Delta + VD^* + V\Delta G + \frac{1}{\sqrt{n}}\left\{ \qquad \right\}. \quad (4)$$

The expansion of $\bar{P}$ is done in the same way; Δ is replaced by $\bar{\Delta} = I - \Delta$. Since $\bar{D} = I - D$ and therefore

$$\bar{D}^* = \sqrt{n}\,(\bar{D} - \bar{\Delta}) = -\sqrt{n}\,(D - \Delta),$$

D^* is replaced by $-D^*$. Defining $\bar{H} = (\Lambda'_V)^{-1} \bar{X} \Lambda_H^{-1}$, we have

$$\bar{H} = F'V(I - \Delta) + N^*(I - \Delta) - VD^* + V(I - \Delta)G + \frac{1}{\sqrt{n}}\left\{ \qquad \right\}. \quad (5)$$

The sum of H and $\bar{H}$ is

$$H + \bar{H} = F'V + N^* + VG + \frac{1}{\sqrt{n}}\left\{ \qquad \right\}. \quad (6)$$

Then

$$H - (H + \bar{H})\Delta = H(I - \Delta) - \bar{H}\Delta = VD^* + V\Delta G - VG\Delta$$

$$+ \frac{1}{\sqrt{n}}\left\{ \qquad \right\}, \quad (7)$$

$$H - \Delta(H + \bar{H}) = (I - \Delta)H - \Delta\bar{H} = VD^* + F'V\Delta - \Delta F'V$$

$$+ \frac{1}{\sqrt{n}}\left\{ \qquad \right\}. \quad (8)$$

The α, αth element of either equation gives

$$\frac{(1 - \delta^{\alpha})h^{\alpha\alpha} - \delta^{\alpha}\bar{h}^{\alpha\alpha}}{\nu^{\alpha}} = d^{*\alpha} + \frac{1}{\sqrt{n}}\left\{ \quad \right\}, \tag{9}$$

where δ^{α} is the αth diagonal element of Δ and $d^{*\alpha}$ is the αth diagonal element of D^*. From this, we argue that $d^{*\alpha}$ is distributed asymptotically like the left-hand side of (9).

Now, consider an off-diagonal element of (7). We have

$$h^{\alpha\beta}(1 - \delta^{\beta}) - \bar{h}^{\alpha\beta}\delta^{\beta} = \nu^{\alpha}\delta^{\alpha}g^{\alpha\beta} - \nu^{\alpha}g^{\alpha\beta}\delta^{\beta} + \frac{1}{\sqrt{n}}\left\{ \quad \right\}; \tag{10}$$

that is,

$$\frac{(1 - \delta^{\beta})h^{\alpha\beta} - \delta^{\beta}\bar{h}^{\alpha\beta}}{\nu^{\alpha}(\delta^{\alpha} - \delta^{\beta})} = g^{\alpha\beta} + \frac{1}{\sqrt{n}}\left\{ \quad \right\}, \qquad \alpha \neq \beta. \tag{11}$$

Since the first columns of Λ_H and L_H are composed of ones, the first column of L_H^* is composed of zeros. However, $L_H^* = G\Lambda_H$; each element of the first column of L_H^* is the sum of the elements in that row of G; therefore, $\sum_{\beta} g^{\alpha\beta} = 0$. Although (7) does not define $g^{\alpha\alpha}$, we obtain this from $g^{\alpha\alpha} = -\sum_{\beta \neq \alpha} g^{\alpha\beta}$.

If we now consider the off-diagonal elements of (8), we have

$$\frac{(1 - \delta^{\beta})h^{\beta\alpha} - \delta^{\beta}\bar{h}^{\beta\alpha}}{\nu^{\alpha}(\delta^{\alpha} - \delta^{\beta})} = f^{\alpha\beta} + \frac{1}{\sqrt{n}}\left\{ \quad \right\} \tag{12}$$

and $f^{\alpha\alpha} = -\sum_{\beta \neq \alpha} f^{\alpha\beta}$. If we now return to (6), we have

$$n^{*\alpha} = h^{\alpha\alpha} + \bar{h}^{\alpha\alpha} - \nu^{\alpha}(f^{\alpha\alpha} + g^{\alpha\alpha}) + \frac{1}{\sqrt{n}}\left\{ \quad \right\}$$

$$= h^{\alpha\alpha} + \bar{h}^{\alpha\alpha} + \nu^{\alpha} \sum_{\beta \neq \alpha} (f^{\alpha\beta} + g^{\alpha\beta}) + \frac{1}{\sqrt{n}}\left\{ \quad \right\}$$

$$= h^{\alpha\alpha} + \bar{h}^{\alpha\alpha} + \sum_{\beta \neq \alpha} \frac{(1 - \delta^{\beta})h^{\beta\alpha} - \delta^{\beta}\bar{h}^{\beta\alpha} + (1 - \delta^{\beta})h^{\alpha\beta} - \delta^{\beta}\bar{h}^{\alpha\beta}}{\delta^{\alpha} - \delta^{\beta}}$$

$$+ \frac{1}{\sqrt{n}}\left\{ \quad \right\}$$

$$= h^{\alpha\alpha} + \bar{h}^{\alpha\alpha} + \sum_{\beta \neq \alpha} \frac{(1 - \delta^{\beta})(h^{\beta\alpha} + h^{\alpha\beta}) - \delta^{\beta}(\bar{h}^{\beta\alpha} + \bar{h}^{\alpha\beta})}{\delta^{\alpha} - \delta^{\beta}}$$

$$+ \frac{1}{\sqrt{n}}\left\{ \quad \right\}. \tag{13}$$

We have Equations (9), (11), (12), and (13) for $d^{*\alpha}$, $f^{\alpha\beta}$, $g^{\alpha\beta}$, and $n^{*\alpha}$ in terms of $h^{\alpha\beta}$ and $\bar{h}^{\alpha\beta}$ and residuals of order $1/\sqrt{n}$. As $n \to \infty$, we argue that the terms of order $1/\sqrt{n}$ can be neglected and hence that $d^{*\alpha}$, $f^{\alpha\beta}$, $g^{\alpha\beta}$, and $n^{*\alpha}$ are distributed as linear combinations of $h^{\alpha\beta}$ and $\bar{h}^{\alpha\beta}$, which, in turn, are linear combinations of x_{gi} and $\bar{x}_{gi}$. Then, since x_{gi} and $\bar{x}_{gi}$ are asymptotically normally distributed, so are $d^{*\alpha}$, $f^{\alpha\beta}$, $g^{\alpha\beta}$, and $n^{*\alpha}$. Since the $l_h^{*\alpha}$ (g,h will run over the items in Λ_V, 0, 1, ..., $m-1$, and i,j will run over the items in Λ_H, 0, m, $m+1$, ..., $2m-2$) are linear combinations of $f^{\alpha\beta}$, and $l_i^{*\alpha}$ are linear combinations of $g^{\alpha\beta}$, then $d^{*\alpha}$, $l_h^{*\alpha}$, $l_i^{*\alpha}$, and $n^{*\alpha}$ have, asymptotically, a joint normal distribution. We shall now prove this result.[5]

Since

$$H = \sqrt{n}\,[(\Lambda'_V)^{-1}P\Lambda_H^{-1} - (\Lambda'_V)^{-1}\Pi\Lambda_H^{-1}]$$

and

$$\bar{H} = \sqrt{n}\,[(\Lambda'_V)^{-1}\bar{P}\Lambda_H^{-1} - (\Lambda'_V)^{-1}\bar{\Pi}\Lambda_H^{-1}],$$

they are asymptotically normally distributed as $(\Lambda'_V)^{-1}X\Lambda_H^{-1}$ and $(\Lambda'_V)^{-1}\bar{X}\Lambda_H^{-1}$ by a trivial application of the lemma (with the components of Z_n, for this application, being the components of P and $\bar{P}$ suitably arranged as a vector). Now, let the components of $(\Lambda'_V)^{-1}P\Lambda_H^{-1}$ and $(\Lambda'_V)^{-1}\bar{P}\Lambda_H^{-1}$ as random variables compose the vector Z_n; let the elements of $(\Lambda'_V)^{-1}\Pi\Lambda_H^{-1}$ and $(\Lambda'_V)^{-1}\bar{\Pi}\Lambda_H^{-1}$ similarly arranged compose the vector μ. Let the nontrivial elements of $L_V\Lambda_V^{-1}$, $L_H\Lambda_H^{-1}$, N, and D as random variables compose the vector W_n (of $2m^2$ components), and as nonrandom variables, the vector w. We know that w is a function of z, say $w = f(z)$, and z is a function of w, say $z = g(w) = f^{-1}(w)$. Since the elements of z are polynomials in the elements of w, the partial derivatives of z with respect to w are continuous functions of w. Now Equations (4) and (5) are in the form

$$\sqrt{n}\,(z - \mu) = \left(\frac{\partial g(\nu)}{\partial w}\right)\sqrt{n}\,(w - \nu) + \left\{ \quad \right\}, \qquad (14)$$

where $\nu = f(\mu)$ and where $\{\quad\}$ contains terms of higher degree in this Taylor's series. Equations (9), (11), (12), and (13) solve

$$\sqrt{n}\,(z - \mu) = \left(\frac{\partial g(\nu)}{\partial w}\right)\sqrt{n}\,(w - \nu) \qquad (15)$$

for $\sqrt{n}\,(w - \nu)$, thus showing that $\left(\dfrac{\partial g(\nu)}{\partial w}\right)$ is nonsingular. Since $\left(\dfrac{\partial g(w)}{\partial w}\right)$ is continuous and nonsingular in a neighborhood of $w = \nu$, the matrix

$$\left(\frac{\partial f(z)}{\partial z}\right) = \left(\frac{\partial g(w)}{\partial w}\right)^{-1}$$

is continuous (and nonsingular) in a neighborhood of $z = \mu$. Thus the lemma may be applied. Finally, (9), (11), (12), and (13) are of the form

$$\sqrt{n}\,(w - \nu) = \left(\frac{\partial f(\mu)}{\partial z}\right)\sqrt{n}\,(z - \mu) + \left\{ \quad \right\}. \qquad (16)$$

The lemma says that, asymptotically, we can treat $\sqrt{n}\,(W_n - v)$ as

$$\left(\frac{\partial f(\mu)}{\partial z}\right)\sqrt{n}\,(Z_n - \mu).$$

The asymptotic distribution of L_V, L_H, N, and D is obtained from that of $L_V\Lambda_V^{-1}$, $L_H\Lambda_H^{-1}$, N, and D by another trivial application of the lemma.

Now, let us find the limiting covariance matrix of the elements of D^*, L_V^*, L_H^*, and N^*. First, we find the variances and covariances of the elements of

$$H = (\Lambda_V')^{-1}X\Lambda_H^{-1} \qquad \text{and} \qquad \overline{H} = (\Lambda_V')^{-1}\overline{X}\Lambda_H^{-1}.$$

Let

$$(\Lambda_V')^{-1} = C = (c_g^\alpha)(\alpha = 1, \ldots, m, \; g = 0, 1, \ldots, m - 1)$$

and let

$$(\Lambda_H')^{-1} = B = (b_i^\alpha)(\alpha = 1, \ldots, m, \; i = 0, m, \ldots, 2m - 2).$$

Then

$$h^{\alpha\beta} = \sum_{g,i} c_g^\alpha x_{gi} b_i^\beta,$$

$$\overline{h}^{\alpha\beta} = \sum_{g,i} c_g^\alpha \overline{x}_{gi} b_i^\beta. \tag{17}$$

The means are

$$EH = ECXB' = 0,$$
$$E\overline{H} = EC\overline{X}B' = 0.$$

The variances and covariances of the h's are

$$Eh^{\alpha\beta}h^{\gamma\delta} = \sum_{g,i,h,j} c_g^\alpha b_i^\beta c_h^\gamma b_j^\delta(\pi_{gihjk} - \pi_{gik}\pi_{hjk}).$$

Since

$$(\pi_{gik}) = \Pi = \Lambda_V'V\Delta\Lambda_H, \; C\Lambda_V' = I, \text{ and } \Lambda_H B' = I,$$

$$C\Pi B' = V\Delta;$$

that is,

$$\sum_{g,i} c_g^\alpha b_i^\beta \pi_{gik} = \delta_{\alpha\beta}v^\alpha \delta^\alpha,$$

where $\delta_{\alpha\beta} = 0$, $\alpha \neq \beta$, and $\delta_{\alpha\alpha} = 1$. Thus

$$Eh^{\alpha\beta}h^{\gamma\delta} = \sum_{g,i,h,j} c_g^\alpha b_i^\beta c_h^\gamma b_j^\delta \pi_{gihjk} - \delta_{\alpha\beta}v^\alpha \delta^\alpha \delta_{\gamma\delta}v^\gamma \delta^\gamma. \tag{18}$$

Similarly,

$$E\overline{h}^{\alpha\beta}\overline{h}^{\gamma\delta} = \sum_{g,i,h,j} c_g^\alpha b_i^\beta c_h^\gamma b_j^\delta \pi_{gihj\overline{k}} - \delta_{\alpha\beta}v^{\alpha\overline{\delta}}\delta^\alpha \delta_{\gamma\delta}v^{\gamma\overline{\delta}}\delta^\gamma, \tag{19}$$

where $\overline{\delta}^\alpha = 1 - \delta^\alpha$, and

$$Eh^{\alpha\beta}\overline{h}^{\gamma\delta} = -\delta_{\alpha\beta}v^\alpha \delta^\alpha \delta_{\gamma\delta}v^\gamma \overline{\delta}^\gamma. \tag{20}$$

For convenience, we make the following definitions. Let

$$\theta^{\alpha\beta\gamma\delta} = \sum_{g,i,h,j} c_g^\alpha b_i^\beta c_h^\gamma b_j^\delta \pi_{gihjk},$$ (21)

$$\bar{\theta}^{\alpha\beta\gamma\delta} = \sum_{g,i,h,j} c_g^\alpha b_i^\beta c_h^\gamma b_j^\delta \pi_{gihj\bar{k}}.$$ (22)

Now, let us find the variances and covariances of the limiting distribution of D^*, F, G, and N^*. We shall denote these by $\mathcal{C}[\ \ ]$. The variance of an element is the covariance of it with itself. For the elements of D^*, that is,

$$d^{*\alpha} \sim [\bar{\delta}^\alpha h^{\alpha\alpha} - \delta^\alpha \bar{h}^{\alpha\alpha}]/\nu^\alpha$$

(where $\sim$ means "asymptotically equivalent to") we have

$$\mathcal{C}[d^{*\alpha}, d^{*\gamma}] = \frac{E[\bar{\delta}^\alpha h^{\alpha\alpha} - \delta^\alpha \bar{h}^{\alpha\alpha}][\bar{\delta}^\gamma h^{\gamma\gamma} - \delta^\gamma \bar{h}^{\gamma\gamma}]}{\nu^\alpha \nu^\gamma}$$

$$= \frac{1}{\nu^\alpha \nu^\gamma} [\bar{\delta}^\alpha \bar{\delta}^\gamma (\sum c_g^\alpha b_i^\alpha c_h^\gamma b_j^\gamma \pi_{gihjk} - \nu^\alpha \delta^\alpha \nu^\gamma \delta^\gamma)$$

$$+ \delta^\alpha \delta^\gamma (\sum c_g^\alpha b_i^\alpha c_h^\gamma b_j^\gamma \pi_{gihj\bar{k}} - \nu^\alpha \bar{\delta}^\alpha \nu^\gamma \bar{\delta}^\gamma) + 2\bar{\delta}^\alpha \delta^\gamma \nu^\alpha \delta^\alpha \nu^\gamma \bar{\delta}^\gamma]$$

$$= \frac{\bar{\delta}^\alpha \bar{\delta}^\gamma \theta^{\alpha\alpha\gamma\gamma} + \delta^\alpha \delta^\gamma \bar{\theta}^{\alpha\alpha\gamma\gamma}}{\nu^\alpha \nu^\gamma}.$$ (23)

Now, consider the asymptotic variances and covariances of

$$f^{\alpha\beta} \sim [\bar{\delta}^\beta h^{\beta\alpha} - \delta^\beta \bar{h}^{\beta\alpha}]/[\nu^\alpha(\delta^\alpha - \delta^\beta)].$$

We have

$$\mathcal{C}[f^{\alpha\beta}, f^{\gamma\delta}] = \frac{E[\bar{\delta}^\beta h^{\beta\alpha} - \delta^\beta \bar{h}^{\beta\alpha}][\bar{\delta}^\delta h^{\delta\gamma} - \delta^\delta \bar{h}^{\delta\gamma}]}{\nu^\alpha(\delta^\alpha - \delta^\beta)\nu^\gamma(\delta^\gamma - \delta^\delta)}$$

$$= \frac{\bar{\delta}^\beta \bar{\delta}^\delta \theta^{\beta\alpha\delta\gamma} + \delta^\beta \delta^\delta \bar{\theta}^{\beta\alpha\delta\gamma}}{\nu^\alpha \nu^\gamma(\delta^\alpha - \delta^\beta)(\delta^\gamma - \delta^\delta)}, \qquad \alpha \neq \beta, \gamma \neq \delta.$$ (24)

To obtain such terms if $\alpha = \beta$, or $\gamma = \delta$, or both, we use the fact that $f^{\beta\beta} = -\sum_{\alpha \neq \beta} f^{\beta\alpha}$.

For

$$g^{\alpha\beta} \sim [\bar{\delta}^\beta h^{\alpha\beta} - \delta^\beta \bar{h}^{\alpha\beta}]/[\nu^\alpha(\delta^\alpha - \delta^\beta)],$$

we have

$$\mathcal{C}[g^{\alpha\beta}, g^{\gamma\delta}] = \frac{E[\bar{\delta}^\beta h^{\alpha\beta} - \delta^\beta \bar{h}^{\alpha\beta}][\bar{\delta}^\delta h^{\gamma\delta} - \delta^\delta \bar{h}^{\gamma\delta}]}{\nu^\alpha(\delta^\alpha - \delta^\beta)\nu^\gamma(\delta^\gamma - \delta^\delta)}$$

$$= \frac{\bar{\delta}^\beta \bar{\delta}^\delta \theta^{\alpha\beta\gamma\delta} + \delta^\beta \delta^\delta \bar{\theta}^{\alpha\beta\gamma\delta}}{\nu^\alpha \nu^\gamma(\delta^\alpha - \delta^\beta)(\delta^\gamma - \delta^\delta)}, \qquad \alpha \neq \beta, \gamma \neq \delta.$$ (25)

For $g^{\alpha\beta}$ and $f^{\gamma\delta}$, we have

$$\mathcal{C}[g^{\alpha\beta}, f^{\gamma\delta}] = \frac{E[\bar{\delta}^\beta h^{\alpha\beta} - \delta^\beta \bar{h}^{\alpha\beta}][\bar{\delta}^\delta h^{\delta\gamma} - \delta^\delta \bar{h}^{\delta\gamma}]}{\nu^\alpha(\delta^\alpha - \delta^\beta)\nu^\gamma(\delta^\gamma - \delta^\delta)}$$

$$= \frac{\bar{\delta}^\beta \bar{\delta}^\delta \theta^{\alpha\beta\delta\gamma} + \delta^\beta \delta^\delta \bar{\theta}^{\alpha\beta\delta\gamma}}{\nu^\alpha \nu^\gamma(\delta^\alpha - \delta^\beta)(\delta^\gamma - \delta^\delta)}, \qquad \alpha \neq \beta, \gamma \neq \delta.$$ (26)

Now, consider $n^{*\alpha}$. We have

$$
\mathcal{C}[n^{*\alpha}, n^{*\gamma}]
$$

$$
= E(h^{\alpha\alpha} + \bar{h}^{\alpha\alpha})(h^{\gamma\gamma} + \bar{h}^{\gamma\gamma})
$$

$$
+ \sum_{\delta \neq \gamma} \frac{E(h^{\alpha\alpha} + \bar{h}^{\alpha\alpha})[\delta^{\delta}(h^{\delta\gamma} + h^{\gamma\delta}) - \delta^{\delta}(\bar{h}^{\delta\gamma} + \bar{h}^{\gamma\delta})]}{\delta^{\gamma} - \delta^{\delta}}
$$

$$
+ \sum_{\beta \neq \alpha} \frac{E(h^{\gamma\gamma} + \bar{h}^{\gamma\gamma})[\delta^{\beta}(h^{\beta\alpha} + h^{\alpha\beta}) - \delta^{\beta}(\bar{h}^{\beta\alpha} + \bar{h}^{\alpha\beta})]}{\delta^{\alpha} - \delta^{\beta}}
$$

$$
+ \sum_{\substack{\beta \neq \alpha \\ \delta \neq \gamma}} \frac{E[\delta^{\beta}(h^{\beta\alpha} + h^{\alpha\beta}) - \delta^{\beta}(\bar{h}^{\beta\alpha} + \bar{h}^{\alpha\beta})][\delta^{\delta}(h^{\delta\gamma} + h^{\gamma\delta}) - \delta^{\delta}(\bar{h}^{\delta\gamma} + \bar{h}^{\gamma\delta})]}{(\delta^{\alpha} - \delta^{\beta})(\delta^{\gamma} - \delta^{\delta})}
$$

$$
= \theta^{\alpha\alpha\gamma\gamma} + \bar{\theta}^{\alpha\alpha\gamma\gamma} - \nu^{\alpha}\nu^{\gamma}
$$

$$
+ \sum_{\delta \neq \gamma} \frac{\bar{\delta}^{\delta}(\theta^{\alpha\alpha\delta\gamma} + \theta^{\alpha\alpha\gamma\delta}) - \delta^{\delta}(\bar{\theta}^{\alpha\alpha\delta\gamma} + \bar{\theta}^{\alpha\alpha\gamma\delta})}{\delta^{\gamma} - \delta^{\delta}}
$$

$$
+ \sum_{\beta \neq \alpha} \frac{\bar{\delta}^{\beta}(\theta^{\beta\alpha\gamma\gamma} + \theta^{\alpha\beta\gamma\gamma}) - \delta^{\beta}(\bar{\theta}^{\beta\alpha\gamma\gamma} + \bar{\theta}^{\alpha\beta\gamma\gamma})}{\delta^{\alpha} - \delta^{\beta}}
$$

$$
+ \sum_{\substack{\beta \neq \alpha \\ \delta \neq \gamma}} \left[\frac{\bar{\delta}^{\beta}\bar{\delta}^{\delta}(\theta^{\beta\alpha\delta\gamma} + \theta^{\beta\alpha\gamma\delta} + \theta^{\alpha\beta\delta\gamma} + \theta^{\alpha\beta\gamma\delta})}{(\delta^{\alpha} - \delta^{\beta})(\delta^{\gamma} - \delta^{\delta})} \right.
$$

$$
\left. + \frac{\delta^{\beta}\delta^{\delta}(\bar{\theta}^{\beta\alpha\delta\gamma} + \bar{\theta}^{\beta\alpha\gamma\delta} + \bar{\theta}^{\alpha\beta\delta\gamma} + \bar{\theta}^{\alpha\beta\gamma\delta})}{(\delta^{\alpha} - \delta^{\beta})(\delta^{\gamma} - \delta^{\delta})} \right]. \tag{27}
$$

The asymptotic covariances between $d^{*\alpha}$ and $f^{\gamma\beta}$ are

$$
\mathcal{C}[d^{*\alpha}, f^{\gamma\beta}] = E \frac{(\bar{\delta}^{\alpha}h^{\alpha\alpha} - \delta^{\alpha}\bar{h}^{\alpha\alpha})(\bar{\delta}^{\beta}h^{\beta\gamma} - \delta^{\beta}\bar{h}^{\beta\gamma})}{\nu^{\alpha}\nu^{\gamma}(\delta^{\gamma} - \delta^{\beta})}
$$

$$
= \frac{\bar{\delta}^{\alpha}\bar{\delta}^{\beta}\theta^{\alpha\alpha\beta\gamma} + \delta^{\alpha}\delta^{\beta}\bar{\theta}^{\alpha\alpha\beta\gamma}}{\nu^{\alpha}\nu^{\gamma}(\delta^{\gamma} - \delta^{\beta})}, \tag{28}
$$

between $d^{*\alpha}$ and $g^{\gamma\beta}$ are

$$
\mathcal{C}[d^{*\alpha}, g^{\gamma\beta}] = E \frac{(\bar{\delta}^{\alpha}h^{\alpha\alpha} - \delta^{\alpha}\bar{h}^{\alpha\alpha})(\bar{\delta}^{\beta}h^{\gamma\beta} - \delta^{\beta}\bar{h}^{\gamma\beta})}{\nu^{\alpha}\nu^{\gamma}(\delta^{\gamma} - \delta^{\beta})}
$$

$$
= \frac{\bar{\delta}^{\alpha}\bar{\delta}^{\beta}\theta^{\alpha\alpha\gamma\beta} + \delta^{\alpha}\delta^{\beta}\bar{\theta}^{\alpha\alpha\gamma\beta}}{\nu^{\alpha}\nu^{\gamma}(\delta^{\gamma} - \delta^{\beta})}, \tag{29}
$$

and between $d^{*\alpha}$ and $n^{*\gamma}$ are

$$
\mathcal{C}[d^{*\alpha}, n^{*\gamma}]
$$

$$
= E \frac{(\bar{\delta}^{\alpha}h^{\alpha\alpha} - \delta^{\alpha}\bar{h}^{\alpha\alpha})}{\nu^{\alpha}} \left\{ h^{\gamma\gamma} + \bar{h}^{\gamma\gamma} + \sum_{\beta \neq \gamma} \frac{\bar{\delta}^{\beta}(h^{\beta\gamma} + h^{\gamma\beta}) - \delta^{\beta}(\bar{h}^{\beta\gamma} + \bar{h}^{\gamma\beta})}{\delta^{\gamma} - \delta^{\beta}} \right\}
$$

$$
= \frac{\bar{\delta}^{\alpha}\theta^{\alpha\alpha\gamma\gamma} + \delta^{\alpha}\bar{\theta}^{\alpha\alpha\gamma\gamma}}{\nu^{\alpha}} + \sum_{\beta \neq \gamma} \frac{\bar{\delta}^{\alpha}\bar{\delta}^{\beta}(\theta^{\alpha\alpha\beta\gamma} + \theta^{\alpha\alpha\gamma\beta}) + \delta^{\alpha}\delta^{\beta}(\bar{\theta}^{\alpha\alpha\beta\gamma} + \bar{\theta}^{\alpha\alpha\gamma\beta})}{\nu^{\alpha}(\delta^{\gamma} - \delta^{\beta})}. \tag{30}
$$

$$\mathcal{C}[n^{*\alpha}, f^{\gamma\beta}]$$

$$= E \frac{(\bar{\delta}^\beta h^{\beta\gamma} - \delta^\beta \bar{h}^{\beta\gamma})}{\nu^\gamma(\delta^\gamma - \delta^\beta)} \left\{ h^{\alpha\alpha} + \bar{h}^{\alpha\alpha} + \sum_{\epsilon \neq \alpha} \frac{\bar{\delta}^\epsilon(h^{\epsilon\alpha} + h^{\alpha\epsilon}) - \delta^\epsilon(\bar{h}^{\epsilon\alpha} + \bar{h}^{\alpha\epsilon})}{\delta^\alpha - \delta^\epsilon} \right\}$$

$$= \frac{\bar{\delta}^\beta \theta^{\beta\gamma\alpha\alpha} + \delta^\beta \bar{\theta}^{\beta\gamma\alpha\alpha}}{\nu^\gamma(\delta^\gamma - \delta^\beta)} + \sum_{\epsilon \neq \alpha} \frac{\bar{\delta}^\beta \bar{\delta}^\epsilon(\theta^{\beta\gamma\epsilon\alpha} + \theta^{\beta\gamma\alpha\epsilon}) + \delta^\beta \delta^\epsilon(\bar{\theta}^{\beta\gamma\epsilon\alpha} + \bar{\theta}^{\beta\gamma\alpha\epsilon})}{\nu^\gamma(\delta^\gamma - \delta^\beta)(\delta^\alpha - \delta^\epsilon)}. \quad (31)$$

$$\mathcal{C}[n^{*\alpha}, g^{\gamma\beta}]$$

$$= E \frac{(\bar{\delta}^\beta h^{\gamma\beta} - \delta^\beta \bar{h}^{\gamma\beta})}{\nu^\gamma(\delta^\gamma - \delta^\beta)} \left\{ h^{\alpha\alpha} + \bar{h}^{\alpha\alpha} + \sum_{\epsilon \neq \alpha} \frac{\bar{\delta}^\epsilon(h^{\epsilon\alpha} + h^{\alpha\epsilon}) - \delta^\epsilon(\bar{h}^{\epsilon\alpha} + \bar{h}^{\alpha\epsilon})}{\delta^\alpha - \delta^\epsilon} \right\}$$

$$= \frac{\bar{\delta}^\beta \theta^{\gamma\beta\alpha\alpha} + \delta^\beta \bar{\theta}^{\gamma\beta\alpha\alpha}}{\nu^\gamma(\delta^\gamma - \delta^\beta)} + \sum_{\epsilon \neq \alpha} \frac{\bar{\delta}^\beta \bar{\delta}^\epsilon(\theta^{\gamma\beta\epsilon\alpha} + \theta^{\gamma\beta\alpha\epsilon}) + \delta^\beta \delta^\epsilon(\bar{\theta}^{\gamma\beta\epsilon\alpha} + \bar{\theta}^{\gamma\beta\alpha\epsilon})}{\nu^\gamma(\delta^\gamma - \delta^\beta)(\delta^\alpha - \delta^\epsilon)}. \quad (32)$$

Now, let us find the asymptotic variances and covariances of $L_V^* = F\Lambda_V$ (i.e., $l_g^{*\alpha} = \sum_\beta f^{\alpha\beta}\lambda_g^\beta$). We have for $g, h \neq 0$

$$\mathcal{C}[l_g^{*\alpha}, l_h^{*\gamma}] = \sum_{\beta, \delta} \lambda_g^\beta \lambda_h^\delta \mathcal{C}[f^{\alpha\beta}, f^{\gamma\delta}]$$

$$= \sum_{\substack{\beta \neq \alpha \\ \delta \neq \gamma}} \lambda_g^\beta \lambda_h^\delta \mathcal{C}[f^{\alpha\beta}, f^{\gamma\delta}]$$

$$- \sum_{\delta \neq \gamma} \lambda_g^\alpha \lambda_h^\delta \sum_{\epsilon \neq \alpha} \mathcal{C}[f^{\alpha\epsilon}, f^{\gamma\delta}]$$

$$- \sum_{\beta \neq \alpha} \lambda_g^\beta \lambda_h^\gamma \sum_{\phi \neq \gamma} \mathcal{C}[f^{\alpha\beta}, f^{\gamma\phi}]$$

$$+ \lambda_g^\alpha \lambda_h^\gamma \sum_{\substack{\epsilon \neq \alpha \\ \phi \neq \gamma}} \mathcal{C}[f^{\alpha\epsilon}, f^{\gamma\phi}]$$

$$= \sum_{\substack{\beta \neq \alpha \\ \delta \neq \gamma}} (\lambda_g^\beta - \lambda_g^\alpha)(\lambda_h^\delta - \lambda_h^\gamma)\mathcal{C}[f^{\alpha\beta}, f^{\gamma\delta}]$$

$$= \sum_{\substack{\beta \neq \alpha \\ \delta \neq \gamma}} \frac{(\lambda_g^\beta - \lambda_g^\alpha)(\lambda_h^\delta - \lambda_h^\gamma)(\bar{\delta}^\beta \bar{\delta}^\delta \theta^{\beta\alpha\delta\gamma} + \delta^\beta \delta^\delta \bar{\theta}^{\beta\alpha\delta\gamma})}{\nu^\alpha \nu^\gamma(\delta^\alpha - \delta^\beta)(\delta^\gamma - \delta^\delta)}. \quad (33)$$

For $L_H^* = G\Lambda_H$ (i.e., $l_i^{*\alpha} = \sum_\beta g^{\alpha\beta}\lambda_i^\beta$), we have for $i, j \neq 0$,

$$\mathcal{C}[l_i^{*\alpha}, l_j^{*\gamma}] = \sum_{\beta, \delta} \lambda_i^\beta \lambda_j^\delta \mathcal{C}[g^{\alpha\beta}, g^{\gamma\delta}]$$

$$= \sum_{\substack{\beta \neq \alpha \\ \delta \neq \gamma}} \frac{(\lambda_i^\beta - \lambda_i^\alpha)(\lambda_j^\delta - \lambda_j^\gamma)(\bar{\delta}^\beta \bar{\delta}^\delta \theta^{\alpha\beta\gamma\delta} + \delta^\beta \delta^\delta \bar{\theta}^{\alpha\beta\gamma\delta})}{\nu^\alpha \nu^\gamma(\delta^\alpha - \delta^\beta)(\delta^\gamma - \delta^\delta)}. \quad (34)$$

The other asymptotic variances and covariances are for L_V^* and L_H^*

$$\mathcal{C}[l_g^{*\alpha}, l_i^{*\gamma}] = \sum_{\substack{\beta \neq \alpha \\ \epsilon \neq \gamma}} \frac{(\lambda_g^\beta - \lambda_g^\alpha)(\lambda_i^\epsilon - \lambda_i^\gamma)(\bar{\delta}^\beta \bar{\delta}^\epsilon \theta^{\beta\alpha\gamma\epsilon} + \delta^\beta \delta^\epsilon \bar{\theta}^{\beta\alpha\gamma\epsilon})}{\nu^\alpha \nu^\gamma(\delta^\alpha - \delta^\beta)(\delta^\gamma - \delta^\epsilon)}, \quad i, h \neq 0, \quad (35)$$

for D^* and L_V^*

$$\mathcal{C}[d^{*\alpha}, l_g^{*\gamma}] = \sum_{\beta \neq \gamma} \frac{(\lambda_g^\beta - \lambda_g^\gamma)(\bar{\delta}^\alpha \bar{\delta}^\gamma \theta^{\alpha\alpha\beta\gamma} + \delta^\alpha \delta^\gamma \bar{\theta}^{\alpha\alpha\beta\gamma})}{\nu^\alpha \nu^\gamma(\delta^\gamma - \delta^\beta)}, \quad g \neq 0, \quad (36)$$

282

for $D*$ and L_H^*

$$\mathbb{C}[d^{*\alpha}, l_i^{*\gamma}] = \sum_{\beta \neq \gamma} \frac{(\lambda_i^\beta - \lambda_i^\gamma)(\bar{\delta}^\alpha \bar{\delta}^\gamma \theta^{\alpha\alpha\gamma\beta} + \delta^\alpha \delta^\gamma \bar{\theta}^{\alpha\alpha\gamma\beta})}{\nu^\alpha \nu^\gamma (\delta^\gamma - \delta^\beta)}, \quad i \neq 0, \quad (37)$$

for $N*$ and L_V^*

$$\mathbb{C}[n^{*\alpha}, l_g^{*\gamma}] = \sum_{\beta \neq \gamma} \frac{(\lambda_g^\beta - \lambda_g^\gamma)}{\nu^\gamma (\delta^\gamma - \delta^\beta)}$$

$$\times \left\{ \bar{\delta}^\beta \theta^{\beta\gamma\alpha\alpha} + \delta^\beta \bar{\theta}^{\beta\gamma\alpha\alpha} + \sum_{\epsilon \neq \alpha} \frac{\bar{\delta}^\beta \bar{\delta}^\epsilon (\theta^{\beta\gamma\epsilon\alpha} + \theta^{\beta\gamma\alpha\epsilon}) + \delta^\beta \delta^\epsilon (\bar{\theta}^{\beta\gamma\epsilon\alpha} + \bar{\theta}^{\beta\gamma\alpha\epsilon})}{\delta^\alpha - \delta^\epsilon} \right\},$$

$$g \neq 0, \quad (38)$$

and for $N*$ and L_H^*

$$\mathbb{C}[n^{*\alpha}, l_i^{*\gamma}] = \sum_{\beta = \gamma} \frac{(\lambda_i^\beta - \lambda_i^\gamma)}{\nu^\gamma (\delta^\gamma - \delta^\beta)}$$

$$\times \left\{ \bar{\delta}^\beta \theta^{\gamma\beta\alpha\alpha} + \delta^\beta \bar{\theta}^{\gamma\beta\alpha\alpha} + \sum_{\epsilon \neq \alpha} \frac{\bar{\delta}^\beta \bar{\delta}^\epsilon (\theta^{\gamma\beta\epsilon\alpha} + \theta^{\gamma\beta\alpha\epsilon}) + \delta^\beta \delta^\epsilon (\bar{\theta}^{\gamma\beta\epsilon\alpha} + \bar{\theta}^{\gamma\beta\alpha\epsilon})}{\delta^\alpha - \delta^\epsilon} \right\},$$

$$i \neq 0. \quad (39)$$

This completes the proof of the theorem.

It will be noticed that the variances and covariances are functions of the parameters being estimated and the probabilities of joint occurrences π_{gihjk} and $\pi_{gih j\bar{k}}$. From the sample, we have consistent estimates of all of these parameters, for p_{gihjk} and $p_{gih j\bar{k}}$ are consistent estimates of π_{gihjk} and $\pi_{gih j\bar{k}}$.

4. Simplification of Formulas

The expressions given above are valid if Π and $\bar{\Pi}$ have the structure indicated earlier. It is not necessary that other π's satisfy the usual structure. However, if the π_{gihjk} do satisfy the usual structure, $\theta^{\alpha\beta\gamma\delta}$ and $\bar{\theta}^{\alpha\beta\gamma\delta}$ can be simplified. We need the following equations:

$$\pi_{gihjk} = \sum_\epsilon \lambda_g^\epsilon \lambda_i^\epsilon \lambda_h^\epsilon \lambda_j^\epsilon \lambda_k^\epsilon \nu^\epsilon, \qquad g \neq h, i \neq j,$$

$$\pi_{gigjk} = \pi_{gijk} = \sum_\epsilon \lambda_g^\epsilon \lambda_i^\epsilon \lambda_j^\epsilon \lambda_k^\epsilon \nu^\epsilon, \qquad i \neq j, \quad (40)$$

$$\pi_{gihik} = \pi_{gihk} = \sum_\epsilon \lambda_g^\epsilon \lambda_i^\epsilon \lambda_h^\epsilon \lambda_k^\epsilon \nu^\epsilon, \qquad g \neq h.$$

If $g = h$ and $i = j$, we use $\pi_{gigik} = \pi_{gik}$. In these formulas, $\lambda_0^\epsilon = 1$; g can equal i (or j) only if both are 0. $\pi_{gih j\bar{k}}$ is defined as in (40), except that λ_k^ϵ is replaced by $\lambda_{\bar{k}}^\epsilon$.

To obtain $\theta^{\alpha\beta\gamma\delta}$, we evaluate

$$\theta^{\alpha\beta\gamma\delta} = \sum_j b_j^\delta \left\{ \sum_i b_i^\beta \left[\sum_h c_h^\gamma \left(\sum_g c_g^\alpha \pi_{gihjk} \right) \right] \right\} \quad (41)$$

by finding ( ), then [ ], then { } and, finally, the entire expression.

Since $C\Lambda'_V = I$ (i.e., $\sum_g c_g^\alpha \lambda_g^\epsilon = \delta_{\alpha\epsilon}$) and $\lambda_f^\epsilon = (\lambda_f^\epsilon)^2 + \lambda_f^\epsilon \lambda_{\bar{f}}^\epsilon$, we have

$$\sum_g c_g^\alpha \pi_{gihjk} = \sum_{g \neq h} \sum_\epsilon c_g^\alpha \lambda_g^\epsilon \lambda_i^\epsilon \lambda_{\bar{h}}^\epsilon \lambda_j^\epsilon \lambda_k^\epsilon \nu^\epsilon + c_h^\alpha \sum_\epsilon \lambda_{\bar{h}}^\epsilon \lambda_i^\epsilon \lambda_j^\epsilon \lambda_k^\epsilon \nu^\epsilon$$

$$= \sum_g \sum_\epsilon c_g^\alpha \lambda_g^\epsilon \lambda_i^\epsilon \lambda_{\bar{h}}^\epsilon \lambda_j^\epsilon \lambda_k^\epsilon \nu^\epsilon + c_h^\alpha \sum_\epsilon \lambda_h^\epsilon \lambda_{\bar{h}}^\epsilon \lambda_i^\epsilon \lambda_j^\epsilon \lambda_k^\epsilon \nu^\epsilon$$

$$= \lambda_i^\alpha \lambda_{\bar{h}}^\alpha \lambda_j^\alpha \lambda_k^\alpha \nu^\alpha + c_h^\alpha \sum_\epsilon \lambda_h^\epsilon \lambda_{\bar{h}}^\epsilon \lambda_i^\epsilon \lambda_j^\epsilon \lambda_k^\epsilon \nu^\epsilon, \qquad i \neq j. \qquad (42)$$

Similarly,

$$\sum_g c_g^\alpha \pi_{gihik} = \lambda_{\bar{h}}^\alpha \lambda_i^\alpha \lambda_k^\alpha \nu^\alpha + c_h^\alpha \sum_\epsilon \lambda_h^\epsilon \lambda_{\bar{h}}^\epsilon \lambda_i^\epsilon \lambda_k^\epsilon \nu^\epsilon. \qquad (43)$$

The next step gives us

$$\sum_h c_h^\gamma \left(\sum_g c_g^\alpha \pi_{gihjk} \right) = \sum_h c_h^\gamma \lambda_{\bar{h}}^\alpha \lambda_i^\alpha \lambda_j^\alpha \lambda_k^\alpha \nu^\alpha + \sum_h c_h^\gamma c_h^\alpha \sum_\epsilon \lambda_h^\epsilon \lambda_{\bar{h}}^\epsilon \lambda_i^\epsilon \lambda_j^\epsilon \lambda_k^\epsilon \nu^\epsilon$$

$$= \delta_{\gamma\alpha} \lambda_i^\alpha \lambda_j^\alpha \lambda_k^\alpha \nu^\alpha + \sum_h c_h^\gamma c_h^\alpha \sum_\epsilon \lambda_h^\epsilon \lambda_{\bar{h}}^\epsilon \lambda_i^\epsilon \lambda_j^\epsilon \lambda_k^\epsilon \nu^\epsilon, \quad i \neq j, \quad (44)$$

and

$$\sum_h c_h^\gamma \left(\sum_g c_g^\alpha \pi_{gihik} \right) = \delta_{\gamma\alpha} \lambda_i^\alpha \lambda_k^\alpha \nu^\alpha + \sum_h c_h^\gamma c_h^\alpha \sum_\epsilon \lambda_h^\epsilon \lambda_{\bar{h}}^\epsilon \lambda_i^\epsilon \lambda_k^\epsilon \nu^\epsilon. \qquad (45)$$

Then

$$\sum_i b_i^\beta \left[\sum_h c_h^\gamma \left(\sum_g c_g^\alpha \pi_{gihjk} \right) \right] = \delta_{\gamma\alpha} \left\{ \sum_i b_i^\beta \lambda_i^\alpha \lambda_j^\alpha \lambda_k^\alpha \nu^\alpha + b_j^\beta \lambda_j^\alpha \lambda_{\bar{j}}^\alpha \lambda_k^\alpha \nu^\alpha \right\}$$

$$+ \sum_i b_i^\beta \sum_h c_h^\gamma c_h^\alpha \sum_\epsilon \lambda_h^\epsilon \lambda_{\bar{h}}^\epsilon \lambda_i^\epsilon \lambda_j^\epsilon \lambda_k^\epsilon \nu^\epsilon$$

$$+ b_j^\beta \sum_h c_h^\gamma c_h^\alpha \sum_\epsilon \lambda_h^\epsilon \lambda_{\bar{h}}^\epsilon \lambda_j^\epsilon \lambda_{\bar{j}}^\epsilon \lambda_k^\epsilon \nu^\epsilon$$

$$= \delta_{\gamma\alpha} \{ \delta_{\beta\alpha} \lambda_j^\alpha \lambda_k^\alpha \nu^\alpha + b_j^\beta \lambda_j^\alpha \lambda_{\bar{j}}^\alpha \lambda_k^\alpha \nu^\alpha \}$$

$$+ \sum_h c_h^\gamma c_h^\alpha \lambda_h^\beta \lambda_{\bar{h}}^\beta \lambda_j^\beta \lambda_k^\beta \nu^\beta$$

$$+ b_j^\beta \sum_h c_h^\gamma c_h^\alpha \sum_\epsilon \lambda_h^\epsilon \lambda_{\bar{h}}^\epsilon \lambda_j^\epsilon \lambda_{\bar{j}}^\epsilon \lambda_k^\epsilon \nu^\epsilon. \qquad (46)$$

Finally,

$$\theta^{\alpha\beta\gamma\delta} = \delta_{\gamma\alpha} \delta_{\beta\alpha} \delta_{\delta\alpha} \lambda_k^\alpha \nu^\alpha$$

$$+ \delta_{\gamma\alpha} \sum_j b_j^\delta b_j^\beta \lambda_j^\alpha \lambda_{\bar{j}}^\alpha \lambda_k^\alpha \nu^\alpha$$

$$+ \delta_{\beta\delta} \sum_h c_h^\gamma c_h^\alpha \lambda_h^\beta \lambda_{\bar{h}}^\beta \lambda_k^\beta \nu^\beta$$

$$+ \sum_{j,h,\epsilon} b_j^\delta b_j^\beta c_h^\gamma c_h^\alpha \lambda_h^\epsilon \lambda_{\bar{h}}^\epsilon \lambda_j^\epsilon \lambda_{\bar{j}}^\epsilon \lambda_k^\epsilon \nu^\epsilon. \qquad (47)$$

Similarly,

$$\bar{\theta}^{\alpha\beta\gamma\delta} = \delta_{\gamma\alpha} \delta_{\beta\alpha} \delta_{\delta\alpha} \lambda_{\bar{k}}^\alpha \nu^\alpha$$

$$+ \delta_{\gamma\alpha} \sum_j b_j^\delta b_j^\beta \lambda_j^\alpha \lambda_{\bar{j}}^\alpha \lambda_{\bar{k}}^\alpha \nu^\alpha$$

$$+ \delta_{\beta\delta} \sum_h c_h^\gamma c_h^\alpha \lambda_h^\beta \lambda_{\bar{h}}^\beta \lambda_{\bar{k}}^\beta \nu^\beta$$

$$+ \sum_{j,h,\epsilon} b_j^\delta b_j^\beta c_h^\gamma c_h^\alpha \lambda_h^\epsilon \lambda_{\bar{h}}^\epsilon \lambda_j^\epsilon \lambda_{\bar{j}}^\epsilon \lambda_{\bar{k}}^\epsilon \nu^\epsilon. \qquad (48)$$

These expressions can be used to modify the form of the variances and co-variances. For example,

$$\mathcal{C}[d^{*\alpha}, d^{*\gamma}] = \delta_{\gamma\alpha} \frac{\lambda_k^\alpha \lambda_{\bar{k}}^\alpha}{\nu^\alpha} \Bigg[1 + \sum_j (b_j^\alpha)^2 \lambda_j^\alpha \lambda_{\bar{j}}^\alpha + \sum_h (c_h^\alpha)^2 \lambda_h^\alpha \lambda_{\bar{h}}^\alpha \Bigg]$$
$$+ \sum_{j,h,\epsilon} b_j^\gamma b_j^\alpha c_h^\gamma c_h^\epsilon \lambda_h^\epsilon \lambda_{\bar{h}}^\epsilon \lambda_j^\epsilon \lambda_{\bar{j}}^\epsilon \nu^\epsilon \frac{(\lambda_{\bar{k}}^\alpha \lambda_{\bar{k}}^\gamma \lambda_k^\epsilon + \lambda_k^\alpha \lambda_{\bar{k}}^\gamma \lambda_{\bar{k}}^\epsilon)}{\nu^\alpha \nu^\gamma}. \quad (49)$$

5. Asymptotic Distributions of Sample Unstratified Determinants and Discriminants

Two other functions of the sample response proportions that we may be interested in are the sample unstratified determinant and the discriminant (for $m = 3$). Each of these is asymptotically normally distributed (as a consequence of the lemma of Section 3).

The population unstratified determinant $|\Pi^*|$ is the determinant of $\Pi^* = (\pi_{gi}) = \Pi + \bar{\Pi}$, and the corresponding sample unstratified determinant $|P^*|$ is a consistent estimate of it. Then $\sqrt{n}\,(|P^*| - |\Pi^*|)$ has the same limiting distribution as

$$\sum_{g,i} \frac{\partial |\Pi^*|}{\partial \pi_{gi}} x_{gi}^*, \quad \text{where } x_{gi}^* = \sqrt{n}\,(p_{gi} - \pi_{gi}). \quad (50)$$

The latter have a limiting joint normal distribution with means 0 and variances and covariances given by

$$Ex_{gi}^* x_{hj}^* = \pi_{gihj} - \pi_{gi}\pi_{hj}. \quad (51)$$

This result is a corollary or analogue of Theorem 1. Since

$$|\Pi^*| = \sum_j \Pi_{gj}^* \pi_{gj}, \quad (52)$$

where Π_{gj}^* is the cofactor of π_{gj} in $|\Pi^*|$, we have

$$\frac{\partial |\Pi^*|}{\partial \pi_{gi}} = \Pi_{gi}^*. \quad (53)$$

Then, from the lemma, we see that $\sqrt{n}\,(|P^*| - |\Pi^*|)$ has a limiting normal distribution with mean 0 and variance

$$\sum_{g,i,h,j} \frac{\partial |\Pi^*|}{\partial \pi_{gi}} \frac{\partial |\Pi^*|}{\partial \pi_{hj}} (\pi_{gihj} - \pi_{gi}\pi_{hj}) = \sum_{g,i,h,j} \Pi_{gi}^* \Pi_{hj}^* \pi_{gihj} - m^2 |\Pi^*|^2. \quad (54)$$

These quantities can be estimated consistently from the observed proportions.

For a polynomial of degree m with roots $d^1, \ldots, d^m$, the discriminant is $[\prod_{\alpha<\gamma} (d^\alpha - d^\gamma)]^2$. We shall treat its asymptotic distribution in one case. In principle, other cases can be treated similarly.

In the case of $m = 3$, let the determinantal equation $-|P - tP^*|/|P^*| = 0$ be written

$$t^3 - c_1 t^2 + c_2 t - c_3 = 0. \quad (55)$$

The roots of this equation are d^1, d^2, d^3. The discriminant is

$$f = [(d^1 - d^2)(d^1 - d^3)(d^2 - d^3)]^2; \tag{56}$$

it can be written in terms of the coefficients as

$$f = 18c_1c_2c_3 - 4c_1^3c_3 + c_1^2c_2^2 - 4c_2^3 - 27c_3^2. \tag{57}$$

The three roots are real if and only if f is nonnegative, and they are different if and only if f is not 0.

Let ϕ be the corresponding population discriminant, that is, the discriminant for $-|\Pi - \theta\Pi^*|/|\Pi^*| = 0$, where it is assumed that $|\Pi^*| \neq 0$; this equation can be written

$$\theta^3 - \gamma_1\theta^2 + \gamma_2\theta - \gamma_3 = 0. \tag{58}$$

Then f is a consistent estimate of ϕ and $\sqrt{n}\,(f - \phi)$ has a limiting normal distribution with mean 0. Application of the lemma to the form (57) shows that $\sqrt{n}\,(f - \phi)$ has the same limiting distribution as

$$\begin{aligned}
&[18\gamma_2\gamma_3 - 12\gamma_1^2\gamma_3 + 2\gamma_1\gamma_2^2]\sqrt{n}\,(c_1 - \gamma_1) \\
&+ [18\gamma_1\gamma_3 + 2\gamma_1^2\gamma_2 - 12\gamma_2^2]\sqrt{n}\,(c_2 - \gamma_2) \\
&+ [18\gamma_1\gamma_2 - 4\gamma_1^3 - 54\gamma_3]\sqrt{n}\,(c_3 - \gamma_3).
\end{aligned} \tag{59}$$

Since c_1, c_2, and c_3 are rational functions of P and P^*, $\sqrt{n}\,(c_1 - \gamma_1)$, $\sqrt{n}\,(c_2 - \gamma_2)$, and $\sqrt{n}\,(c_3 - \gamma_3)$ have a limiting joint normal distribution. The variance of the limiting distribution of $\sqrt{n}\,(f - \phi)$ can now be found from (59).

Application of the lemma to the form (56) shows that $\sqrt{n}\,(f - \phi)$ has the same limiting distribution as $\sum_{\alpha=1}^{3} \beta_\alpha d^{*\alpha}$, where

$$\beta_1 = \frac{\partial\phi}{\partial\delta^1} = 2\sqrt{\phi}\,(2\delta^1 - \delta^2 - \delta^3)(\delta^2 - \delta^3),$$

$$\beta_2 = \frac{\partial\phi}{\partial\delta^2} = 2\sqrt{\phi}\,(\delta^1 - 2\delta^2 + \delta^3)(\delta^1 - \delta^3), \tag{60}$$

$$\beta_3 = \frac{\partial\phi}{\partial\delta^3} = 2\sqrt{\phi}\,(-\delta^1 - \delta^2 + 2\delta^3)(\delta^1 - \delta^2),$$

and

$$\sqrt{\phi} = (\delta^1 - \delta^2)(\delta^1 - \delta^3)(\delta^2 - \delta^3).$$

If $\delta^1 \neq \delta^2 \neq \delta^3 \neq \delta^1$, then $\delta^{*\alpha} = \sqrt{n}\,(d^\alpha - \delta^\alpha)$ have a limiting joint normal distribution, and the variance of the limiting normal distribution of $\sqrt{n}\,(f - \phi)$ is

$$\sum_{\alpha,\gamma=1}^{3} \beta_\alpha\beta_\gamma \mathcal{C}(d^{*\alpha}, d^{*\gamma}), \tag{61}$$

where the $\mathcal{C}(d^{*\alpha}, d^{*\gamma})$ are given by Equation (23) or Equation (49).

286

Notes

1. That an estimate t of θ is consistent means that for sufficiently large sample size, t is arbitrarily near θ with arbitrarily high probability; that is, given $a > 0$, $b > 0$, there exists an n_0 such that for $n > n_0$

$$\Pr\{|t - \theta| < a\} > 1 - b.$$

This is sometimes written plim $t = \theta$. Suppose $y = f(x)$ is a function continuous at $x = \theta$; then $f(t)$ is a consistent estimate of $f(\theta)$. Continuity of $f(x)$ means that if x is near θ, $y = f(x)$ is near $f(\theta)$; that is, given $c > 0$, there exists a d such that for $|x - \theta| < d$, then $|y - f(\theta)| < c$. The proposition is that for sufficiently large n, t is near θ and hence $f(t)$ is near $f(\theta)$ with arbitrarily high probability; that is, given $c > 0$, $b > 0$, there exists an n_0 such that for $n > n_0$

$$\Pr\{|f(t) - f(\theta)| < c\} > 1 - b.$$

This follows by taking $a = d$. The proposition also holds when $f(x)$ is a function of several variables.

p_{gik} is a consistent estimate of π_{gik}, for np_{gik} is a binomial variable, and it is well-known that a relative frequency is a consistent estimate of the corresponding probability.

The elements of D are the roots of $|P - d(P + \bar{P})| = 0$. When the determinant is expanded, the coefficients of the powers of d are continuous functions of P and $\bar{P}$ (polynomials), and the roots of a polynomial equation are continuous functions of the coefficients. In a similar way, we can demonstrate that the elements of L_V, L_H, and N are continuous functions of P and $\bar{P}$.

2. The lemma is a special case of the theorem at the bottom of page 575 of "The asymptotic properties of estimates of the parameters of a single equation in a complete system of stochastic equations," T. W. Anderson and Herman Rubin, *Annals of Mathematical Statistics*, Vol. 21 (1950), pp. 570–582.

3. The Taylor's series expansion is

$$f(z) = f(\mu) + \left(\frac{\partial f(\mu)}{\partial z}\right)(z - \mu) + r,$$

where r is a remainder that can be neglected. Then

$$\sqrt{n}\,[f(Z_n) - f(\mu)] = \left(\frac{\partial f(\mu)}{\partial z}\right)\sqrt{n}\,(Z_n - \mu) + R,$$

where R is a random variable which is a consistent estimate of 0 (that is, can be neglected for large sample sizes).

4. It might be noted that

$$\Pi = \Lambda_V' V \Delta \Lambda_H, \quad \bar{\Pi} = \Lambda_V' V(I - \Delta)\Lambda_N, \quad \text{and} \quad \lambda_0^\alpha = 1$$

define Λ_V, V, Δ, and Λ_H uniquely. $\sum \nu^\alpha = 1$ follows from these and $\pi_{00k} + \pi_{00\bar{k}} = 1$. An ordering on α is assumed.

5. The terms of order $1/\sqrt{n}$ in Equations (9), (11), (12), and (13) depend on L_V^*, L_H^*, N^*, and D^*; if they depended on H and $\bar{H}$, we could argue straightforwardly that they could be neglected.

Bibliography

Almendinger, V. V., 1961. "Topics in the Regional Growth Model," *Report of the Penn Jersey Transportation Study*: (mimeo)

Anderson, T. W., 1954. "On Estimation of Parameters in Latent Structure Analysis," *Psychometrika*, Vol. 19, pp. 1–10.

———, 1954. "Probability Models for Time Changes in Attitudes, "*Mathematical Thinking in the Social Sciences*, P. F. Lazarsfeld, ed., New York: The Free Press.

———, 1958. *An Introduction to Multivariate Statistical Analysis*, New York: John Wiley & Sons, Inc.

———, 1959. "Some Scaling Methods and Estimation Procedures in the Latent Class Model," *Probability and Statistics*, Ulf Grenander, ed., New York: John Wiley & Sons, Inc., pp. 9–38.

———, and R. Carleton, n.d. *A Sampling Experiment and Its Implications*. Bureau of Applied Social Research. (mimeo)

———, and L. A. Goodman, 1957. "Statistical Inference about Markov Chains," *Annals of Mathematical Statistics*, Vol. 28, pp. 89–110.

Apostol, T., 1961. *Calculus*, Vol. I, Waltham, Mass.: Blaisdell Publishing Co.

Baker, Frank, 1962. "Information Retrieval Based on Latent Class Analysis," *Journal of the Association for Computing Machinery*, Vol. 9, No. 4, pp. 512–521.

Birnbaum, A., 1957. "Efficient Design and Use of Tests of Mental Ability for Various Decision Making Problems," USAFSAM *Series in Statistics*, Report 58–16, Randolph AFB, Texas: School of Aviation Medicine.

Blumen, I., M. Kogan, and P. McCarthy, 1955. *The Industrial Mobility of Labor as a Probability Process*, Cornell University, School of Industrial and Labor Relations.

Boudon, R., 1962. "Le Modèle des Classes Latentes," *Revue Française de Sociologie*, Vol. 3, pp, 3. 259–300.

Chaillou, J., and M. Delabré, 1964. "A Propos de la Division d'une Population en Classes Latentes et de l'Analyse Factorielle," *Bulletin du C.F.R.P.*, Vol. 13, pp. 259–275.

Coleman, J. S., 1964a. *Introduction to Mathematical Sociology*, New York: The Free Press.

———, 1964b. *Models of Change and Response Uncertainty*. Englewood Cliffs, N. J.: Prentice-Hall, Inc.

Cramér, H., 1946. *Mathematical Methods of Statistics*, Princeton: Princeton University Press.

Daval, Roger, F. Bourricaud, Y. Delamotte, and R. Doron, 1963. *Traité de Psychologie Sociale*, Vol. I, Paris: Presses Universitaires de France, Chapter 3.

Elderton, W. P., 1938. *Frequency Curves and Correlation* (3rd edition), Cambridge: Cambridge University Press.

Faddeeva, V. N., 1959. *Computational Methods of Linear Algebra*, New York: Dover Publications, Inc.

Finney, D. J., 1947. *Probit Analysis: A Statistical Treatment of the Sigmoid Response Curve*, Cambridge: Cambridge University Press.

Gibson, W. A., 1951. "Applications of the Mathematics of Multiple-Factor Analysis to Problems of Latent Structure Analysis," unpublished Ph.D. dissertation, University of Chicago. Also in Paul F. Lazarsfeld *et al.*, "The Use of Mathematical Models."

———, 1955. "An Extension of Anderson's Solution for the Latent Structure Equations," *Psychometrika*, Vol. 20, pp. 69–73.

———, 1956. "Proportional Profiles and Latent Structure," *Psychometrika*, Vol. 21, pp. 135–144.

———, n.d. "Multiple Factors and Latent Structure," unpublished manuscript.

———, 1959. "Three Multivariate Models: Factor Analysis, Latent Structure Analysis, and Latent Profile Analysis," *Psychometrika*, Vol. 24, pp. 229–252. Also in *Readings in Mathematical Social Science*, P. F. Lazarsfeld and N. W. Henry, eds., Chicago: Science Research Associates, Inc., 1966.

———, 1960. "Non-Linear Factors in Two Dimensions," *Psychometrika*, Vol. 25, pp. 381–392.

———, 1962a. "Extending Latent Class Solutions to Other Variables," *Psychometrika*, Vol. 27, pp. 73–81.

———, 1962b. "Latent Structure and Positive Manifold," *British Journal of Statistical Psychology*, Vol. 15, pp. 149–160.

Gilliam, Sylvia, 1948. "The Latent Structure of a Thurstone-Chave Scale," unpublished Master's Essay, Columbia University.

Green, Bert F., 1951. "A General Solution for the Latent Class Model of Latent Structure Analysis," *Psychometrika*, Vol. 16, pp. 151–166.

———, 1952. "Latent Structure Analysis and Its Relation to Factor Analysis," *Journal of the American Statistical Association*, Vol. 47, pp. 71–76.

Guttman, Louis, 1954. "The Principal Components of Scalable Attitudes," *Mathematical Thinking in the Social Sciences*, P. Lazarsfeld, ed., New York: The Free Press, Chapter 5.

Harman, H. H., 1960. *Modern Factor Analysis*, Chicago: University of Chicago Press.

Harper, Dean H., 1966. "Some New Applications of Dichotomous Algebra to Survey Analysis and Latent Structure Analysis," unpublished Ph.D. dissertation, Columbia University.

———, 1967. "Relaxing the Axiom of Local Independence," unpublished manuscript.

Hays, D. G., and E. F. Borgatta, 1954. "An Empirical Comparison of Restricted and General Latent Distance Analysis," *Psychometrika*, Vol. 19, pp. 271–279.

Henry, Andrew F., 1952. "A Method of Classifying Non-Scale Response Patterns in a Guttman Scale," *Public Opinion Quarterly*, Vol. 16, pp. 94–106.

Hohn, Franz E., 1964. *Elementary Matrix Algebra* (2nd edition) New York: The Macmillan Company.

Horst, Paul, 1963. *Matrix Algebra for Social Scientists*, New York: Holt, Rinehart and Winston, Inc.

Jonassen, C. T., 1959. *The Measurement of Community Dimensions and Elements*, Center for Educational Administration, Ohio State University.

———, and Peres, S., 1960. *Interrelationships of Dimensions of Community Systems*, Columbus: Ohio State University Press.

Kadushin, Charles, 1966. "The Friends and Supporters of Psychotherapy," *American Sociological Review*, Vol. 31, pp. 786–802.

Katz, Leo, and C. Proctor, 1959. "The Concept of Configuration of Interpersonal Relations in a Group as a Time Dependent Stochastic Process," *Psychometrika*, Vol. 24, pp. 317–327.

Kemeny, J. G., H. Mirkil, J. L. Snell and G. L. Thompson, 1959. *Finite Mathematical Structures*, Englewood Cliffs, N. J.: Prentice-Hall, Inc.

Kemeny, J. G., and J. L. Snell, 1961. *Finite Markov Chains*. Princeton: D. Van Nostrand Co., Inc.

Kendall, P. L., 1954. *Conflict and Mood*, New York: The Free Press.

Koopmans, T. C., 1949. "Identification Problems in Economic Model Construction," *Econometrica*, Vol. 17, pp. 125–144.

———, 1951. "Identification Problems in Latent Structure Analysis," Cowles Commission Discussion Paper: Statistics No. 360. (mimeo)

———, and O. Reiersol, 1950. "The Identification of Structural Characteristics," *Annals of Mathematical Statistics*, pp. 165–181.

Lambert, R., 1959. "L'Analyse de la Structure Latente de Lazarsfeld," *Bulletin C.F.R.P.*, Vol. 8, pp. 1–2, 101–120.

Lazarsfeld, Paul F., 1950a. "The Logical and Mathematical Foundation of Latent Structure Analysis," *Measurement and Prediction*, S. A. Stouffer *et al.*, Princeton: Princeton University Press, Chapter 10.

———, 1950b. "Some Latent Structures," *Ibid.*, Chapter 11.

———, 1951, *et al.* "The Use of Mathematical Models in the Measurement of Attitudes," RAND Corporation Research Memorandum No. 455, Santa Monica. (mimeo)

———, 1954. "A Conceptual Introduction to Latent Structure Analysis,"

Mathematical Thinking in the Social Sciences, P. F. Lazarsfeld, ed., New York: The Free Press, Chapter 7.

———, 1955. "Recent Developments in Latent Structure Analysis," *Sociometry*, Vol. 18, pp. 391–403. Also in *Sociometry and the Science of Man*, J. L. Moreno, ed., New York: Beacon House, 1956, pp. 647–659.

———, 1959a. "Latent Structure Analysis," *Psychology: A Study of a Science*, S. Koch, ed., New York: McGraw-Hill Book Company, Vol. 3, pp. 476–535.

———, 1959b. "Latent Structure Analysis," *Contributions to Scientific Research in Management*, UCLA Graduate School of Business Administration.

———, 1960. "Latent Structure Analysis and Test Theory," *Psychological Scaling-Theory and Applications*, H. Gulliksen and S. Messick, eds., New York: John Wiley & Sons, Inc., pp. 83–95. Also in *Readings in Mathematical Social Science*, P. F. Lazarsfeld and N. W. Henry, eds., Chicago: Science Research Associates, Inc., 1966, pp. 78–88.

———, 1961. "The Algebra of Dichotomous Systems," *Studies in Item Analysis and Prediction*, Herbert Solomon, ed., Stanford: Stanford University Press.

———, 1965. "Latent Structure Analysis," *Mathematics and Social Sciences*, S. Sternberg *et al.*, eds., The Hague: Mouton, pp. 37–54.

———, and N. W. Henry, 1965. "The Application of Latent Structure Analysis to Quantitative Ecological Data," *Mathematical Explorations in Behavioral Science*, F. Massarik and P. Ratoosh, eds., Homewood, Ill.: Richard D. Irwin Inc. and The Dorsey Press, pp. 333–348.

Lord, F. M., 1952. "A Theory of Test Scores," *Psychometric Monographs*, No. 7.

———, 1953a. "The Relation of Test Score to the Trait Underlying the Test," *Educational Psychological Measurement*, Vol. 13, pp. 517–549. Reprinted in *Readings in Mathematical Social Science*, P. F. Lazarsfeld and N. W. Henry, eds., Chicago: Science Research Associates, Inc., 1966.

———, 1953b. "An Application of Confidence Intervals and of Maximum Likelihood to the Estimation of an Examinee's Ability," *Psychometrika*, Vol. 18, pp. 56–76.

Madansky, A., 1959. *Partitioning Methods in Latent Class Analysis*, Report P-1644, RAND Corporation.

———, 1960. "Determinantal Methods in Latent Class Analysis, *Psychometrika*, Vol. 25, pp. 183–198.

McCarthy, P. J., 1951. "A Special Review of *The American Soldier*, Vol. IV," *Psychometrika*, Vol. 16, pp. 247–255.

McDonald, Roderick P., 1962a. "A General Approach to Non-Linear Factor Analysis," *Psychometrika*, Vol. 27, pp. 397–415.

———, 1962b. "A Note on the Derivation of the General Latent Class Model," *Psychometrika*, Vol. 27, pp. 203–206.

McHugh, R. B., 1954. "On the Scaling of Psychological Data by Latent Structure Analysis," unpublished Ph.D dissertation, University of Minnesota.

———, 1956. "Efficient Estimation and Local Identification in Latent Class Analysis," *Psychometrika*, Vol. 21, pp. 331–347; Correction, Vol. 23, pp. 273–274.

MacRae, D., Jr., 1956. "An Exponential Model for Assessing Four-fold Tables," *Sociometry*, Vol. 19, pp. 84–94.

Miller, C. R., and E. W. Butler, 1966. "Anomia and Eunomia: A Methodological Evaluation of Srole's Anomia Scale," *American Sociological Review*, Vol. 31, pp. 400–406.

Miller, C. R., G. Sabagh, H. F. Dingman, 1962. "Latent Class Analysis and Differential Mortality," *Journal of the American Statistical Association*, Vol. 57, pp. 430–438.

Mood, A. and F. Graybill, 1963. *Introduction to the Theory of Statistics*, New York: McGraw-Hill, Inc.

Neyman, J., 1949. "Contribution to the Theory of the Chi-Square Test," *Proceedings of the Berkeley Symposium on Mathematical Statistics and Probability*, J. Neyman, ed., Berkeley: University of California Press.

Parzen, E., 1960. *Modern Probability Theory and Its Applications*, New York: John Wiley & Sons, Inc.

———, 1962, *Stochastic Processes*, San Francisco: Holden-Day, Inc.

Rao, C. R., 1952. *Advanced Statistical Methods in Biometrical Research*, New York: John Wiley & Sons, Inc.

Rasch, G., 1960. *Probabilistic Models for Some Intelligence and Attainment Tests*, Danmarks Paedagogiske Institut.

———, 1966. "An Individualistic Approach to Item Analysis," in P. F. Lazarsfeld and Neil W. Henry, eds., *Readings in Mathematical Social Science*, Chicago: Science Research Associates.

Rietz, H. L., 1927. *Mathematical Statistics*, Carus Mathematical Monograph No. 3, The Mathematical Association of America.

Rossi, Peter H., 1951. "Latent Structure Analysis and Research on Social Stratification," unpublished Ph.D. dissertation, Columbia University.

Saaty, T., and J. Bram, 1964. *Non-Linear Mathematics*, New York: McGraw-Hill, Inc.

Solomon, H., 1961. Editor's Introduction to *Studies in Item Analysis and Prediction*, Stanford: Stanford University Press.

Somers, Robert H., 1961. "Latent Content Model of Latent Structure," unpublished Ph.D. dissertation, Columbia University.

Stouthard, Ph.C., 1965. "Data Modellen. Enkele Toepassingen en een Methodologische Kritiek," Tilburg: Katholieke Hogeschool te Tilburg.

Stouffer, S. A., *et al.*, 1950. *Measurement and Prediction*, Princeton: Princeton University Press. (Reprinted 1966 by John Wiley & Sons, Inc.)

Thurstone, L. L., 1947. *Multiple Factor Analysis*, Chicago: University of Chicago Press.

Torgerson, W., 1958. *Theory and Methods of Scaling*, New York: John Wiley & Sons, Inc.

Tucker, L. R., 1946. "Maximum Validity of a Test with Equivalent Items," *Psychometrika*, Vol. 11, pp. 1–13.

Wiggins, Lee M., 1955. "Mathematical Models for the Interpretation of Attitude and Behavior Change," unpublished Ph.D. dissertation, Columbia University.

INDEX

Accounting equations, 22, 27, 44, 47ff, 125
Allport, G., 4
Anderson, T. W., 11, 47, 71, 79, 80, 92–99, 226, 247, 273–287
Apostol, T., 100fn
Ascending matrices, 152, 205
Association, 18
Asymptotic efficiency, 79–80
Asymptotic normal distribution, 79–80, 274–275

BAN estimation, 80–83, 105
Basic matrix, 50, 201
    stratified, 51, 203
Basic solution, 52
Birnbaum, A., 221, 223
Borgatta, E. F., 140

Carleton, R. O., 92–99
Carnap, R., 2
Cattell, R. B., 6
Characteristic roots, 56, 272
Characteristic vectors, 56, 272
Chi-square measure, 76–77, 99–105
Chi-square test, 81–82, 148
Classification, 36
Cofactor, 269
Coleman, J. S., 252, 254
Conditions of reducibility, 11, 34, 211–217
Consistent estimator, 78, 287
Continuous variables, 228ff
Covariance, 35
Cramér, H., 79, 82, 101fn
Cross product, 27
    conditional, 35
    stratified, 27

Density function, 158
Determinant, 267–270
Determinantal equation, 53, 271
Dewey, J., 3
Diagonal matrix, 266
Dichotomous items, 226
Dudman, J., 10
Durkheim, E., 4

Elderton, W. P., 206
Empirical examples:
    attitude toward army, 106–111
    community characteristics, 233–235
    job satisfaction, 210–211
    magazine readership, 251
    psychiatric sophistication, 88–92
    radio listening, 113–120
    role conflict, 142–148
    social rigidity, 185–189
    sociometric choices, 258–263
Estimation algorithms, 77, 98

Factor analysis, 6, 11, 106, 111, 240–244
Faddeeva, V. N., 56, 272
Finney, D. J., 220
Fitting data, 39–41, 75–76, 142–145, 190, 210
Friedrich, C. J., 5

Gibson, W. A., 13, 47, 71, 105, 111, 113–120, 226, 233
Goodman, L. A., 247
Graybill, F., 101fn
Green, B. F., 11, 112
Guttman, L., 7–10

Harman, H. H., 111, 113fn
Harper, D. H., 228
Hays, D. G., 140
Hempel, C. G., 2, 3
Hohn, F. E., 56, 264
Horst, P., 7fn
Hyperbolic rotation, 169–170

Identification, 23, 59
    of number of classes, 64–65
Indeterminacy
    in latent distance model, 132
    in located class model, 150
Intervening variable, 5
Inverse, 266

James, W., 3

Kadushin, C., 88–91
Katz, L., 258–260
Kemeny, J. G., 245, 264
Kendall, P. L., 251

Latent class model, 46ff
    basic solution of, 55–56
    classification in, 36–39, 68–70
Latent content model, 160ff
    estimation techniques in, 189–190
    solution of, 177–181
    symmetric parameters of, 163
Latent continuum, 148, 157

ABCDEFGHIJ – R –7654321 0/698